SUCCESSFUL
PRACTICE
TRANSITIONS

TO CONTACT DR. DAVID GRIGGS

Dr. David Griggs
The Transition Group
105 Harrison Avenue
Belleair Beach, FL 33786

Toll Free: 888-593-5852
Web: www.thetransitiongroup.com

email: clientservices@thetransitiongroup.com

SUCCESSFUL PRACTICE TRANSITIONS

Tulsa, Oklahoma

PennWell Publishing Company
1421 South Sheridan / P.O. Box 1260
Tulsa, OK 74112-6619

ISBN: 0-87814-617-2

Printed in the United States of America

1 2 3 4 5 01 00 99 98 97

TABLE OF CONTENTS

INTRODUCTION

What is the prognosis for the successful transition of my practice? Am I aware of the benefits to be enjoyed as well as the pitfalls to avoid during the life cycle of my practice? Do I know how to begin the process of examining all of my transition options? Am I on track for an end result that I truly want?

If you haven't already answered these questions, at what point in your career do you think you'll have to seriously consider them—at retirement? Sooner? What would your answers be *now*? Ten years from now?

Do you even understand the questions?

The answers to these very important questions depend on you. However, in today's rapidly changing dental marketplace, the timing required for the needed answers to these questions is rapidly accelerating.

Dentists at all career levels—including early, mid- and late career — now are being affected by increased competition for available discretionary dollars, managed care, corporate management of practices, discount dentistry, practice-downsizing, group practice and other practice expansion modalities, and a gradual shift from solo to duo practice and beyond. As dentists actively seek sound advice and constantly strive to become better educated in the process of practice transition, many find more questions than answers.

Through my work at W. David Griggs, DDS, & The Transition Group, I've come in contact with dentists from all around the world. I'm constantly impressed by what they represent. They're ethical, hardworking, competent, caring people, dedicated to making a difference in the health of the patients they treat. Yet, these same dentists consistently tell me of the tremendous struggles they face when making decisions about practice transitions.

Why is it that we so often hear tragic stories about the dentist who was an excellent clinician, worked hard for many years to build a practice, but failed to plan for the inevitable transition of his practice until far too late in the transition cycle? Other stories include failed associateships and partnerships, all of which began with optimism and the desire for freedom from the daily constraints and pressures of sole proprietorship. They ended in disappointment, damaged or lost practice value and, in many cases, the more significant loss of a business relationship with a fellow colleague.

Many dentists will spend much of their dental careers struggling with the overall transition concept, causing them to make poor business decisions in the process.

From the frustrated, angry dentist faced with having the practice appraised due to a divorce, to the heartbroken widow or widower of a dentist who left the family with little direction about what to do with the practice, the scenarios continue to unfold.

For years, dentists have been given methods, techniques, tools, and information to enable them to provide excellent dental care. In dental school, we mastered an intensive learning process, spending many long, hard hours in basic sciences and clinical training. Most of us completed dental school feeling a true sense of accomplishment and confidence in our newfound knowledge and clinical abilities.

The fact remains, however, that while we made a tremendous investment in our education and training, we were not given any real tools to make decisions about practice *establishment.* We were not told about acquisitions and buy-ins, practice *expansion* through associateships and mergers, or practice *exit strategies* through deferred, pre-retirement, and other practice sale models—the present-day language of "practice transitions."

As associateships to buy-in arrangements, practice mergers, and practice acquisitions and sales continue to prove to be excellent business opportunities for dentists, a strategic transition plan may well be the best "insurance policy" for a dentist to invest in.

In this book, I present a dramatically different approach to successfully planning your practice transition. Together, we will explore what I believe to be some of the most exciting options available in dentistry today—options which allow dentists to prosper more than ever before, by getting what they deserve through effectively planning for the transition of their practice.

This information transcends the traditional prescriptions of simply *hoping* that the practice will be successfully transferred to the "right" person, and that the value of the practice will be protected throughout the transition cycle. It addresses the challenges of bringing in an associate to the practice, successfully selling a portion of the practice in early, mid-, and late career, and anxiously awaiting retirement in order to "cash-in" the remaining equity of a lifelong endeavor.

Rather than continuing to assume these risks, many dentists are not only envisioning the future, but also planning a route to it. In one sense, this approach is very different; in another, some of our answers are deeply rooted in classic, timeless principles.

Unfortunately, past transition approaches often left dentists with little to show for the practices they established, purchased, and sold. There is no shortcut to planning a successful transition or protecting yourself (as well as the value of your practice) throughout the cycle; however, there is a path. Through this path, we hope you will get what you deserve, by planning for what you get.

I'll teach you exactly what to plan for in your practice transition. To get the most out of this material, you must read it carefully and then examine your goals and motives in the transition cycle. You must also examine how well equipped you are to construct and implement your plan without the help of advisors in the process. However, most importantly, I am going to challenge you to be willing to change your thought patterns surrounding the transition process.

You'll become aware of exciting new options that can lead to personal and financial rewards. The information contained in this book continues to empower many dentists to become better decision-makers, ensure smooth transitions, and guarantee a solid return on the investment made in all types of practice transitions.

Let's take a look at what you can expect from this book:

- In Chapter One, "The Practice Transition Life Cycle: A Commentary About Today's Rapidly Changing Dental Marketplace," we'll explore the rapidly changing marketplace that dentists now find themselves in, and how it impacts the transition of their practices. You'll determine *where you are* in this changing marketplace, as well as where you are in your own practice transition You will then begin to understand the need to develop a strategic-transition plan for your future.

- In Chapter Two, "Options for Practice Transitions: Available Options for Dentists at All Career Levels," we'll discuss various transition options for dentists to consider in early, mid-, and late career. We'll examine, as well, the importance of looking at all the available strategies for practice transitions *prior* to developing a strategic-transition plan. As you study the various available options, you'll learn how to best determine which option will best help you to meet your individual career goals.

- In Chapters Three through Six, "Successful Sales Strategies"; a Creating 'Win-Win' Associateship to Co-Ownership Arrangements"; "Practice Mergers"; and "New Practice Establishment," we'll clearly define a specific path for each and outline the steps required for a "win-win" approach to successful end results. Learn how to sell part or all of your practice years *before* as well as upon retirement from dentistry. You'll learn how to structure these different transitions and become aware of the importance of each step in the process.

- In Chapter Seven, "Determining the Value of Your Practice: Identify, Maximize, and Preserve Your Investment," We'll look at a logical and comprehensive approach to determining the value of your practice. You'll also learn *how* to enhance the value of your practice and avoid practice-value destroyers.

- In Chapter Eight, "Structuring Your Agreements: An Equitable Approach to Making Agreements Work for All Parties Involved," we'll take an in-depth look at the specifics required in structuring "win-win" practice-transition agreements. We'll show you how to save thousands of dollars in the negotiation process, and preserve your dreams of a prosperous transition by avoiding adversarial approaches commonly used in this arena. You'll continue to refer back to this chapter to make sure the crucial points of your comprehensive agreement are not overlooked.

- In Chapter Nine, "Get What You Pay For: How To Best Utilize Your Financial, Legal, and Business Advisors," we'll evaluate how to best utilize the support of your transition consultant, CPA, attorney, practice broker, and various financial advisors. We'll help you to know how to measure the quality of the advice you're receiving, as well as how to locate knowledgeable, experienced advisors to help you. We'll also explain what to look for, should you choose a transition specialist to become the overall *coordinator* of your transition.

- In Chapter 10, "Purchasing or Buying Into a Practice: Advice for Early-Career Dentists," we'll walk you through a comprehensive checklist to help you cover all your bases when purchasing or buying into a practice. You'll learn what to look for, how to best protect your investment, and how to secure financing for your venture.

- In Chapter 11, "Cashing in the Equity in Your Practice: Advice for Early-, Mid-, or Late-Career Dentists," we'll provide an overview of the "cashing-in practice equity" process, from the sale of part or all of the practice, prior to as well as upon retirement. Letters from other dentists who have sold their practices for various reasons are included in this chapter. See how they based *their* decisions to sell, and what challenges and benefits they encountered throughout the process.

- In Chapter 12, "When You Finally Decide To Sell Your Practice: Advice From the Late-Career Perspective," we look at the underlying emotions experienced (but often not considered) by many dentists during transitions. You'll recognize the emotional motivators and concerns which surface during the overall transition process—from the beginning, during, and through the ending of the practice life cycle. We'll leave you with the stories of those who received positive end results...dentists who actually enjoyed the process and reaped the rewards of *Successful Practice Transitions.*

- In Chapter 13, "Developing a Strategic-Transition Plan: Structuring Your Comprehensive-Transition Plan," we'll help you to develop your own strategic-practice-transition action plan. Choosing the right transition option, when to begin an initial financial and personal analysis, and how to implement your plan are all covered in this chapter. You'll utilize this action plan to meet your personal and professional goals.

- In Appendix I, "Pitfalls, Myths, and Misconceptions," you will learn how to identify and avoid common pitfalls encountered in practice transitions, as well learn about some of the many myths and misconceptions that can cause serious "roadblocks" for dentists when they plan their transition. This section will help save you a great deal of time, money, and aggravation.

- In Appendix II, "Specialty Practices—Special Considerations," we will explain to the dental specialist some of the major differences to be aware of between specialty practices and general practices when planning a transition. Differences in practice valuation, associate compensation, and overall transition requirements will be covered.

- In Appendix III, "Commonly Asked Questions and Answers," you will be provided with answers to questions that are consistently asked by dentists from across the United States and Canada.

A Note from the Author

I practiced dentistry in Atlanta, Georgia for 10 years and have been a practice transition consultant for 17 years. During these years, I have observed dentists experience a higher quality of life, enhance their profitability, and enjoy peace of mind. A key element for these dentists was planning well in advance for *all* phases of their practice transition.

Conversations with these dentists were revealing. It was obvious that at some point in their careers, they began looking at their practices in a new way. For many early-and mid-career dentists, the decision to *step beyond the limitations of solo practice* became the first step in the path to success. For the late-career dentists, success resulted from planning—*at least five years in advance of retirement*—the transfer of their practice to a successor.

Regardless of career stage, dentists who strongly believe in a well-planned transition and find a clear and equitable means of transferring the value of their practice to a successor can enjoy exciting new options in practice transitions. You'll be interested to learn how the practice value (along with the desire to acquire and build practice equity) drives much of the transition process as we know it today.

Do we, as dentists, know how to build successful practice arrangements that expand *and* transfer practice value to a successor? Unfortunately, most of us do not have this critical knowledge.

Until retirement, few dentists enjoy any of the value "locked" inside their practices. Based on available statistics, dentists who wait until retirement to sell rarely receive more than *half* the potential value of their practices.

However, with proper planning (and at any time during early, mid, or late career), practice value can be converted into a passive-income stream. In the spirit of fair exchange, dentists buying in can benefit from the immediate income and career stability created in the process. As buyers enjoy the steady accumulation of practice value, they also begin to reap the benefits of practice succession.

In this book, I will provide you with the latest "win-win" recommendations for associateships, partnerships, mergers, and buy-ins, as well as important considerations for the purchase or sale of a practice. This information is designed to help you determine which options are best for you and to know when to implement them into your transition plan.

This book is a "must read" for dentists at all career levels:

- the early-career dentist seeking low-risk methods to establish a practice in today's competitive marketplace;

- the mid-career dentist wishing to expand a patient base, enhance practice profitability and cash in practice value, incrementally, throughout his or her career; and

- the late-career dentist wanting to maximize, preserve, and insure the value of a practice, while properly positioning it for a future sale.

As we move full-speed toward the 21st century, many dentists feel they are losing control over their personal and professional lives. There just isn't enough time to get everything done. Stress mounts daily. Life sometimes is just not what we think it should be. We often ask the question, "Is it really worth it?"

This seemingly never-ending rat race has many dentists yearning for a simpler, more meaningful approach to the practice of dentistry and to practice-succession planning. It is for these dentists that this book is written.

Successful Practice Transitions can be the answer you've been looking for to change your business future in dentistry. My goal in writing this book is to provide dentists with innovative strategies to successfully establish, expand, and convert practice value, thus allowing dentists everywhere the personal, professional, and financial enjoyment of practice succession.

Whether you are in private or group practice, a general dentist or a specialist, whether you're intent on building your own practice or purchasing additional practices, whether you want to find a way to play more golf, take more time off to travel, or simply retire, this book will help you to find your focus, develop a plan, and successfully glide through any type of practice transition. Put these strategies to work and you'll find the tools you need to make your practice transition be whatever you want it to be—today, tomorrow, and for years to come.

Much success.

W. David Griggs, DDS

1

THE PRACTICE TRANSITION LIFE CYCLE: A COMMENTARY ABOUT TODAY'S RAPIDLY CHANGING DENTAL MARKETPLACE

The Transition Life Cycle

Until recently and throughout most of dentistry's history, the life cycle of a dental practice has remained relatively unchanged. Traditionally, practices have gone through four phases: establishment, expansion, plateaus, and, as the owner transitioned into retirement, declines. (Figure 1.1)

However, in the mid- to late-1970s, a new phase of the transition began to appear: the practice conversion/succession cycle. This was named for the conversion of the equity in the practice (primarily good-will-equity) into a cash flow stream, in the process of transferring this

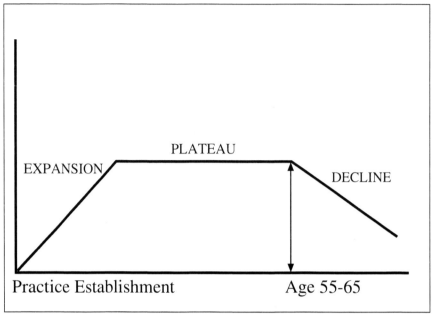

Fig. 1.1 *The transition life cycle, traditional model*

goodwill base to a successor. This part of the transition cycle developed when dentists began to discover that they could sell their practices on a consistent basis as a growing concern, by selling something that was essentially valueless in the past—goodwill.

As this conversion-succession process was refined over time, dentists soon found that this exchange process could not only happen years in advance of retirement, but could occur more than once during the life cycle of the practice. Dentists who traditionally allowed their practices to fall into the normal declining phase were now able to expand the true potential of the practice. They could sell part or all of the equity and decrease their own personal production within the practice if they so chose (*i.e.,* a decline in the dentist's personal production without a decline in the practice or its value). (Figure 1.2)

In the early years of dentistry, practice establishment was somewhat risk-free. Given that a practitioner made good choices (i.e., location, facility, staff, etc.), beginning a practice from "scratch" was quite common and, in most cases, financially rewarding. Since successful practice establishment was relatively easy for most new graduates, there was little demand for purchasing established practices from those dentists who were retiring. Practice owners thought little (if at all) of the eventual sale

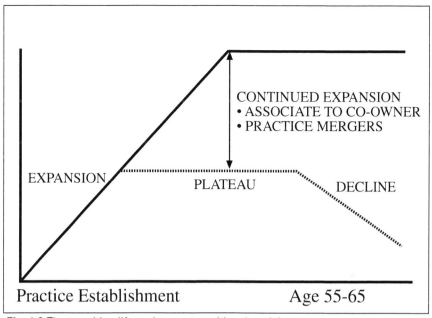

Fig. 1.2 *The transition life cycle, new transitional model*

of their practices. It was not uncommon to see retirement-bound dentists simply send an emotional good-bye letter to their patients thanking them for their loyalty and trust, encouraging them to continue to seek dental care, and wishing them well. Often, with no thoughts of financial gain, dentists felt honored to refer their patients to a colleague who would continue to provide excellent care to their patients. As changes in the market (as well as new ideas and concepts) began to surface in the 1970s and 1980s, dentists became more creative in planning the establishment, expansion, and transition of their practices.

With the introduction of dental insurance, practice expansion for many dentists was greatly enhanced. Dentistry clearly entered an era of diversification. Despite the overall benefits of dental insurance for both dentists and patients, relationships were altered. Patients, who in the past paid directly for dental services, assumed less responsibility for payment. Dental insurance allowed dentists to quickly establish large, successful practices and they certainly were grateful for increased treatment-plan acceptance due to this shift in financial responsibility.

Through the process of public awareness, better patient education, and the major corporations providing dental insurance to their employees, dental patients became more motivated than ever before. Practices everywhere began to flourish. Competition was not a threat. In fact, many dentists became so busy that few had any concerns with new dentists setting up practices in their area. New techniques and effective ways of painlessly treating patients added to the benefits for patients seeking dental care.

Staff loyalty was high and often resulted in lifetime relationships. As practices continued to prosper and provide dentists with secure incomes, planning for retirement was easy. The timing for this phase of the cycle was solely dependent upon the practitioner's own personal goals.

With good health and a sincere desire to continue practicing, many dentists chose to practice well into their 70s.

New developments in dentistry began to shift the emphasis toward preventative care. With an overall reduction in tooth decay, along with patients being encouraged to seek regular care, dental practices began to feel a slight shift in productivity. In addition, new forms of health-care delivery in dentistry were evolving. Rumblings of a new concept referred to as capitation began to surface, followed shortly thereafter by another unfamiliar term called managed care.

The dental market began to fragment as these nontraditional delivery systems began their slow arrival. With this shift came the effects of rising costs of dental supplies, increased staff salaries, and higher operational expenses. As patients became better educated in all aspects of dental care, they became better consumers as well. Having the luxury of choice, many patients started to evaluate where they would spend their dental dollars. Due to the fact that dentistry had become a very popular career path for individuals interested in the health care industry, competition began to surface.

These changes in the dental marketplace planted "seeds" in the minds of new graduates and dramatically impacted the way they looked at beginning their careers. Rapidly passing were the days of "starting from scratch" and gracefully climbing the ladder of success. The uncertainty of this changing environment created an opportunity — established practitioners could now look to the possibility of selling part or all of their practices on or before retirement as opposed to just "closing the doors."

The relative guarantee of cash flow that came with acquiring a well-established patient base became a base of security for many new graduates. For dentists needing help in handling increased workloads, hiring an associate became a welcomed solution to the daily pressures of practice ownership. The fact that many practitioners considering retirement were now promoting the perpetuation process of their practice led to a new phase in the transition cycle. This phase is now referred to as the *practice conversion cycle* or *practice succession cycle*.

As dentists began to take advantage of planning for converting the equity in their practice into cash, new challenges arose. These included determining the fair market value of a practice; successfully transferring the doctor's goodwill (and the staff's loyalty) to a successor; understanding complex buy-in and sale agreements; considering widely divergent opinions of financial advisors; and deciding whether or not to owner-finance the transaction, and more.

While development of this phase of the transition cycle brought a newfound excitement to many practitioners, the need for specialized transition-planning became more apparent. Dentists in the changing dental marketplace grew unsure of their decisions surrounding practice transitions, creating a need for advice from trained transition specialists to help develop a plan and insure the overall success of the transition process.

The rapidly changing dental marketplace has modified the evolution of the transition cycle. This ever-changing environment presents today's dentist with a variety of challenges.

Today's Changing Dental Marketplace

When I graduated from dental school in the 1970s, few models of dental practice existed other than the solo cottage-industry dentist. Few, if any, early-career dentists were purchasing established practices. Setting up practice from "scratch" was still relatively risk-free. I believed that setting up my own practice was the only way to go. Like many others, I opened a practice in a new medical complex in a rapidly growing suburb.

Group practices, partnerships, and other non-solo practice arrangements were rare. The prevailing attitude among most dentists was characterized by strict independence. Why lose your identity (and complicate your life) by entering into a partnership, group practice, associateship, or merger?

The "employee-only" dentist and the dentist with no present desire for future practice ownership were common only in the non-private sector (military, public health, and university systems). Newly graduated dentists, anxious to set up their own practices, looked upon established practices strictly as short-term associateship positions serving as springboards to building their own practices. They rarely considered buying into or purchasing an already established practice. Why pay for what you could quickly build on your own?

But, times have changed. Today, many dentists struggle emotionally and financially with the changes happening around them. Increased competition for new patients, rising overhead costs, decreased dental insurance benefits, practice management issues challenges—all these conditions exist in a market simultaneously affected by the climate of managed care.

General dentists and specialists, fee-for-service, managed care, and "hybrid" practices (combining both fee-for-service and managed care)—the speed and magnitude of these changes influenced all. Though common for other businesses, dentistry (until recently) has enjoyed relative immunity from such crises. As the profession undergoes fragmentation, many dentists celebrate prosperity, while others see themselves as unsuccessful. An increasingly large number of dentists feel caught somewhere in the middle.

Dentists quickly are changing their attitudes toward practice transitions. In fact, we now see radical changes in the practice transition cycle. Some of the reasons for these changes include:

- Fewer dentists set up practices from "scratch" due to the pressures of greater financial risks. Many fear that this avenue no longer provides immediate income security. Why take such a risk when purchasing or buying into a practice often allows the benefit of an immediate income stream?

- A growing number of dentists are now opting out of traditional private practice ownership. Employee-only dentists now are commonplace (with many choosing never to aspire to any type of practice ownership). This group consists of dentists who have chosen to concentrate specifically on the clinical aspects of dentistry, either foregoing future ownership or giving up existing ownership. For others looking at quality-of-life issues (reflective of shorter workweeks and fewer management responsibilities), the employee-only status is appealing. Sensing uncertainty in the changing dental marketplace, some dentists are temporarily relying on this option to provide security. Why not seek the safe haven of an employee-only position until the dust settles in the market-place?

- Non-solo practices are becoming increasingly popular as expense-sharing arrangements are re-explored. Why not consider working arrangements that might result in lower overhead, professional camaraderie, and shared practice responsibilities?

- Many dentists now can take advantage of buy-in or purchase opportunities within the practices in which they already work. Established practices now serve as internal spring-boards for ownership for early-career dentists. (In the past, established practices were used as external springboards, i.e; using the practice as an experience tool from which to eventually build a practice elsewhere.) In these cases, the associate no longer views the practice strictly as a short-term employment opportunity. Owner-dentists are less at risk of creating a future exit-platform for the early-career associate.

- Many dentists choose not to face the challenges ahead. Unable to cope with new, emerging dental practice models (while feeling these winds of change), some practitioners in their 40s and 50s now are looking at other career paths.

- Owner-dentists now are reversing roles with their associates earlier. Enjoying a passive income stream generated from the sale of the equity in the practices, freeing themselves from the day-to-day management and overhead responsibilities, they feel fewer concerns about the future.

Other dentists simply are retiring from practice early, no longer choosing to deal with the changes ahead.

Needless to say, the typical dental practice of 20 years ago is slowly becoming a thing of the past. New, innovative working arrangements and practice concepts now are emerging. The marketplace is varied: downsizing of existing practices, practice purchase and mergers, establishment of multi-office locations, and a multitude of practice buy-in and sale arrangements now exist. Equity buy-ins, production-acquisitions, deferred sales, and pre-retirement sales are all part of a new lingo in the new face of practice transitions.

Due to increased competition, many dentists are expanding hours and services in an effort to attract new patients. Practice expansion methods such as merger-acquisitions are becoming popular and there is a rebirth of interest in the associateship to buy-in arrangement.

Dentists are becoming less vested in the idea of total autonomy and independence. They now are willing to explore more non-solo practice arrangements and venture into non-traditional options. As dentists focus on the benefits of consolidating individual efforts into well-structured group arrangements, the need for transition-planning will become extremely important.

Dentistry will soon mirror the image of other professions, with most practice models establishing a natural business-succession cycle. When positioned for transition, these dentists will be less dependent upon buyer or seller locating services. These practices also will include general dentists and specialists who will provide a wide array of services. Common in law firms and accounting firms, future transition-planning will be structured to allow practice perpetuation long after the efforts of the original founders have retired from practice. Have you noticed that other professional firms often print the names of their founders and pre-vious partners on their stationary and proudly display their portraits in the hallways? Why shouldn't we, as dentists, look at our practices with the same sense of historical pride and perpetuity?

This marriage of mutual interests among dentists within the same practice group will occur frequently in the future. Those groups who emphasize the concept of age-staggering will enjoy the greatest benefits of this transition model. This model joins practitioners at different pivotal career points (i.e., early, mid-, and late career) with late-career dentists to form a group practice model that will allow practice succession and perpetuation. This model will be quite different from the previously common group-practice approach. Age-staggering arrangements will allow transitions to occur naturally among the members of the group, with clearly understood benefits to all parties involved. In most traditional group practice models, transition becomes each individual's separate task.

Unlike traditional models, delicate issues regarding patients, staff, and doctors will become easier to conquer when they arise during a prac-tice transition. When these issues surface in a well-defined group struc-

THE CHANGING MARKETPLACE
- FEWER NEW PRACTICE START-UPS
- MORE ESTABLISHED PRACTICE ACQUISITIONS
- PRACTICES SOLD EARLIER & INTERNALLY
- INCREASED SPACE-SHARING
- MORE NON-OWNER DENTISTS

Fig. 1.3 *The changing marketplace*

ture, they will have little effect on the overall success of the transition plan. (Figure 1-3)

The Multi-Layered Delivery System

With changes rapidly occurring in the transition cycle, several distinctive layers now exist in how dental services are provided and reimbursed. Each layer represents a uniquely independent niche in the marketplace.

Fee-for-service dentistry is alive and well today, co-existing side-by-side with neighboring managed-care practices.

An increasing number of dentists across the country now are attempting to incorporate these two contrasting delivery systems into the same practice (the "hybrid-practice"). Mixing fee-for-service dentistry with managed-care dentistry is becoming more commonplace. Some dentists attempting this model are prospering. But, many that entered the managed-care arena without a thorough understanding of its dynamics are failing at this new hybrid form of practice.

Dentists who are physically separating their fee-for-service practices from their managed-care practices represent the greatest success stories for hybrid practice. A successful division of this practice model sets the stage for the dental entrepreneur—the practitioner who owns two separate practices—one providing fee-for-service dentistry, the other providing dentistry through managed-care plans. As each delivery system requires a drastically different approach, the separation will allow the overall management structure to be simplified. This separation also will facilitate the independent sale of these practices in the future. When combining managed care with fee-for-service dentistry within the same facility, the future sale may become complicated, negatively affecting the value of the practice. The attitudes and desires of buyers greatly influence the market, and, at present, fee-for-service practices are in greater demand. (Note: Some regions of the country are beginning to experience a shift in this market mentality, with managed-care practices and hybrids showing enhanced sale-marketability.) The absentee-owner or manageri-al-only owner presents another new twist in the transition cycle. These dentists retain ownership, but maintain minimal, if any, clinical involve-ment in the practice. Some absentee-owners establish multiple facilities within several different geographic locations, often scattered throughout one state or entire regions. Many rely on strategic-marketing plans that include media advertising and direct mail.

The growth of absentee-ownership has led to the birth of corpo-rately-managed dental practices. In most states, ownership still is limited to licensed dentists. However, corporate-management companies are now pursuing dentists who are interested in this new model. Through networked systems, these companies centrally manage and operate mul-tiple practices from a single corporate center. Stock options offered by these corporations have sparked interest from outside investors. Those seeking new investment opportunities purchase the stocks of these com-panies when they "go public," offering shares on a traded exchange.

Dentists whose practices were absorbed into these companies express a wide range of feelings about their current situations. Responses are largely dependent upon how pleased (or displeased) they were with their pre-sale practice situations, their goals after the sale, and their over-all attitudes about change. It's difficult to predict the long-term viability of these management companies. In some cases, we already are seeing dentists restructuring their agreements with these companies in order to regain autonomy, control, and previous income levels.

Physicians experienced a similar metamorphosis in their market-place as hospitals and other health-care companies acquired their prac-tices. Some physicians are pleased with the results, some are not. In many situations, the physicians have been locked into long-term contracts with the companies, continuing to provide services for essentially the same patients at reduced pay. Some receive cash compensation or down-pay-ments for their practices, with the remaining purchase paid out via stock in the management company. (These physicians are obviously "betting" on the fact that their stock will only increase in value.)

Some dentists, too, are receiving "stock-only" compensation (*i.e.*, receiving most, if not all, of the purchase price in stock in the acquiring company). Though I certainly understand the motivation behind selling this way, we may see some "win/lose" transactions on the horizon in this arena. It all depends on the solvency and management of the particular company in the future.

Can We Predict the Future of Practice Transitions?

Good question! We cannot know what lies in the future for dental practice transitions. However, there are a few things we can be sure of.

Now, more than ever, dentists need to be clear about their direction. We have entered an era in which dentists need to quickly determine if they want to build, downsize, level off, convert ownership, or phase out their practices. In addition, they should evaluate their philosophy regarding managed care and stand by their decisions. All these decisions greatly impact future practice income, value, and transitions. Dentists interested in successful practice transitions will find it difficult to choose the correct transition option without being absolutely clear about their direction.

Immediately, dentists must begin to construct comprehensive, well-thought-out, ready-to-be-implemented transition plans. Without these types of plans in place, the future of many dental practices will be driven by default, not by design. The plan-driven transition will become the most successful model for practice transitions in the future.

From an economic perspective, enhanced productivity and overhead control are two keys to developing and maintaining successful practices in the future. Productivity and overhead control always have been important. However, due to the challenges we will face in the future, focus in this area will become a requirement for survival of the private practice.

Better use of existing facilities through group practice models, utilizing the advantages of staggered scheduling, as well as practice expansion through practice mergers are only a few of the opportunities that will be explored.

Many dentists now are choosing to sell their practices early. Because the future seems so uncertain, practice brokers presently are experiencing sky-rocketing practice sales. Based on this trend (along with fewer buyers entering the marketplace), many experts believe that more sellers than buyers will exist in the near future. If so, a downshift in the market value of dental practices will occur. In some areas of the country, this situation already exists, further reinforcing the need for advanced planning on the part of all dentists.

The way in which sellers are compensated for their practice value may change. In the future, determining purchase price and constructing a payment plan may involve some creativity. Currently, compensation for a practice sale generally results in the seller receiving a fixed price. Most often, the seller is compensated in the form of a cash down payment with the remaining balance financed by the seller and paid in monthly installments. In some cases, the seller is fortunate to receive payment in full upon the sale. (Other than the tax consequences of such a transaction, there's a great advantage to receiving cash.) New lending institutions (like the Matsco Companies) have emerged, willing to finance such a venture.

Changes We Can Expect in the Future

Should buyer-dentists become less confident of receiving a guaranteed income stream, they may seek sellers who are willing to base the selling price on future practice performance. With this approach, the price, as well as the payout terms, are based on how the practice performs economically after the sale. In this situation, the buyer is at least partially protected from future economic downswings or any radical changes that might occur in health-care delivery. Of course, this means that the selling dentist must have faith in the buyer's ability to produce and properly manage the practice following the sale. The buyer will need to produce enough income to pay overhead expenses and honor his or her commitment to make payments to the seller.

To receive full price for his practice, the transitioning dentist may be required to remain in the practice, working for the purchasing dentist for a period of time after the sale. (By and large, this working arrangement is an option for most selling dentists, and not a requirement.) Despite initial skepticism, statistics show that some sellers who have already chosen to sell their practices this way have benefited from a more rapid pay-off than they would have received from a traditional sale in which the payments were based on a fixed monthly amount. (See Chapter 3, "Successful Sales Strategies.")

In order for dentists to maintain the integrity of their existing patient bases and enhance their market share of new patients, they must begin a relentless exploration of all available practice-enhancement options. As dentists utilize the vast array of information sources available to them, they will become better educated in practice-transition options. This new found ability to make clear financial decisions regarding practice-transition options also should result in emotional rewards.

To maintain balance, dentists will need to seek options that are both practice and life-enhancing. What is financial success without the balancing force of happiness? Many dentists still think only in terms of "solo practice," believing that they alone are responsible for all day-to-day clinical production. They are unclear and even fearful about the future. The tide is rapidly changing. Dentists willing to examine new practice options will be rewarded by an enhanced bottom line and quality of life. The happiest dentists I know have a healthy mix of both.

Making the most of today's changing environment requires that dentists understand the importance of looking at all available options. Thorough knowledge of these options will allow you to later develop a strategic-transition plan. As you study the various options, you'll learn how to best determine which options best fit your individual career goals and help you to "position for transition."

2

OPTIONS FOR PRACTICE TRANSITION: AVAILABLE OPTIONS FOR DENTISTS AT ALL CAREER LEVELS

When the alarm clock goes off, you jump out of bed and hit the floor running. You rush to the office, where you work your way—somewhat wildly—through a day filled with taking care of patients and being a good leader for your staff, while also trying to manage the business. Before you know it, you're falling—exhausted—back into bed. You should be counting sheep, but instead, you think about all the patients that you haven't seen in awhile and wonder if they're "lost in the cracks." You ask yourself the same question three times—"Is there a better way?"—before you drop off to sleep. You dream of all the things you must do tomorrow and wake up wondering what other practice options are available to you as a dentist.

Welcome to Another Day in Dentistry

"Is there a better way?" represents a typical question posed by most dentists today. The answer varies, depending on your circumstance. In Chapter 1, we reflected on the history of the dental practice. Now, we see the ever-changing face of the dental-practice model. We feel the effects of the rapidly changing dental marketplace. Yet, so many of us are so caught up in the day-to-day challenges of practicing dentistry that we don't take the time to look at all of our options. Why is it that, too often, we wait until we're forced to look at other options before we do take action?

During the past 17 years, I've spent numerous hours lecturing to local, state, and national groups. I feel heartbroken when I look out into the audience and see the sadness in the eyes of dentists who feel that they have no available options. The good news is that you always, always, always have options.

It's not only important for you to explore all available options, but to develop a working knowledge and a complete understanding of the option you have chosen to pursue. Timing is just as important—now is the time to look at all your practice-transition options.

Take advantage of every information source to become better educated in all aspects of practice transitions. Review each option carefully. Make a list of the pros and cons. Decide which option works best for your professional and personal goals. Determine the option that will allow you the highest return on your investment—from both a financial as well as a quality-of-life perspective. Set goals for your transition and develop a strategic-action plan. (See Chapter 13, "Developing a Strategic-Transition Plan.")

The word transition means change, and the term practice transition should no longer be restricted to the stereotype late-career dentist who is thinking of bringing in an associate and/or selling the practice. In today's market, several transition options are available for consideration by dentists at all career levels. In this chapter, I will outline them and describe the general approach to each. As you get an overall view of all the possibilities, refer to other chapters in the book for detailed definitions and methods for implementation. As we look at real-life examples of dentists who have explored all these options, study their experiences. If you currently are implementing one of these options, use this information to evaluate your progress. Whether your plans require immediate action or allow you the luxury of waiting until later, this is an exciting time to look at all available practice-transition options.

Practice-Transition Options

Practice-Establishment Options. Dentists at all career stages have a potential interest in this option. It used to be limited to opening a practice from "scratch" and, in today's marketplace, may not be the most desirable option. Risks in this area are higher than in the past. Dentists considering starting their own practice should invest time in research and have a strategic-transition plan in place prior to approaching this. Careful consideration should be given to location and marketing. A solid financial plan should be developed, allowing external cash flow for the first year. The stress of a "cash-flow" crunch causes many new businesses to fail. By following a structured transition plan and having the cash flow to operate without having to rely on the initial productivity of the practice, chances for success are higher. (See Chapter 6, "New Practice Establishment.")

Practice establishment through the acquisition of an already established practice is more often than not the preferred route to pursue in today's environment. The purchase of an established practice can be one of the most important decisions a dentist will make in his or her career. The good news is that the track record for this venture is excellent, and the majority of dentists who buy established practices are economically far ahead of those that go into associateships or set up practices from scratch. (See Chapter 10, "Purchasing or Buying Into a Practice.")

Associateship to Co-Ownership Options. The associateship to co-ownership approach is one of the lowest-risk options available to the dentist wishing to establish a practice. In this situation, the associate dentist buys in to part of the equity (usually 50%) of the practice. This transition scenario involves the evolution of an employee-employer relationship to that of practice co-ownership. When desired, this arrangement can be preprogrammed to lead to the eventual sale of the entire practice. The unique characteristic of this concept is the ability of this expansion-and-sale cycle to repeat itself endlessly, perpetuating the practice indefinitely. Selling practice equity to associates can occur multiple times in the life cycle of a practice. Dentists now can enjoy the benefits of the "firm" concept common in other professions, yet almost nonexistent in dentistry. Utilizing the vehicle of age-staggering, the perpetuation and transition process is enhanced, and this process has facilitated excellent growth potential for all practitioners involved. (See Chapter 4, "Creating 'Win-Win' Associateship to Co-Ownership Arrangements.")

Practice Merger Options. Practice mergers often are compared to the group practice model; however, they are entirely different. In this scenario, two practices are joined into a single practice entity through the purchase of one dentist's practice. For dentists who already have an established patient base, purchasing and merging with another practice is an extremely effective way to expand. This avenue literally increases profitability overnight. The selling dentist, on the other hand, enjoys the benefits of continued practice, as well as the security of knowing that the practice was sold to an individual who was already a proven entity in the community. As with any transition, proper planning is a key element in the success of this venture. (See Chapter 5, "Practice Mergers.")

Practice Sale Options. Selling a practice once meant immediate retirement. Though, in many cases, this approach (i.e., a retirement sale) benefits both the seller and the buyer—others wish to implement this event early, but they are confused about the right time to sell their practices. Due to all of the other many creative sale options available to dentists today, the sale of a practice followed by immediate retirement is becoming less common. (See Chapter 3, "Successful Sales Strategies.")

Group Practice Options. This model has been given different names by different people—i.e., space sharing, group practice, solo group, cluster group, etc. The arrangement generally refers to more than one dentist, (usually with separate practice ownership), sharing the same space in one or more locations. Dentists entering a space-sharing situation often are seeking benefits such as shared overhead expenses, office coverage, and professional camaraderie. Historically, these practice models have not always been successful, particularly from a transition perspective. Though I do not recommend space-sharing when other non-solo options exist (such as practice mergers and associateship to co-ownership), success can be enhanced through the use of "win-win" agreements that allow for transition of the practices internally. (See Chapter 5, "Practice Mergers.")

Deferred Sale Options. Dentists often overlook the deferred sale option. This option simply involves locking in the terms, price, and structure of a practice sale prior to the actual event. Most often, this option is used by the selling dentist who wants to guarantee the current value and eventual sale of the practice, but prefers to retain ownership for some period of time. The deferred sale greatly benefits the dentist whose practice requires the assistance of an associate to maintain the growing workload, still needs and/or wants to continue practicing, has perhaps experienced a revolving-door syndrome of associates in the past, and would like to establish future goals for the practice sale while protecting practice value. The buyer-dentist also benefits from this deferred-ownership model. Many new dentists find this to be an ideal way to secure the future purchase of a practice, while having the security of an associate salary during an initial mentoring period. (See Chapter 3, "Successful Sales Strategies," and Chapter 10, "Purchasing or Buying Into a Practice.")

Pre-retirement Sale Options. Pre-retirement sale options exist in many models of available practice transitions for today's dentist. In a pre-retirement sale, the actual sale of the practice occurs well in advance of retirement. The seller then continues practicing, but in an overhead and management-free environment, working as an employee or independent contractor of the buyer. Each pre-retirement sale is unique, and planning early is the best way to insure success.

Some dentists are using this vehicle to explore other career options, or to transition from their existing practices to smaller versions of the same in other areas where they desire to relocate. By selling while the value is at its peak—and having the freedom to explore a new location, staff, or patient base—many preretirement dentists are excited about starting new practices from "scratch." These preretirement dentists continue to repeat the cycle, often selling the new established practice and taking yet another plunge. After all, years of experience, combined with a surge of fresh energy, can make for a very successful venture. (See Chapter 3, "Successful Sales Strategies.")

Retirement Sale Options. Selling upon retirement still is the most common sale option pursued by dentists. In the retirement sale, the selling dentist plans to retire from practice immediately upon, or within a short period of time following, the sale. The selling dentist generally stays just long enough to complete any treatment in progress. Choosing the option of retirement generally involves late-career dentists; however, dentists who have looked at other career options often choose practice retirement as a vehicle to approach careers outside of dentistry. For the most part, accomplishing a successful, fulfilling retirement-sale option involves careful planning. As with other options, a strategic plan for a retirement sale can greatly affect the long-term success of the venture and the happiness of the practitioner. Prior to considering the retirement sale strategy as an option, dentists should clearly know all available transition options, choose the best one for designing an effective transition-retirement plan, develop a comprehensive financial-retirement plan, and remain open to evaluating other personal transition plans. One chapter in this book assists the dentist looking at this option. (See Chapter 3, "Successful Sales Strategies.")

Goodwill-Only Sale Options. The sale and transfer of the dentist's goodwill (through the transfer of the patient records) often has been a "gray" area in practice-transition options. The terms and structure of this type of sale frequently are determined by the potential productivity inherent in the pending treatment needs of the patients, as well as the potential of establishing a long-term doctor-patient relationship. There exist many creative ways to determine the value of this potential. Points to consider include the number of current active patients; the number of new patients per month: the productivity of the hygiene department; and the availability of staff transfer (where desired by the buyer). In the event you consider this option, seek the advice of a trained transition specialist to help structure the plan and determine the true value of the patient-record transfer. These transfers have proven to be financially rewarding to dentists who plan properly.

In the chapters ahead, we will explore in more detail the most viable transition options to consider in early, mid-, and late career. The information will show you how to plan, as well as implement, various practice transitions, allowing you to establish a better foundation for your own future decisions surrounding the establishment, expansion, or sale of your practice.

When the term "practice transition" is used, most dentists immediately think of the *sale* of the practice. Though practice transition encompasses the entire life cycle of the practice, information on its eventual sale is certainly one of the most sought-after components.

The following chapter, "Successful Sales Strategies," will give you a broad overview of this very important part of the transition cycle.

3

SUCCESSFUL SALES STRATEGIES: HOW TO SELL YOUR PRACTICE AND HAVE A GOOD END RESULT

Jim was a dentist in private practice. On the surface, things were going well, but he began to wonder if selling his practice would lead to increased security and freedom, as he had hoped.

As I began consulting with him, Jim started to understand the benefits of why dentists always should be in a position to sell.

Jim and I graduated from dental school at about the same time; we're the same age. During our first meeting, we talked about the typical things dentists talk about these days—primarily, the state of dentistry today and the coming changes. However, the most interesting part of my conversation with Jim was the reason for his call.

During our discussion, Jim told me about his childhood friend, Rick. Rick and Jim graduated from high school in the 1960s. Jim went off to college to study biology; Rick intended to go into the hardware business. Every few years, they called each other to catch up. By the time Jim had graduated from college and decided to go to dental school, Rick owned his hardware store.

Four years later, when Jim graduated from dental school, Rick's business was prospering. In an effort to expand it, Rick hired an associate. He couldn't keep up with all the customers by himself, so it made sense to bring in another person.

Ten years later, Jim was in private practice. On the surface, things were going well. His student loans and practice debts were paid in full and he had been able to put away some money for his children's education. At last, he had arrived—he'd reached his goals. But why did he feel so trapped?

Overhead costs and day-to-day responsibilities of private practice were consuming. He felt pressured. It was hard for him to give himself permission to take time off. He felt as if there were always tasks and details demanding his attention. He had thought about looking for an associate, as Rick had done in his hardware business, but these relationships didn't seem to work out well in dentistry—or so Jim thought.

After a particularly hard day, Jim called Rick to talk things over with him. Rick still was riding high. His business had grown by leaps and bounds. He had sold part of the hardware business to his associate, who was now his partner. He was enjoying passive income from the sale and his management responsibilities had been cut in half. Jim was happy for his friend, but he couldn't help being somewhat envious.

Theoretically, Jim still thought that he had made a sounder career choice than Rick. Although dentistry had required extensive education, the profession allowed the potential for a good, stable income.

Yet, as the years went by, Jim's friend, Rick, continued to experience more freedom. Jim's practice seemed to require more time than ever before. Rick reduced his work hours, while Jim continued to feel trapped.

Jim began to question if solo practice would ever lead to the increased security and freedom that Rick had with his hardware store.

Eventually, Rick sold his hardware business to a large company. The corporation hired Rick as a consultant and allowed him to continue working in the store. No longer burdened by the pressures of managing the business, Rick enjoyed his time with customers. Most of all, he enjoyed the cash-flow stream created by selling his interest in the business. In short, Rick was financially secure. It appeared that he would never have to struggle again.

Jim, still envious, was now intrigued. He questioned Rick about how he had pulled this off. "I just did what all business people do," Rick replied. "I expanded, found a partner to buy-in, and later took advantage of the opportunity to sell my share to a major competitor. I was presented with an offer too good to refuse. Doesn't this happen in dentistry?"

Jim had to admit that dentists could benefit from this type of business thinking. In fact, he realized that many dentists (like him) were so vested in independence, they often passed up opportunities to expand, thus never reaping the benefits of passive income and shared management responsibilities.

Jim began to wonder if independence was worth the price. He decided to look for a way to change his future. His next call was to me, to explore what opportunities dentists could seize to experience greater freedom.

As I began consulting with Jim, he started to understand why all dentists should always be in a position to sell part or all of their practices. He recognized that while the decision to sell or take on an associate could be stressful, waiting too long to make changes could be devastating. His lack of decision-making had made the entire experience much more traumatic than it needed to be.

Once we completed a comprehensive transition plan for Jim, he was able to put it into play—with excellent results. As it did for his friend, Rick, life for Jim became exhilarating once again.

When To Plan for a Practice Sale

Selling your practice is both an ominous and appealing concept. You don't know which is stronger—the excitement or the butterflies you are feeling. There are countless questions coming to mind. When's the right time to sell? Should I finance all or part of the sale? No matter how young or old you are, begin now to think about the future sale of your practice. Certain life and career events can occur that make it advantageous to be "positioned to sell." Some of these events are positive, some are not so positive. In either case, it pays to be well-postured for the possibility. Properly timed and structured, it can set the stage for a financially secure retirement.

After all the blood, sweat, and tears you pour into your practice, selling is where it all ends up—and, hopefully, you'll be receiving a profitable return on your lifelong investment.

As a consultant, I've worked with hundreds of dentists faced with the decision of whether to sell their practices—and when. Having previously been in that position myself, I'm acutely aware of the emotional issues involved. (In fact, I spent two sleepless weeks wondering if selling my practice was the right thing to do.)

Perhaps, before we explore the options for selling a practice, it would be advantageous for us to understand the emotional aspects of a practice sale.

Don't Wait Too Long

It is interesting to look at the psychological aspects of selling a dental practice. Selling has always been viewed as an acceptable option during the final years of practice. Late-career dentists do not have the need to justify their decision to sell. However, the problem many older dentists face is not planning well for retirement, both financially and psychologically. Some late-career dentists feel forced to delay retirement until they are simply too old to continue practicing. Even those who are financially prepared have a great deal of uncertainty about the process of selling their practices, as well as what awaits them in their retirement years.

Mid-career dentists often feel a need to have a good reason to sell their practices. In other professions, business owners are proud of building, selling, retiring, or starting new ventures. Often, these entrepreneurs consider a mid-career sale a sign of their versatility and talents.

Until recently, selling a dental practice in mid-career was sometimes viewed as a sign of failure. We're now seeing a shift in this attitude. More mid-career dentists are choosing to sell their practices, while the value is high. Many then look for another small practice to buy and build and repeat the process. Other mid-career dentists finally are giving themselves permission to pursue other business interests outside of dentistry (Where is it written that you must stay in the same career or profession your entire life? I faced this emotional "roadblock" myself in the early 1980s and, in retrospect, I needlessly suffered a lot of anxiety.)

One area to explore in the emotional aspect of selling a practice is the relationship we have with our patients. As dentists, we develop very close personal relationships with our patients. When we sell our practices, they often feel as if we are selling an essential component of their lives. Some dentists believe that they owe it to their patients to stay in the practice.

It's sad to think that we dedicated professionals choose not to sell when it's right for us, only because we are afraid of feeling guilty for "abandoning" patients. In essence, we are allowing the perceived needs of others to influence our own major life decisions.

Until there is a good reason to sell, many dentists never look at other options. Unfortunately, illness too frequently forces a sale.

I've had many late-career dentists call me for advice about selling their practices, worrying that they have waited too late to sell. Some even say they'll probably end up "dying at the chair," as if they see no way of cashing in their practice value at that point. (In fact, we've all heard stories about dentists who have died at the chair.)

I recently was saddened to learn of the death of one of my elderly clients. He suffered a heart attack while doing an extraction and fell over the patient during the procedure. His staff pulled his lifeless body off the patient. This was a man who, only two years before his death, told me that he "just wasn't ready to begin planning for the sale of his practice." His reason for waiting was good health, and he was sure that he could continue his rigorous routine for several more years. Though he often spoke about how he "wanted to be sure his wife would be well taken care of," he neglected to focus any attention on the eventual transition of his practice.

His widow, already traumatized by his sudden death, was devastated to learn that his practice would sell for only about 20% of its pre-death value (if it sold at all).

Had a comprehensive transition plan been in place, a future buyer already could have been in place in the practice, and the purchase of the practice would have occurred automatically. Prior to his death, this dentist could have benefited from cashing in part or all of his practice value, while continuing to work in the practice as a co-owner or in a preretirement sale arrangement. Selling practice equity (or at least planning for the sale) did not have to mean the end of his practicing years.

Perhaps my client was having a difficult time adjusting to letting go of his practice. I've noticed that dentists who retire before 65 years of age tend to adjust easier than do those who remain in practice much longer. Perhaps those who do retire prior to age 65 do so because they have planned for it financially — and perhaps they have something to retire to.

Dentists who sell at an earlier age usually have planned for their retirement lifestyles. They often have developed many outside interests and look forward to spending time with their families. Dentists who plan for retirement are most apt to make wise decisions about their practice sales. Because they look forward to a happy retirement, they plan for it early.

The point remains — all dentists should plan for the future. Whether you're a recent dental school graduate or have practiced for 40 years, it's never too early to think about positioning your practice for a potential sale. We dentists often fail to realize that planning to sell doesn't always mean it's actually time to sell. There is a big difference. First, planning for a practice sale means knowing the details of all viable practice-exit strategies. Second, planning means developing a successful sale strategy at all points of your practice life cycle. And last, planning means always, always being in a position to sell.

The graph entitled the "Practice Growth Cycle" (Figure 3.1) will give you a better understanding of how the various practice-sale options fit into the typical practice life cycle. There are several key points to notice here as it relates to the profitability and value of your practice as you go through various phases in the transition of your practice.

The Growth Phase

During the normal growth phase of the practice, profitability and practice values are in a steady climb once a certain monthly base production required for paying the overhead has been achieved. This rise is almost a proportional one. Below this base production, the practice is not profitable, and may have little, if any, true market value. A sound practice management program and/or bringing in an associate could augment this growth quite rapidly, or if a merger opportunity were available in the area, that also would create immediate expansion of the practice. (See Chapter 5, "Practice Mergers.")

The Plateau Phase

This phase is reached when the owner dentist either becomes financially comfortable with the existing production of the practice or is unable to produce beyond a certain point due to limitations of the practice. Frequently, capacity has peaks and the dentist has no desire to expand. This stage often is referred to as the mature phase of the practice life cycle. Many dentists complain when they reach various plateau phases in their practices. (There are often multiple plateau phases—not just one.) Some are able to move beyond these plateaus while others are not.

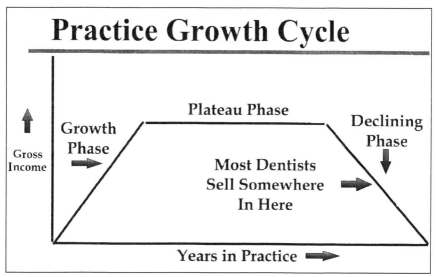

Fig. 3.1

The Declining Phase

Inevitably, a declining phase becomes a natural part of the cycle of a solo practice (Quite often, this decline is viewed as a natural event). At some point, the solo owner slows down, gets sick, retires, or dies. Some serious decisions need to be made prior to any voluntary or involuntary reduction in the productivity of the practice. At this point, the following options should be considered: bringing in an associate to maintain and/or expand the production of the practice; selling the practice early while the value is at a maximum; and/or hiring a practice management consultant to assist in the continued growth of the practice. (Figure 3.2)

The time to make decisions about a practice sale is prior to the so-called "declining" phase. Income, combined with practice value, begins to slip away during the decline of any practice. Advantageous preretirement-sale options begin to diminish without proper presale planning.

Once practice production declines, practice value and profitability is affected dramatically ("profit squeeze"). There will come a time when your desire to slow down will be greater than your desire to continue working at your current level.... Upon cutting back, the rate of return on your production dollars will decrease (as will the value of your practice). At this point, it makes sense to either sell or bring in an

```
┌─────────────────────────────────────────────────┐
│        THE DECLINING PHASE:                       │
│        OPTIONS TO CONSIDER                        │
├─────────────────────────────────────────────────┤
│                                                   │
│   •  BRINGING IN AN ASSOCIATE                     │
│                                                   │
│   •  SELLING THE PRACTICE EARLY                   │
│                                                   │
│   •  HIRING A CONSULTANT                          │
│                                                   │
└─────────────────────────────────────────────────┘
```

Fig. 3.2

associate to first expand the practice and eventually purchase part or all of it.

Considering the "time value" of money, the sooner you sell and convert practice equity into an interest-bearing cash stream, the greater amount of money you will receive. Knowing the best "timing" for this can give you a great deal of "peace of mind," as well as put you tens of thousands of dollars ahead, if not much more. This information should be part of your comprehensive transition plan.

In many cases, it's as if we dentists believe that we have the luxury of just letting our practices die. After all, we built our own business, why can't we do with it what we want? While true in the literal sense, allowing a practice to simply decline before retirement may be a luxury today's dentists can't afford. Dentists must examine their options for expanding, selling, or, at least, securing the sale of the equity in their practices prior to this declining phase.

Practice-Sale Strategies

In this section, I'll present a description of the most common practice-sale strategies to consider for the outright sale of a dental practice. It's important that you understand each so that you can choose the strategy that will yield your desired results. Four basic options exist. (Figure 3.3)

Most of you will find one of these strategies better fits your particular situation than the others. Hopefully, none of you will be forced to choose one option over another because of events and circumstances beyond your control. I urge you to plan ahead so that your strategy-of-choice is well thought out and chosen voluntarily.

In exploring which option is right for you, we'll discuss the timing for each of these sale options and how you can begin to develop a

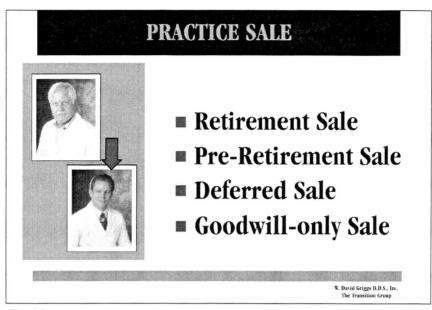

Fig. 3.3

strategic plan for the eventual sale of your practice. (See Chapter 13, "Developing a Strategic Transition Plan.")

Retirement Sale Option

In the retirement sale option, the practice is sold and the dentist retires. (This is why this option often is referred to as the "walk-away sale.") There generally is very little transition time between the sale and retirement. The seller stays long enough to finish uncompleted cases and moves on to retirement life. Patients receive letters announcing that their "continued care has now been turned over to Dr. Smith, someone who was hand picked by their dentist."

The Retirement Sale: Advantages. The retirement-sale transition eliminates a common problem: insufficient patients in the practice to keep both the seller and buyer busy, particularly through a prolonged transition. Few dentists nearing retirement have sufficient patient load to support two dentists through any lengthy post-sale working relationship, unless both buyer and seller are able to work on a part-time basis.

Many sellers pursue the retirement-sale route because of concerns they have about other sale arrangements—arrangements that require them to work together with the buyer following the sale, sometimes for extended periods. Since many sellers who are close to retirement have worked alone throughout most of their careers, they have concerns as to how happy they would be working with (or for) another dentist. (Figure 3.4)

This is the most common and the least complicated type of sale. It also requires the least amount of advanced planning when compared to other sale options. There are minimal relationship challenges in this transition, because the working relationship between the buyer and seller is brief and in some situations, nonexistent (i.e., the seller exits the practice immediately upon the sale). It's been the traditional approach for most dentists for many years.

The Retirement Sale: The Basic Steps. Dentists wanting to sell upon retirement should begin the process at least one to two years prior to their anticipated exit date. This time frame allows time for the dentist to get his "house in order," and conduct a proper search for the right candidate. (The "right" candidate generally means someone who is both mentally and financially ready to purchase.) The time can be shorter in areas where there is a high demand for established practices, but it can be much longer in smaller towns or rural areas where fewer dentists are seeking opportunities. Gauge your situation accordingly, and, as always, plan a little further ahead than what you think you need.

While many dentists adjust well to newer practice-transition arrangements as described in this chapter, many still tend to sell upon retirement. This can work out well, but I'm concerned that the decision to wait is driven more from lack of information of all available options and/or procrastination than by conscious design.

The fact is, lack of planning causes problems, and I urge you not to procrastinate. Even if you decide to remain a solo practitioner, you should begin planning for a successor well before your target-retirement date. I also believe that keeping an open mind will help you see the benefits of other options. No matter which choice you make, you should enter it with your eyes open and not because you delayed making a decision for so long that you have few options left. In my experience, the biggest disadvantage of a retirement sale is that it often ends up being the only choice.

RETIREMENT SALE ADVANTAGES

- LESS PLANNING REQUIRED
- NO RELATIONSHIP CHALLENGES
- SMALLER PATIENT BASE NEEDED

Fig. 3.4

Dentists who are displeased with new marketing philosophies and other trends in dentistry generally are happy to "sell by nine and be out by noon." There's no question that those who want to make a quick, clean exit generally prefer retirement sales. No matter what disadvantages exist, the ability to transition into retirement quickly is the primary advantage in this kind of sale.

Late-career dentists often choose the retirement sale as their preferred sale option. However, keep in mind that circumstances may remove true choice for the seller. Disability or death often forces a sale by the dentist or the estate. Sometimes, the practice must be sold at a price substantially below market value. (See Chapter 7, "Determining the Value of Your Practice.")

The Retirement Sale: Disadvantages. Since most dentists have traditionally chosen the retirement-sale path as their preferred sale option, it's been possible to observe some of the consequences of such a decision.

Because life is unpredictable, many dentists have found they lose much of the value of their practice in the last three to five years. Sometimes, it's a voluntary occurrence; oftentimes, it is not. Waiting until retirement to sell can be equated to a "crap shoot," when compared to other options in which value can be protected.

In addition, passive income from an early sale is not a benefit that dentists selling at retirement will be able to enjoy. Having to maintain the ownership and management responsibilities of a practice to the end may minimize certain quality-of-life pursuits that are more easily available using other sale options.

Another factor further complicating the situation is something I refer to as the *profit squeeze*. This happens when gross collections drop off in late career, squeezing the normal profit percentage as much as 50%. (Dentists making 35% or 38% of their net find that, late in retirement, it drops 15% to 20% when their production drops.) When all these factors are combined, it forces you to take a serious look at other options before pursuing the retirement-sale option. (Figure 3.5)

The Retirement Sale: Early-Career Considerations. Many early-career dentists find the retirement-sale scenario to be an excellent "entryway" into private practice. All of the practice-sale strategies offer the purchasing dentist low-risk options for establishing practice ownership. The degree of success enjoyed by the buyer in the retirement-sale scenario will depend on the profile of the practice (i.e., size, production history, and potential), and the overall clinical and communication skills of the purchasing dentist. The quick transfer of patients that occurs in this scenario is one of the most important factors to consider in this type of transition. The selling dentist who chooses this scenario often desires this. Despite the fact that the transition relationship between the buyer and seller may be brief, the successful transfer of patients can occur provided the transition is properly managed and well-thought through. Transition management (part of the new lingo used by transition consultants) certainly is important in any type of sale, particularly in a retirement-sale scenario. The services of a professional should be sought. (Figure 3.6)

The Retirement Sale: Mid-Career Considerations. Mid-career dentists who already have established practices can greatly benefit from buying a retiring dentist's practice in their area (Note: Retiring dentists are not the only ones selling. See Chapter 5, "Practice Mergers.") The two practices can be merged into one facility or they can be operated as separate facilities (i.e., a second location of the practice). Merging into one facility is almost always more profitable, although there are some situations

---

RETIREMENT SALE DISADVANTAGES

- PRACTICE VALUE LOSS

- NO PASSIVE INCOME

- PROFIT *SQUEEZE*

Fig. 3.5

EARLY-CAREER CONSIDERATIONS

LOW-RISK PRACTICE START

MINIMAL TRANSITION TIME

QUICK PATIENT TRANSFER

NO RELATIONSHIP CHALLENGES

Fig. 3.6

where operating them as separate facilities may make the most sense. Either way, this type of purchase can enhance greatly the purchaser's profitability and can facilitate the expansion needed to add an associate to the practice. This way, the combined practices can be expanded even further. (See Chapter 4, "Associateship to Co-Ownership.")

For the most part, mid-career dentists are in a better position to purchase practices in a retirement-sale scenario than the average early-career dentist is. In general, the lesser-experienced new dentist requires a longer transition time to adequately transfer patients. Mid-career dentists can usually accomplish this transfer in less time. As we've seen, however, there is no hard and fast rule about this. It will depend on the size of the practice being purchased and the personal and clinical skills of the buyer. (See Chapter 10, "Purchasing or Buying Into a Practice.") (Figure 3.7)

Preretirement-Sale Option

A second practice sale option is the pre-retirement sale, which simply means the practice is sold prior to retirement, sometimes even years before.

There are specific benefits to a pre-retirement sale, and dentists evaluating this type of transition usually have personal requirements and reasons for choosing it. Selling dentists at any career level can consider a pre-retirement sale. It's extremely important for pre-retirement sale arrangements to be designed and developed on a case-by-case basis, as the needs of the individuals may widely vary. A structured,

```
┌─────────────────────────────────────────────────────┐
│               THE RETIREMENT SALE:                    │
│             MID-CAREER CONSIDERATIONS                 │
├─────────────────────────────────────────────────────┤
│  • PRACTICE EXPANSION                                 │
│     - MERGER                                          │
│     - SECOND OFFICE LOCATION                          │
│  • INCREASED PROFIT                                   │
│  • FACILITATES ASSOCIATE ENTRY                        │
│  • PRACTICE-VALUE ENHANCEMENT                         │
└─────────────────────────────────────────────────────┘
```

Fig. 3.7

preplanned exit strategy for the dentist considering retirement, relocation, or other types of transition is integral to the design of the pre-retirement sale.

This option is popular for the seller-dentist who has the desire to explore career opportunities outside of practicing dentistry. The advantage of selling and continuing to work in the practice (while pursuing other ventures) is one that few business owners get to enjoy. Knowing that the option to return to private practice exists, these dentists can enjoy the freedom of trying new ventures. In fact, this is the option I chose when I sold my practice in Atlanta, Georgia. My initial transition plan was to sell my practice, work for the buyer, look for a practice to purchase in Florida, and then move. As it turned out, my practice sold well before my anticipated date of relocation to Florida. I worked in the practice for only one year after the sale. In my agreement, however, I had the security of knowing that I had the option to remain in the practice for several years, should I so choose.

This created all sorts of possibilities for me to consider. The freedom created by my sale allowed me to pursue numerous avenues that otherwise would have been difficult for me to explore. This "posture" allowed me the opportunity to receive extensive training and education in the consulting field. Having the freedom of choice, I made the decision to change my career direction and help others to explore their options as well.

The pre-retirement sale offers a number of other advantages, such as the opportunity to lock in practice value years before retirement and continue working until retirement in an overhead-free and management-free environment.

This option also protects the seller-dentist from possible problems in the future. Often, during the five-year period proceeding retirement, the productivity level of many dental practices drops. When this happens, the practice value decreases significantly. Other unforeseen problems, such as death or disability, can obviously have a tremendous effect on practice value. By choosing the pre-retirement option, this potential downward trend in practice value can be eliminated.

Another benefit to the seller-dentist is the opportunity to make the entire retirement experience less stressful by planning ahead. The sooner the equity of a practice is converted into a cash-flow stream, the greater the return on investment. In some cases, this provides not only peace of mind, but also tens of thousands of dollars for future retirement investments.

In addition, the gradual phase-out plan created by the pre-retirement sale facilitates a smooth transition for patient transfer. The patients know that they have been turned over to someone who worked side-by-side with you before you retired.

The financial benefits of selling early are numerous, particularly for those dentists who intend to cut back on their production. (Figure 3.8)

Here's an example of a dentist who was considering selling. He had his practice valued in an effort to understand the economic impact that the sale might have on his retirement and estate-planning. It was valued at $210,000. He planned to immediately cut back his work schedule from four days to three, then to two. Also, he determined that by selling his practice early, he was going to preserve his practice value by approximately $70,000 by the end of year three. Here's why:

Assuming his practice was currently worth $210,000 (70% of his $300,000 gross annual income) and he decreased production to $200,000

THE PRE-RETIREMENT SALE: BENEFITS

- PRACTICE VALUE SECURED
- PASSIVE INCOME
- CONTINUED-PRACTICE OPTION
- NO MANAGEMENT *OR* OVERHEAD RESPONSIBILITIES
- SMOOTHER TRANSITION

Fig. 3.8

by year three (the last year he planned to work) and sold his practice at that time, then it might sell for $140,000 (again, 70% of a $200,000 gross-annual income). The difference in the price received was going to be $70,000. (Figure 3.9)

He also determined that if he sold early, he would receive investment income on the net selling price (the selling price, minus taxes and any other expenses involved in the sale). Conversely, he calculated what his net profit percentage would be on his production income if he maintained ownership and overhead responsibilities himself.

He presently was netting 35% of his gross collections. He determined that as he decreased his production, his net percentage would be squeezed to less than 30%. However, if he sold his practice early and worked for the buyer (who was going to compensate him at 35% of collections), he could continue to maintain his present net percentage. In essence, he was going to enjoy at least a 5% higher net on the dollars produced once he gave up ownership of the practice. (Note: In this scenario, the seller is not normally paid for the services provided directly by the hygienist.)

Finally, he had one additional windfall form of income to add to the equation: the rental of the real estate. Since he owned the building in which he practiced, he could now receive rent (from someone other than himself) years in advance of, as well as beyond, retirement. (As an option, the real estate could also have been sold.)

In the final analysis, this dentist was happy to see that, by selling early, he was many thousands of dollars ahead of where he would have been had he worked until the end and then sold.

Since many late-career dentists want to approach retirement in a scenario similar to this one, the pre-retirement sale could be of great benefit to them.

Note: Each situation needs to be looked at individually. In some situations, where the seller wants or needs to cut back production as retirement approaches, this scenario is ideal. However, the dentist who wants to stay at "full throttle" until the end may not benefit from such a program.

Pre-retirement-Sale Benefits: Early Career. The pre-retirement sale also is an ideal way for early-career dentists to buy a practice, even if the buyer is not yet experienced enough to operate the practice alone. A pre-retirement sale offers a longer transition period and more time to prepare clinically and managerially to own a practice. Guidance and

PRE-RETIREMENT SALE PRACTICE VALUE PRESERVATION	
PRESENT PRACTICE GROSS	$300,000
PRESENT PRACTICE VALUE (70%)	$210,000
PRACTICE GROSS INCOME IN 3 YEARS	$200,000
PRACTICE VALUE IN 3 YEARS $140,000	
PRACTICE VALUE PRESERVATION	**$70,000**

Fig. 3.9

mentoring are necessary for success and, for many sellers, it's a rewarding experience. The selling dentist is secure in the knowledge that the practice is sold, making the mentoring even more worthwhile. This is much better than the uneasy feeling dentists may have if they're in a loosely structured associate arrangement that may lead nowhere. (Usually, neither party wins in that scenario.)

The transition time—during which the buyer and seller work together—needs to be tailored to suit the buyer's needs. Buyers often need both mentoring and production income from the seller. The buyer and seller establish a minimum period of time the seller is obligated to stay with the practice, after which the relationship can continue by mutual consent. This way, the buyer has time to refine clinical and managerial skills and to help assure the seller that the practice is in good hands. (Figure 3.10)

Pre-retirement Sale: Choosing the Right Candidate. Once the seller has found the "right" candidate, it's wise to stay in the practice for whatever length of time it takes to make the transition work. This usually requires a minimum of between 12 and 18 months, but the seller can stay in the practice much longer based on the needs and desires of both parties. Having the seller stay in the practice during some minimal transition time is far better than turning away a good candidate (with less experience) in order to search for a more experienced candidate. Another candidate may better match the seller's time frame, but may not be the right person. Every dentist wants to leave the practice feeling good about the successor, so spending a little extra time in the practice usually is a worthwhile investment in future peace of mind.

<table>
<tr><td>

THE PRE-RETIREMENT SALE: EARLY-CAREER BENEFITS

- REQUIRES LESS CLINICAL EXPERIENCE
- PROVIDES EXTENDED MENTORING PERIOD
- ALLOWS TAILORED TRANSITION TIME

</td></tr>
</table>

Fig. 3.10

Pre-retirement Sale as Part of a Merger. In a pre-retirement sale that involves a merger, the seller becomes a built-in, associate clinician for the buyer. He or she assists with the transition and helps maintain overall practice productivity until the selling dentist retires. The seller gradually phases out of the practice and patients transfer to the buyer, as well as to a buyer's present or future associate. The seller has helped in the growth of both dentists' practices. The profit generated from the additional production will almost always pay for the cost of the practice, even after paying the buyer, seller, or associate reasonable compensation for their services. (See Chapter 5, "Practice Mergers.") (Figure 3.11)

Deferred Sale Option

The next practice-sale option is the deferred sale. In this situation, the buyer and/or seller are not yet ready to exchange ownership of the practice, but both parties are willing to proceed with a plan for the eventual sale. The deferred sale can prove to be an interesting approach to this common scenario.

To provide you with a classic example of this situation, let's use the scenario of the dental school graduate wanting to purchase a practice. The owner wants to sell the practice. However, he would like to delay the effective date of such a sale. The dentists either pre-agree on price and terms of the future sale or agree to a price determination method to be used in the future. The buyer becomes an "employee-dentist" for the seller. They have arranged for the actual sale of the practice to occur automatically on a specific future date. This is called a deferred sale.

In this option, all terms and conditions of the arrangements are programmed to occur in advance. There are no items to negotiate at a later date and few questions left unanswered, provided that a comprehensive agreement has been constructed prior to the arrangement. This

```
┌─────────────────────────────────────────────────────┐
│           THE PRE-RETIREMENT SALE:                    │
│               MERGER BENEFITS                         │
├─────────────────────────────────────────────────────┤
│                                                       │
│  • ENHANCES PROFITS & PRACTICE VALUE                  │
│  • SELLER BECOMES "BUILT-IN" ASSOCIATE                │
│  • PASSIVE INCOME                                     │
│  • FACILITATES FUTURE ASSOCIATE-BUY-IN                │
│                                                       │
└─────────────────────────────────────────────────────┘
```

Fig. 3.11

preplanning strategy helps prevent any misunderstandings from occurring down the road. (Figure 3.12)

Between the initial employment-agreement date and the actual purchase date, the buyer continues to work for the seller. At the time of the sale, the two dentists reverse roles. The buyer is now the owner, and the seller is now the employee. Generally, this transition takes place one to three years after the initial association.

Many dentists prefer this option to the normal and customary associate arrangement, because the pre-arranged agreement offers the owner a better chance of a guaranteed sale. Far too many dentists are disappointed in basing their goals on the hope that their associate eventually will buy the practice. Often, dentists are fooled into thinking that "grooming" an associate to become the buyer is some guarantee of sale. Unfortunately, some associates do not have a buyer's mentality or have other future agendas in mind. Hiring a dentist who has a buyer's mentality and mutually agreeing to a firm plan for a deferred sale eliminates the "going nowhere" syndrome common in many associateships.

After the actual sale occurs (usually in one to three years), the seller has the option of continuing to practice (under pre-arranged terms similar to the pre-retirement sale option) or retiring. This offers the best of both worlds for many late-career dentists.

Early-Career Considerations. This deferred purchase opportunity for the early-career dentist is much more attractive than employment-only opportunities. The seller-dentist often becomes a mentor for the associate dentist, who needs to gain experience and become more prepared for ownership. This extended mentoring period is very much appreciated by many early-career dentists.

DEFERRED SALE BENEFITS
SELLER BENEFITS

- ESTABLISHES AGREED-UPON PRICE
- SECURES FUTURE SALE
- ELIMINATES "ASSOCIATESHIP GOING NOWHERE" SYNDROME
- ALLOWS EXTENDED TRANSITION TIME

Fig. 3.12

Mid-Career Considerations. Mid-career dentists considering future-practice expansion, through mergers or additional locations, also can find some advantages with this approach. Due to the delayed purchase mechanism, a "courtship" period is created, prior to either party making a full commitment to a sale-purchase. In this scenario, however, the mid-career dentist does not become an "employee-dentist" for the seller. The two dentists simply work together in a space-sharing situation, until the effective date of the sale. The selling dentist maintains actual ownership of the practice, with the future buyer managing it. In this situation, the seller often works on a percentage basis.

This type of deferred sale approach also is excellent for the late-career dentist who prefers to sell to an already-experienced practitioner. The greater experience and motivation of the mid-career dentist generally means a shorter transition period in this type of deferred sale. Eventually, this creates the opportunity for the mid-career buyer to enjoy a profitable merger and/or a second practice location, depending on the distance between the buyer's and seller's practices.

Goodwill Sale Option

Often, only the goodwill of the practice is sold. In conjunction with this sale, the patient records of the practice are transferred to the buyer, which is why this type of sale frequently is referred to as a *patient record transfer.*

This type of sale occurs in a number of situations. Sometimes the seller's facility and equipment are not marketable due to location or age. There also are situations in which the buyer is practicing in the same area as the seller and already has a desirable location (i.e., the buyer has no need for the seller's facility and/or equipment). This type of sale often occurs when the seller becomes disabled or dies and another dentist in the area offers to purchase the patient records. Although it's questionable as to the precise amount of goodwill that transfers in a death or disability sale, it's still a good investment for the buyer.

There also are situations in which the seller's location is more marketable as real estate than as a practice. For the seller to maximize his or her return, it's necessary to separate the sale of the location from the sale of the practice. In this situation, the real estate is often sold to a non dentist and used for some type of commercial business. (I frequently have seen dental offices in high-exposure areas replaced with high-rise construction.) The practice goodwill is then sold to a nearby dentist.

How to Sell Goodwill Only. The goodwill value of the practice can be valued as a separate asset. Any good appraisal will provide this value. (See Chapter 7, "Determining the Value of Your Practice.") In a goodwill-only sale, this can become the value that determines where to start negotiating a selling price. Typically, a percentage of the gross collections of the practice determine this value.

This value also can be based on a fixed per-chart cost. I've seen this range from $25 per chart to as much as $100 per chart (for active patients—those seen at least once in the previous 12 months). In the per-chart approach, this amount becomes a fixed price and is paid over time (generally seller-financed) with interest.

Another payment option has the buyer paying the seller a fixed percentage of the collections produced on the seller's patients that transfer. This way, the buyer is in a no-risk position and the seller can potentially receive a far greater amount of money than the per-chart approach will yield.

Note: As a buyer, you should always seek the advice of counsel regarding state laws that govern the purchase and transfer of patient records. The sale of goodwill can become a potential legal issue when looking at the sale of practices with Medicaid (called by different names in different states) or Medicare patients. Because selling and referring these patients may violate federal or state laws, caution should be exercised when selling a practice with such a patient base for more than the value of the tangible assets. Please check with your legal advisor regarding such a sale.

Choosing the Right Option

Choosing the appropriate practice-sale option will depend upon each dentist's situation. The multitude of variables include the target retirement date of the dentist, how early the seller began planning, the health status of the seller, whether the seller wants a continued practice option, and the experience level of the buyer. (Figure 3.13)

Target Retirement Date. Dentists with rapidly approaching target-retirement dates have fewer options. It often takes a full year to get everything in order to sell—i.e., valuing the practice, locating buyer candidates, and completing all the necessary agreements. Those who are one year or less from retirement will most likely leave practice in a retirement-sale scenario based on the limited amount of time remaining. To have the greatest number of possible options, plan early—at least three to five years out.

Health Considerations. Health problems force many dentists to sell early. At the very least, these dentists should be securing the future sale of their practice through a deferred sale or pre-retirement sale program. Otherwise, the value of the practice is placed at risk.

Continued-Practice Option. Many dentists savor the idea of selling their practices prior to actual retirement. This allows the selling dentist to continue working in the practice, taking profit out of their business after it's been sold. For those desiring the continued-practice option, the pre-retirement-sale approach is the one on which to focus.

The Experience Level of the Buyer. In some situations, the experience level of the purchaser will influence the practice sale option that you choose as the proper transition of the practice. From a buyer's perspective, the size of the practice being purchased is often dictated by the buyer's prior practice experience. It makes sense, then, that the greater the purchaser's experience level, the larger the potential practice being purchased can be. In addition, it also may dictate whether the selling dentist needs to stay with the practice following the sale to help maintain production until the buyer is better prepared to "go solo." (In a properly structured transition, the buyer can gradually phase into the responsibilities of the practice while the seller phases out.)

CHOOSING THE RIGHT SALE OPTION
VARIABLES TO CONSIDER

- SELLER'S RETIREMENT DATE
- HOW EARLY THE SELLER BEGAN PLANNING
- SELLER'S HEALTH STATUS
- CONTINUED PRACTICE OPTION BY SELLER
- PURCHASER'S EXPERIENCE LEVEL

Fig. 3.13

Often, a selling dentist who initially desires a quick transition (i.e., a retirement sale) finally chooses a more gradual one (such as a deferred sale or pre-retirement sale), based on the needs of the "perfect" buyer candidate he locates. This way, not only are the transition needs of both parties addressed, but the needs of the patients and practice are, as well. It's sometimes better to adapt your transition approach to fit the situation, particularly if you have the "right" person for your practice.

Planning for the Sale

Planning for the sale of your practice is a complex process and is covered in detail in Chapter 13, "Developing a Strategic-Transition Plan." The process should begin with a valuation of your practice, one that will reflect its true value, and not just its price. Lending institutions involved with the sale and advisors recognize and appreciate that you have taken the process seriously by having your practice appraised. (See Chapter 7, "Determining the Value of Your Practice.")

Once the valuation has been completed, income projections can be constructed, providing an income forecast for the buyer. This generally is projected out for a minimum period of three years, and can be as long as 10 years. Extended projections are not needed as buyers and their lenders are most interested in what their income will be for the one- to two-year period following the sale. Most feel that if they do well through this period, they will continue to do better beyond that time. Besides, who can possibly predict what a practice will be producing in three to five years?

With a practice valuation and the necessary income projections, you then are ready to search for a buyer candidate.

For those dentists who do not want to get involved in advertising, screening, and negotiating with buyer candidates, there are consulting companies and practice brokerage firms that can help you. They screen buyers and present your practice opportunity in a professional manner. Your CPA and attorney frequently will offer to help, but they rarely have any experience in this specialized area and may be considered adversaries to a potential buyer. It's generally better not to have them negotiate the sale. (See Chapter 9, "How To Best Utilize Your Financial, Legal, and Business Advisors.")

Once the candidate has been located and all negotiations have been properly handled, the next step is for a preliminary agreement to be drawn up between the two parties. This outlines the major terms and conditions of the sale. It is crucial that you both agree to the issues covered before proceeding to final sale agreements. These agreements will cover the normal issues—the assets being purchased; how the price was broken down into these assets; how accounts receivable are handled; what to do with treatments in progress; various seller and buyer warranties; how seller financing will be secured; how the seller will work for the buyer after the sale; and specifically how patients and staff will be transferred to the buyer.

These documents can be extensive—40 to 60 pages or more. (See Chapter 8, "Structuring Your Agreements.")

Selling to a Dental-Management Company. Over the last few years, new dental-management companies have emerged into the marketplace. These companies have approached dentists with well-established practices, offering them management contracts in exchange for part of the profits of the practice. In some situations, these companies have actually purchased the practices, with licensed dentists (in most cases) as the actual "purchasers."

These companies offer a number of services including marketing, inventory maintenance, patient scheduling, office systems, billing and collection functions, and so forth. (These companies typically provide these services through the use of an on-site manager.) Once the contract between the dentist and the management company has been signed, the doctor's role generally is limited to providing clinical services, which is an attractive option for many dentists in today's changing and challenging market.

Though some of these dental-management companies limit their operations to specialty practices (such as orthodontics), many of them seek out general practices. The financial gain for specialists appears to be greater. However, it still appears that any time a practice can be sold to a traditional buyer, the seller comes out ahead. The exception is any windfall financial gain the seller might reap from stock in the dental management company received as part of the agreement. When examining any proposed offer from these companies, consider carefully the items listed on Figure 3-14.

To Which Group Do You Belong? Throughout the 16 years that I have been consulting, I have seen three distinct groups form regarding practice sales.

Some dentists still choose to altogether bypass the option to sell, preferring to quietly retire. Some end up transferring their patient records through a goodwill-only sale. Others merely refer their patients to a friend upon retirement. This was a tradition decades ago. Some dentists planned for it to happen this way, others did not. Dentists often think the investment in time, energy, and money needed to successfully sell their practices just isn't worth the inevitable annoyances involved. For those who have thoroughly explored all available options, this decision might be justified.

The second group wants to sell, but prefers to put off the decision until a later date. Dentists in this very large group often are unclear about the worth of their practices and the steps involved in the process. Procrastination sets in and they often wait too long to begin effectively planning for this crucial step. At some point, many feel as if they've missed the boat, when they compare their situations to colleagues who approached their transitions more methodically.

The third group believes in logically and systematically planning for the eventual sale of their practice. Dentists in this group tend to prepare in advance for other aspects of their life and career, such as retirement and estate-planning. They choose a practice sale option that best suits their individual needs and circumstances and, in most instances, secure the sale of their practice one or more years prior to their target-retirement date. They plan carefully and then look forward to the benefits.

Not all dentists are ready to begin planning their exit strategies through some type of outright practice sale. For many mid-career dentists (and those early-career dentists who have been successful

W. David Griggs, DDS
33 N. Garden Avenue
Suite 170
Clearwater, FL 33786
Phone: 813-449-8350
FAX: 813-449-8113

The Transition Group

THINGS TO CONSIDER PRIOR TO SIGNING ON WITH OR SELLING TO A DENTAL-MANAGEMENT COMPANY

The following things should be considered when negotiating the sale of your practice with a dental-management corporation.

General things to consider:

1. Company Profile: Are there dentists involved in the company?

2. Company History: How long has the company been in existence?

3. Dentists Who Have Sold: Have you spoken with any dentists who have been with the dental-management company for a year more? Are they pleased with the situation?

4. Purchase Price: If your practice is being purchased, is the price being offered fair based on appraisal? How much *below* appraisal is the offer?

What's important here is not necessarily whether you are getting full price or not (since traditional buyers may *also* want to negotiate the price with you), but how much *less* than the appraised value they are willing to offer you.

5. Terms: How much of a down payment is being offered? Is this enough to secure the sale in your mind and in the mind of your advisors?

In the past, receiving $50,000 to $75,000 as a down payment was common, with the seller financing the balance for 5-10 years, and typically fixed at 1% above prime at the time of the sale. However, today it's fairly common for a seller to receive 100% cash for the sale of the practice, eliminating the risk involved in seller-financing. Keep this in mind when dealing with dental-management companies, particularly when there *may* be no personal guarantees on the financing.

Fig. 3.14a

enough to build large, established practices) the best approach to cashing in the equity in their practices may be by means of a more gradual transition.

The following chapter lays out the details of just such a plan.

Your overall security in this transaction will also have a lot to do with how long you will be staying in the practice after the sale has been completed. If you *are* staying in the practice after the sale, then you will want to factor in the amount of principal you will have received by the time you "exit".

6. Income From Clinical Services: Here's the part to scrutinize, which is simple to do:

- First determine what the *true* net income from your practice has been. This includes all compensation and perks you receive from the practice. In many practices, these perks can equal 5% to 20% of the total gross income of the practice. In that situation, the pre-tax net income from a practice might *appear* to be 30%, but with these added perks, the *true* net of the practice could be as much as 35% to 50%.

- Next, determine what percentage the dental management company is going to pay you for continuing to provide clinical services (or what percent of the practice gross or net the company is retaining for management), and over what period of time. Calculate the *difference* in compensation you normally receive if you continued "as is" (i.e., as the owner) versus turning the practice over to a management company. This will show you how much of the purchase price of your practice you are contributing to from your earnings.

This exercise should help you to make a final decision regarding an offer from a dental management company, as it will give you a clearer idea as to the *actual* price you are receiving for the practice, and whether the decision is a sound one financially. Of course, there's an intangible part of the equation — if you are wanting to work less and to be freed up from the day-to-day management aspects of the practice, turning your practice over to a dental management company may have some benefits for you to consider. You need to determine how much the trade-off is worth to you. As part of this process, compare offers made by dental management companies to offers from *traditional* purchasers who will actually be working in the practice with you. Some dentists prefer this type of situation over that an "absentee owner" scenario.

Fig. 3.14b

4

CREATING "WIN-WIN" ASSOCIATESHIP TO CO-OWNERSHIP ARRANGEMENTS: A NON-ADVERSARIAL APPROACH

Design Associateship to Co-ownership Arrangements That Work and Stop the Revolving-Door Syndrome of Traditional Associateships

Dentistry is quickly becoming a two (or more) practitioner-per-facility business. Dentists who welcome this change may very well enjoy a new, exciting journey from solo to duo, and beyond. Practitioners who resist this change may find it increasingly more difficult to maintain sole proprietorship status with the lifestyle luxuries of the past that have long been dentistry's "trademark." Over the next decade and a half, there certainly will be solo practices catering to "niche" markets that will survive well economically without associates or partners. There also will be those dentists who prefer a higher overhead and lower income (through inefficient use of their facilities) rather than lose their "autonomy" (as they see it) by bringing in associates to enhance the overall production of the practice. However, it is my belief that the vast majority of dentists could benefit greatly from this arrangement—particularly if approached in a different manner than in the past—with a strategic plan in place prior to the beginning of the association (like a treatment plan prior to beginning a case).

When you hear the word "associate" in this model, it creates enough fear to cause the average dentist to shake in his boots and avoid looking in this direction. His or her reaction often is one of avoidance. Big mistake! The horror stories of relationship associateships gone bad hovers over the traditional solo-practice model like a dark cloud. Once examined, the hidden potential of planned, profitable, and safe associateships makes so much sense, we're often ashamed to admit we didn't look at it before.

Changes in the dental marketplace, such as discounted dentistry and managed care, are forcing dentists to become more overhead conscious. In an effort to maintain productivity, internal and external marketing plans now are becoming a top priority for the survival of the private practice. Many dentists I speak with are desperately seeking relief from these daily pressures inherent in solo-practice ownership. Often, these same dentists struggle in their efforts to enhance profitability, placing unnecessary stress on themselves and their staff and frequently overlooking the opportunity to increase profits by better utilizing their facilities.

Although extensive research programs and comprehensive seminars on controlling overhead are popular today, as business owners, we must begin to capitalize on potential profit opportunities created by enhanced facility utilization to lower practice overhead. Dentists who take advantage of this profit-expansion strategy will position themselves well for the future.

Profit Expansion

Profit expansion occurs when additional gross income (that could be produced by the owner, an associate, or co-owner) is added to the base income of the existing practice. This additional income increases the profit *percentage* of the overall income entering the practice, including the base income being produced prior to the expansion. Since most dental overhead expenses are fixed (remaining constant, regardless of gross income), only the production-related expenses increase (such as supplies and lab). Thus, the profit percentage of the practice should naturally rise as gross income increases (i.e., the net-profit percentage on additional practice production is substantially higher than the net percentage on existing production).

For example: I have seen practices with net profits of 32% on the base (existing) production enjoy as much as a 70% profitability on the *additional* production. The resulting overall net percentage depends on the amount of additional production there was over and above the base production. (Figure 4.1)

The figures show net profit generated from an additional $180,000 of associate production in a given year (i.e., an additional $180,000 over and above the base production that existed prior to the associate's entry into the practice). After paying normal expenses involved with this production, the net profit is 28.6% (after paying the associate 30% for rendering the services). In nonlaboratory-related procedures, such as endodontics and periodontics, the profit margin is substantially higher. Could this become passive income?

ASSOCIATE PROFITABILITY	
Associate's Additional Collections	**$180,000**
Additional Production Expenses	
Clinical Supplies (6%)	$10,800
Office Supplies (2%)	$3,600
Laboratory Costs (10%)	$18,000
Total Assistant Costs	$35,000
Miscellaneous (1%)	$1,800
Total Expenses	$69,200 (38.4%)
Associate Compensation (30%)	$54,000
FICA & Other Payroll Costs (10%)	$5,400
Grand Total Costs	$128,600
Net Profit	$51,400 (28.6%)

Fig. 4.1

The dynamics of profit expansion can be likened to the swing of a pendulum. At the beginning of each month, the pendulum begins to swing toward a fixed point, often referred to as the break-even point (BEP). Total operational expenses vary from one practice to another; however, the BEP is where the gross monthly collections of the practice are sufficient to meet the total monthly operational expenses.

Before the pendulum reaches the BEP, overhead expenses are greater than 100% and profits are in the negative column. Should practice productivity decline for any reason (as in the case of illness, death, or other owner absence), the pendulum swings backwards, causing profit *contraction*. (This fact makes it difficult for many dentists in solo practice to take needed time off.)

As gross collections increase, the pendulum swings beyond the BEP, pushing the business forward to a state of profit expansion. The higher the practice collections during this phase, the greater the percentage of profitability.

Two of the most effective means of pushing the pendulum forward are increased production by the owner and/or increased production by an associate or co-owner. The first method requires greater work (and potentially less quality of life) for the owner. The second method creates income on a more passive basis than the first. Other professions have evolved into similar associateship arrangements and have proven this method to be very profitable, as well as quality-of-life enhancing. It has also allowed them to be more competitive in the marketplace.

A hidden advantage of this arrangement is the opportunity to greatly enhance patient service. Through expanded hours and services, a greater number of patients can be treated with a wider range of available appointment times. This is clearly what much of the dental services market demands today.

Some time ago, I consulted with a new solo practitioner who was in need of management advice. Having started a practice from scratch only 14 months earlier, his monthly gross collections of $10,000 per month were barely covering overhead expenses. With his overhead expenses averaging 100% (or more) of the practice income, he felt he couldn't survive much longer.

As we began to work together, implementing systems for his situation, collections increased. With only a $5,000-per-month increase in collections, his overhead expenses dropped to 86%. Production-related expenses were deducted from the overall profit margin, allowing the remainder of profits to be allocated to providing an income source for the owner.

With all other expenses remaining fixed, net profit went from 0% to 14%. After passing the BEP, it was clear that his profit would rise in direct proportion to any future increase in collections (less any production-related expenses.)

As my client's practice reached $20,000 per month in collections, the net-profit margin increased to 35%. He was now beginning to feel relief and was pleased with the compensation he was receiving from the practice. By the time the practice collected $25,000 per month, the business was operating on a healthy 40% profit margin.

Should he choose to remain in solo practice, this steady increase in profit margin will plateau at some point. The stress of an increased workload will make it difficult for him to maximize true potential of the practice. However, this same model becomes even more profitable when we examine options that can expand the productivity without the restrictions of solo practice.

Stepping Beyond Solo

Dentists should examine all options that allow them to step beyond the limitations of practicing solo. This would include associateships, co-ownership arrangements, and mergers, as well as some space-sharing scenarios based on sound transition plans (see Chapter 5, "Practice Mergers"). The associateship to co-ownership scenario best fits the early or mid-career dentist who has an expandable patient base and wishes to make better use of the existing facility.

Many successful practitioners use the leverage of associateship arrangements to their advantage. A vital part of this successful "key" lies in planning and structuring these arrangements from a long-term perspective. When associateship arrangements are designed to lead into an eventual co-ownership opportunity for the associate, the longevity of the relationship is enhanced as well as the profitability of the practice.

In this chapter, we clearly will define this model and discuss the profit potential of this option.

Associateship to Co-Ownership Dynamics

An associateship to co-ownership arrangement generally evolves from an initial associate-owner (employee-employer) relationship. A new relationship is created under which the former associate becomes a co-owner of the practice through buying in. As opposed to the two dentists practicing as two separate practice entities, a single team practice is formed, with each individual owning an undivided interest in the total. In most cases, the actual co-ownership occurs between the first and second year of the relationship. (Figure 4-2, page 68.) However, it can occur at any time, depending upon the readiness level of the owner and associate, as well as what was prescribed in their written agreement.

Something of a "pre-nuptial" relationship, prior to the actual co-ownership date, is recommended (often referred to as a trial period). A reasonable length of time should be allowed for the owner and associate to form a sound foundation for the co-ownership relationship to come.

There are distinct advantages to practicing co-ownership for both the prospective owner and associate. To become fully aware of the many advantages of this model, it's important to explore the benefits for dentists at all career levels.

What Are the Benefits of the Associateship to Co-ownership Model?

Let's look at how dentists on both sides of the equation stand to gain from an associateship to co-ownership arrangement and the reasons to explore this type of venture:

Low-Risk Practice Establishment: Dentists who have not yet established a patient base of their own will find this approach to be one of the lowest-risk, practice-establishment options available. The associate's safety net lies in the fact that the owner's practice becomes a safe-haven in which to build a practice without the requirement of immediate/direct responsibility of ownership and management. Today, a greater number of dental school graduates are seeking this type of arrangement.

Incentives for Employee Dentists: Many associate dentists are unhappy when they find themselves in employment situations with no chance for future ownership. Some work in two or more practices, just to make ends meet financially. They often feel that the future, as they see it, is not the same career perspective they had when they entered dental school. This problem, in part, is due to the fact that these dentists have sought out jobs, instead of long-term career opportunities. An associateship leading to co-ownership offers a totally different framework for young dentists to build on than just a "job."

Guaranteed Income Stream: Unlike setting up a practice from scratch, there is a guaranteed income stream with an associateship leading to a co-ownership arrangement. The magnitude of this income stream varies, depending on the size of the practice and the willingness of the owner to transfer patients, the compensation plan offered the associate, as well as how quickly the patients accept the associate.

Enhanced Net Income–Decreased Overhead: As the associate brings in production over and above the current practice production, overall overhead (as a percentage of gross) should decrease, while the percentage of practice profitability increases. This expansion has a stabilizing effect on a practice. No longer do we have to rely on the sole-production efforts of one dentist to support an entire practice.

[Note: Enhanced profitability will only occur when the associate and owner together expand the production level beyond the existing base production. Increased profitability for the owner probably will not result in the situation where existing production being done by the owner is merely turned over to an associate. Some situations necessitate this (i.e., owner health problems and/or an associate's need to quickly become productive). Although it is better to have an associate capture the otherwise "lost" production potential by assuming the excess patient flow, a much smaller profit margin is generated from roll-over productivity. The point here is clear—net profit will not increase unless it is attained when the owner and associate expand the *existing* production levels of the practice.]

Additional expenses are obviously incurred when an associate is incorporated into a practice. Some of these expenses include dental and office supplies, laboratory fees, additional equipment, space, and staff costs. Prior to the practice reaching new gross-income levels, practice overhead temporarily can increase as these expenses are incurred. In a well-managed practice (and provided that potential productivity exists), overhead again will decrease as production goals are reached.

The associate's compensation package is another fluctuating cost to consider. Be sure not to set yourself up for failure in this area. A note of advice: protect yourself by basing your associate's compensation on a collections-only basis. When the associate's salary is based on a fixed percentage of collections, with any guaranteed compensation treated as a draw against this percentage, the cost to the practice becomes relative—the higher the associate's compensation, the greater the practice profitability. If we are grooming the associate to be a co-owner, the sooner he or she is compensated on a percentage basis (one of the realities of practice ownership), the better.

Equity-Building Potential: Unlike most employment situations, this transition option positions the associate for "equity-building," potentially leading to equal co-ownership. Practice equity is a real asset, and most dentists want it.

Future Compensation Increases: Once the co-ownership occurs, the associate generally steps up to co-owner-level income, which should be higher than employee-level income. This is one of the primary reasons associates seek co-ownership situations. This income increase comes from both the higher percentage of net profit received as a co-owner and a separate income stream that is based strictly on ownership interest. (This concept of separating ownership income from production income will be covered later in this chapter.) Proper pre-associateship planning must take place to insure that this will be part of the overall "benefits package." (This not only means that compensation should increase upon the co-ownership, but that pre-co-ownership compensation shouldn't be so generous that it does not allow this "jump" to occur.)

Shared Workload: Sharing the day-to-day workload of a practice with another dentist probably is the single most important reason most dentists bring in associates. The presence of an associate allows the owner-dentist the option of working shorter days and/or fewer days per week, with the comfort of knowing that the patients are being cared for and that the overhead is being covered. Owner-dentists often are unaware of the hidden advantages of the associateship to co-ownership model; however, they are very clear about their desire to decrease the stress associated with their existing workload.

Expanded Days and Hours: Few dentists can say that they use their facilities to their fullest potential. The majority of dental offices easily could be opened more days and hours. Today's marketplace demands better accessibility to health-care services, making extended hours (including weekend-appointment availability) advantageous.

Specialty Services: Procedures that traditionally have been referred out by the general practice (such as endodontics, periodontics, orthodontics, implants, and so forth) often can be performed by a competent associate. Not only does it make good economic sense to provide these services in-house, the care-giving aspect of the practice is enhanced in the eyes of patients. Patients often feel more cared for when they know the same dentists, and the same staff can treat them in the same office. They grow accustomed to the environment they've become familiar with, as opposed to being referred outside the practice to an unknown practitioner in a different location. Expanding services also can add tens of thousands of dollars to the bottom line, with little increase in fixed practice-overhead costs.

Increased Practice Value: An additional windfall for many owners is an increase in the overall value of the practice, directly resulting from increased productivity. This benefits both owner and associate—a "win-win" situation. Together, they will very likely create a much more valuable practice than the combined value of their separate practices. What they can build together as a team is much greater than what they could have built independently.

Financially-Committed Associate: I frequently hear the expression, "All sorts of positive forces come out of the woodwork when there is true commitment." Successful clients, with whom we have worked over the years, agree. They believe their success is directly related to the emotional and financial commitments they make and the risks they take. A well-structured associateship to co-ownership arrangement generates a financially and emotionally-committed associate, who will be motivated to build and maintain a profitable practice. Knowing that the opportunity exists to eventually share ownership profits, the associate's commitment level enhances financial security for both the owner and the associate.

The Opportunity to Cash-In Practice Equity: For most dentists, practice value yields no direct return on investment until the practice is sold (usually at retirement). Therefore it's beneficial to learn how to convert this dormant equity into a passive cash-flow stream, long before retirement, while still maintaining an ongoing income stream from the production in the practice. By steadily expanding the practice over time, the necessary framework can be established for cashing in the equity that lies dormant within the practice. Cashing in this equity can occur at any time in early, mid-, or late career. The timing for this opportunity often depends on how early the dentist begins the planning process and how clear and equitable the agreements between the parties are constructed.

The Advantage of Having a Built-In Buyer: Imagine the luxury of knowing that you had, in place, an equitably arranged retirement buy-out, years prior to selling your practice. Why not eliminate the time pressure of searching for a candidate to purchase your practice during your late-career years? Having the security of a built-in buyer, for the sale of the remaining interest in the practice, can be the single, greatest long-term benefit of an associateship to co-ownership arrangement. It is a benefit that cannot be fully appreciated unless you have had to do it the other way–pending an enormous amount of time, money, and energy searching for a buyer in the open market.

The associateship leading to co-ownership option also provides practice owners with life and disability "insurance." It creates a ready, willing, and able party to purchase the practice in the event of death or disability. This benefit alone could be worth hundreds of thousands of dollars!

In a properly constructed associateship to co-ownership arrangement, additional sale opportunities are developed from within the practice. The initial opportunity occurs with the buyer of the first portion (usually 50%) of the practice. At a later date, the same associate (now a co-owner) can purchase the remaining interest in the practice. The co-owners also could jointly sell an equal interest to a third associate that enters the practice. This built-in buyer concept creates opportunities to continually cash in practice equity long after the initial sale.

Buyers Continue to Benefit From Future Co-ownership: Associates also benefit from this co-ownership/buy-out plan, as they can repeat the same process by bringing in associates of their own. With additional co-ownership arrangements in place, the cycle repeats itself.

Continuing this cycle can be compared to the passing of the Olympic torch. Initially, the founder of the practice carries the torch. At given times, the torch is passed to new associates, while the original carriers of the torch (the retiring dentists) continue to run the race, but now at their desired pace. The eventual phase-out and retirement of the senior co-owners prompt the entry of new associates, who eventually become co-owners as well. This repeating cycle perpetuates the practice and is much like what we see in professional firms.

Late-Career Dentists' Considerations. Although it is very common for late-career dentists to bring in associates, for some it will not be the best option to consider. Late-career dentists are looking retirement square in the face. In late career, dentists should first explore options that provide more of a guaranteed buy-out within a shorter time-frame than most associateship to co-ownership arrangements offer. Many new practice-sale strategies offer creative transition plans for retirement, such as selling early to secure the value of the practice, with the option to continue practicing until retirement.

Associateship arrangements that lead to a co-ownership are designed for an eventual buy-out. (This buy-out should be an obligation, and not an option, so that all co-owners can be assured of a successful transition.) However, this option often reflects an approach that is a much slower process and does not have the higher security, or the guaranteed end results, offered with a practice sale option. (See Chapter 3, "Successful Sales Strategies.") Late-career dentists should approach the associateship to co-owner route with caution.

A Word of Caution Before Proceeding

Practitioners who seek quick relief from extant practice overloads sometimes push the quest for finding an associate into high gear. In these situations, associates frequently are brought in too hastily, and often the most important steps of the associateship to co-ownership process are neglected.

Do not allow fatigue to lead to you toward hasty decisions, without thorough evaluation of this serious process. Before expanding your practice with an associate, seek the advice and knowledge of a specialized transition consultant. Consulting a trained professional guarantees you'll be introduced to information on all of the important issues to consider, as well as the specific steps involved in the process. This advisor also may have the ability to act as a third-party mediator, helping both parties to achieve a "win-win" end result. Be sure to start off on "sound footing." Eliminate the possibility of making quick decisions that could lead to high-priced mistakes.

The Importance of a Long-Term Plan

It's impossible to know how the owner and associate will feel about each other in the future. For this reason, dentists often use a "wait-and-see" attitude as an excuse not to establish a plan upfront. The future carries no guarantees. That is why it is imperative to construct a mutually agreed-upon plan right from the start. The plan will allow you to move ahead with the relationship, if desired, or dissolve it peacefully if necessary. Structuring the basic strategies of a plan is the best possible security (and guarantee of success) for an associateship leading to co-ownership arrangement.

The dentist who chooses not to bring in an associate may be much better off than the dentist who does enter into an associate relationship without clearly defining the future details of the relationship.

All associateships should be taken very seriously, from day one. The casual attitude many dentists have had when entering associateship arrangements has proven to be one of the most costly mistakes we continue to make in our profession. In becoming established dentists, we had to take every phase of our education and practice establishment very seriously. Why not enter into associateship arrangements with the same degree of seriousness, caution, and concern? By establishing a clearly defined vision with a fully developed structure for long-term goals, associateship arrangements can be structured with a clear, defined mission from the start. The present and future terms of the initial association, the co-ownership, and the eventual buy-out always should be specified in these agreements—structured upfront.

Planning provides damage control. I frequently come across dentists who have worked together for years without any sort of plan or written agreement. For one reason or another (sometimes out of the blue), they decide to start putting a plan together. Given that so much time has passed, the context of initial discussions regarding the associateship relationship and eventual co-ownership have been lost or clouded. All of a sudden, these dentists may have different ideas about the value of the practice. The tug-of-war that develops over the existence of (or lack of) earned equity on the part of the associate may be only the beginning of their struggles. ("Earned equity" refers to that part of the practice that the associate may feel he or she built.) The treacherous work of structuring agreements with dentists at this juncture can cause the process to be very difficult and fragile.

Quite often, there is damage to be undone, too, before a clear direction can be established. Unfortunately, a common discovery in the after-the-fact planning process is the question, "Should we have gotten together in the first place?" What a shame that sometimes the parties realize that they have wasted time (sometimes years), energy, and money on a relationship based on divergent goals and philosophies.

Preplanning establishes associateship commitment. Without a clear and agreed-upon vision of the future, few owner-dentists are willing to turn over their patient base to an associate. An associate who has no plans (or desire) to become a long-term part of the practice provides the owner with little motivation to advance the patient-transition process. For these reasons, casual relationships rarely create an environment conducive to practice-building for the associate.

For the associateship arrangement to lead to a successful co-ownership arrangement, there must be true commitment between owner and associate. As the foundation is laid in the initial planning stages, both parties need to be involved and clear on the details of a long-term plan.

During the planning stage, owner-dentists can evaluate the timing of bringing in an associate. This also is the time to make sure that the right associate has been chosen.

For the associate, this time should be used to decide if this is the practice where a total commitment can be made. Typically, associates in non-ownership situations have less motivation to build the practice and/or learn how to manage it. With no stake in the practice, the outlook of the non-owner associate is extremely different. Without plans for future ownership, associates frequently choose to remain unaware of the practice overhead costs, have only minimal appreciation for cost control, and rarely spend time learning about in-office systems, which greatly affects many other aspects of the practice.

The structure of the associateship to co-ownership arrangement changes this picture entirely. This option creates a "hope for the future" in the associate. With this model, an opportunity for the associate to take "emotional" ownership in the daily management of the practice is created. The associateship to co-ownership option is the very best cure for the "revolving door syndrome," a term familiar to most dentists. When we hear the term, most of us understand exactly what it means. Some of us have even experienced it. Quite frankly, many practices appear to provide a revolving door for associates—Dr. Smith, one year, Dr. Jones, the next, and so on. Their concept of the short-term associate occurs so frequently, it is almost a given that the arrangement will not be long term.

We can learn from what we see happening to others. It is not hard to find numerous examples of failed associateships and, sadly enough, we don't have to look very far to find them. Several of our friends and colleagues probably could write a book on the topic. You must learn from the mistakes of others and plan for and look forward to a better outcome for your own associateship arrangement.

Before beginning the planning stages of an associateship leading to co-ownership agreement, it's important for both parties to answer a few basic questions.

Questions for the Practice Owner

Are you really serious about moving ahead toward a proposed co-ownership arrangement?

What are some of the forces driving your decision? Is relief from your current workload one of the major ones? (If so, have you questioned whether you would be happier by just downsizing your current patient base and reducing your schedule, rather than bringing in an associate on a long-term basis?)

Are you clear about the long-term benefits of practice co-ownership vs. what you might be giving up in the process?

What level of commitment are you expecting (and do you need) from the associate, before you can be willing to make your own firm commitment? What exactly will you be expecting from the associate in the form of commitment (emotionally and financially)?

Do you have the necessary paperwork and documentation in order before proceeding?

Are you ready to discuss things such as practice value, co-ownership date, price and terms, etc.?

Have you appraised the capacity of your practice to support an additional dentist?

How will you work together in the current space?

Will expansion or relocation to a new space be necessary at some point?

What will be necessary to create "equally equipped" treatment rooms for both doctors? Will staggered hours be required? Expansion?

Is the vitality of the hygiene program adequate enough to support a new associate?

Would a merger-acquisition of another practice be a logical expansion step to consider prior to (or in conjunction with) bringing in an associate?

Questions for the Associate

Are you clear about the short- and long-term benefits of buying in vs. other practice establishment options?

Would you prefer to purchase a practice outright if you could obtain the necessary financing?

Have the price, terms, and time frame for the co-ownership/buy-out been set and agreed upon by both parties?

Has an in-depth production-projection analysis been provided and explained to you so you will have an idea of when you can afford to buy in (i.e., how many years must you wait, or what production level must you reach before being financially and mentally being able to establish a co-ownership)?

Do you know what your net income will be while you are buying in? (Will this income be enough to meet your minimal financial needs at the time?)

Do you understand how a co-ownership structure is repeatable, which also allows you the future opportunity to bring in an associate?

Are you willing to go out and find new patients (and referral sources) on your own, as opposed to expecting the owner's practice to "feed" you with all of the patients you need?

Hopefully, both parties should be able to answer "yes" to the above questions before proceeding.

Owner's "Pre-Associateship To Co-ownership" Checklist

Prior to proceeding into the associate relationship, you should have before you a checklist of important items to consider. The following is a brief checklist of the most important issues to address at this stage. (There are additional items that should be included in your initial employment, co-ownership, and co-ownership agreements with the associate. (See Chapter 8, "Structuring Your Agreements.")

Your Strategic Plan. First on your checklist is your strategic plan. Begin your plan with a financial analysis of the practice, which includes a combined income forecast, business plan, and practice valuation. This analysis will provide a clear path for both parties.

A written plan helps prevent the misunderstandings that almost always occur in most transitions. The majority of failed co-ownership arrangements are due to misunderstandings over financial issues. There literally are dozens of other issues that also can potentially qualify for areas of disagreement. Your goal should be to avoid turning the transition process from a marriage into a divorce. (If you've been through this, you no doubt know what this period is like.) These problems almost always can be avoided with advance planning. It also helps to use a third party as an intermediary. Transition consultants provide an excellent service in this area, smoothing off any "rough edges" that may develop in the process.

Practice Valuation. One of the first steps in your financial analysis is a practice valuation. It's important to know the practice value prior to beginning any relationship leading to co-ownership; obviously, when the intent is for the associate to buy in, it is important that the value be established upfront.

Without the value and payment structure computed in a comprehensive appraisal, the associate will be unable to know what production requirements will be needed to sufficiently fund the future co-ownership. The fear of "costs" causes many associates to shy away from buying in; too often, this is generated because no one has taken the time to show them the value of what they're buying. (This is similar to the way some patients feel about dental fees—until the dentist conveys the value of the service to the patient, the fee may appear too high.)

The associate should be provided with projections, which show net income after the monthly investment costs are paid. With this information projected upfront, it's amazing to see the amount of fear that is instantly removed from associates. You'll be surprised to find that the bottom-line figures usually are "key" motivational factors to the transition. A fully informed associate can more truly appreciate the value of the purchase price.

Practice Co-ownership Format. From the information gathered in the practice valuation, a comprehensive practice-purchase format ("practice co-ownership format") can be constructed.

This format is, in essence, the strategic business plan that the owner-dentist and the associate-dentist use as their blueprint for the future. It represents a five- to 10-year snapshot of the projected income to be received by each party, both during and following the co-ownership.

A common mistake dentists (and their advisors) make in the transition process is to present associates with only the sale price of the practice. Many practice owners feel that their practices are undervalued, and that the co-ownership price being offered to the associate is a bargain. Based on this belief, practice owners often are unaware of the need to supply associates with important additional information to base their decision on. This is a mistake. Instead of placing the main focus on the price, the focus should be on the true value of what is being sold to the associate. A properly structured practice co-ownership format can provide this.

The practice co-ownership format actually:

- shows the "true net" income of the practice;

- explains how practice profits will be distributed after the co-ownership. (Co-owners have several options to consider for dividing the joint profits of the practice—see the section on co-ownership compensation.);

- establishes associate "target" production goals; and

- defines how the buy-in payments impact both owner and associate income.

Co-ownership Price Agreement. The proposed co-ownership price for a specified portion (usually 50%) of the practice should be agreed upon prior to the time that the associate enters the practice. Although an initial practice-value price has been established (in most cases, during the practice-valuation process), agreeing to the final price "up-front" eliminates future disputes as well as any disincentive on the part of the associate to expand the practice during the employee phase. This agreement prevents the associate from equating the efforts made in helping to build the practice with the purchase price required upon buying in. (See the section on associate's earned equity for individualized approaches to this earned equity.)

The co-ownership agreement should contain:

- the co-ownership buy-in price;

- purchase terms and financing requirements;

- payout period;

- interest rate (if owner-financed); and

- co-ownership buy-in date (or production-threshold goal).

Buy Out Provisions. All parties should clearly agree to when the associate will buy out the owner-dentist's interest in the practice. This is important for a number of reasons, particularly in the event of death or disability. For the benefit of all parties, there should be a clear understanding about how additional dentists will be brought into the practice and how they will buy in.

Now that the major framework has been put in place for the proposed co-ownership, it's time to look at how the associate will be compensated.

Determining Associate Compensation. Prior to the actual co-ownership, associate compensation normally is based on a percentage of collections accrued from the associate's production. This percentage can vary, depending upon the true net income of the practice (as determined by the practice valuation). Any salary extended the associate usually is based on a fixed-dollar amount per day and prorated for partial days worked. (It is wise to look at national statistics to determine the average amount per day you should expect to pay.) This salary is generally treated as a "draw" against production-generated income, again based on collections. The following scenario illustrates how this salary-draw is treated:

Determining Associate Compensation Percentages. Until the associate buys in and becomes a co-owner, the standard compensation percentage for associates in your area should be paid. This normally will range from 22% to 35%, with the expenses of the practice paid by the owner. (In some cases, any lab fees or specialty equipment/supplies preferred by the associate may require that you adjust the associate's compensation accordingly.

To understand the economic realities connected with the associate compensation percentage, it's useful to take a hard look at the *real* profitability of the practice. (Again, in most cases, this is determined as part of the initial practice valuation, done prior to the entry of the associate.) Knowing the practice's true profit enables the owner to gauge a fair and reasonable percentage for associate compensation.

As an aside, some dentists who are quite creative with running expenses through the practice find the practice evaluation process to be a pleasant surprise. Often, because they have become so creative with taking advantage of tax loopholes, their profit and loss statements present a picture of "doom and gloom." In their creative efforts, they often lose sight of what the "true-net" picture actually looks like and even convince themselves that the profit margin is low. Oftentimes, their practices are much more profitable than they knew. Unfortunately, for others, this process may be a shock.

Once a real, "true-net" picture of practice profit is established, intelligent decisions about associate compensation can be made. Practices with legitimately high overheads will have to base the associate's compensation on a slightly lower percentage of collections than the national averages.

Associate Lab Expense. There are two common ways to approach compensation as it relates to any laboratory expense incurred by the associate.

1. *Flat percentage.* The first approach says the associate's compensation is based on a flat percentage of the associate's personally generated collections. In this approach, the owner pays for all practice costs (except the associate's malpractice insurance), including the associate's laboratory expense.

2. *Adjusted percentage.* The second approach deducts laboratory costs (generated from associate production only) from the associate's gross-collections figure before applying the compensation percentage to calculate associate compensation. In the example on the next page (Figure 4-2), the associate's lab bill was deducted from the associate's gross collections, with the remaining adjusted gross subject to a percentage. This compensation method often is referred to as paying the lab bill "off the top." The percentage paid to the associate in this scenario usually is higher than the flat percentage paid in those situations where the owner pays all the expenses.

Some practice owners are more comfortable deducting out the lab bill, as they feel that it makes the associate more directly accountable for

ASSOCIATE COMPENSATION Adjusted Percentage	
ASSOCIATE'S COMPENSATION PERCENTAGE (35%)	
ASSOCIATE'S GROSS COLLECTIONS	$10,000
ASSOCIATE'S LAB BILL	$ 1,000
ADJUSTED GROSS COLLECTION	$ 9,000
ASSOCIATE'S COMPENSATION (35%)	$ 3,150

ASSOCIATE COMPENSATION Flat Percentage	
ASSOCIATE'S COMPENSATION PERCENTAGE (30%)	
ASSOCIATE'S GROSS COLLECTIONS	$10,000
ASSOCIATE'S COMPENSATION (30%)	$ 3,000

Fig. 4.2

his or her own lab costs. More often than not, the net compensation received by the associate is relatively the same, whether a higher percentage was paid with the lab bill "off the top" or a lower percentage was paid without deducting out the lab bill.

Additional Expenses. Some practice owners deduct additional expenses from associate collections prior to compensation, but it's a less common practice.

Typical additional expenses include prorated items such as supplies and disposables, as well as the overhead costs of providing the associate with a trained dental assistant. Under these circumstances, the associate's percentage paid is higher than in situations where a flat percentage is paid. This approach also can give the associate the feeling of building a separate practice from the owner (which I do not recommend).

When the associate feels that he or she is merely "renting space," it is not uncommon to feel the presence of "separate camp" mentality. Be aware of the possible impact of this approach and how it may defeat the original purpose of the associateship to co-ownership format. Many dentists feel that this approach to associate compensation is more complex than necessary. In the end, the compensation appears to work out about the same.

Problem: Associate Overcompensation. Some associates have an inflated view of what their compensation should be. Often, they cannot understand why compensation isn't based on the true costs of the associate (i.e., on the additional costs incurred on just the additional production of the associate), rather than being based on the overall overhead costs of the practice.

For example: The associate may request between 40% and 50%, feeling that the owner still is making a nice profit. Sometimes, the owner-dentist (thinking that most of the increases in overhead costs will only be production-related) agrees to a percentage higher than normal. Owner-dentists who have fallen into this trap have created a grossly inequitable situation, not realizing that the associate probably is making a greater percentage on his or her production than is the owner. This is not only unfair to the owner, but it also creates no incentive for the associate to ever want to buy in. (Why buy in and make a lower percentage as an owner? Why not just remain an employee?)

It's critical to maintain a compensation differential of at least 10% between owner and associate. This variance allows the owner at least some reward for the risks and responsibilities of ownership. For the associate, there is the promise of a significantly elevated level of income upon buying into the practice.

It is crucial to maintain this income differential as an incentive. Be careful how generously you compensate your associate.

Associate Status:
Employee or Independent Contractor?

In my opinion, dentists should not take the risk of trying to treat their associates as independent contractors. The IRS appears to disapprove of this arrangement, and, in looking at the multiple requirements involved, it's usually a difficult position to defend. This issue often causes disagreements (usually surrounding the issue of who will be paying the matching FICA). It's interesting that it seems to end up being a wash, anyway.

Independent contractors almost always want to be paid a higher percentage than that given to employees. Owners who pay their associates as employees typically try to pay the lower percentages, due to increased costs.

I recommend structuring associate compensation on an employee-related status and designing the compensation rate according to averages normal for the area. Whether you pay the associate 30% as an employee or 35% as an independent contractor, the net result is nearly the same. As an owner, you're probably in a much safer position with Uncle Sam with the associate as an employee. (Consult your tax and legal advisors for advice in this area.)

Some financial consultants suggest that after a designated trial period (and prior to the time the associate buys in), the associate enters a phase in which he becomes directly responsible for his share of expenses in the practice. At that time, the associate is paid 100% of his collections and is then charged for 100% of his lab fees and other pro-rated expenses, including staff costs, payroll taxes, and office and clinical supplies. After paying these expenses, the associate is then charged a flat percentage of his collections to cover a portion of the practice's fixed overhead. Here's an example:

Practice collections	$60,000
Associate collections	
(25% of total collections)	15,000
Associate direct costs	
Total costs (40%)	$24,000
Multiplied by associate's share (25%)	6,000
Associate net income	
Associate collections	$15,000
Minus associate direct costs	6,000
Associate adjusted net	9,000
Minus flat % charged associate (30%)	4,500
Remaining net income	4,500

This approach may work for some of you, but I always have found it difficult to accurately estimate what an associate's overhead was, separate from the total practice overhead. I also find this approach to be more complicated than necessary when calculating net compensation for an associate. The worst consequence of this approach is that it can create a "separate camp" mentality on the part of the associate (i.e., an attitude that two separate practices exist as opposed to a team), something I see often in arrangements structured this way.

Associateship to Co-Ownership: The Four Phases

An associateship to co-ownership cycle has four distinct phases: trial period, post-trial period, the buy-in, and buy-out.

Phase I:
Trial Period

The first phase of the associateship to co-ownership cycle is the trial period. This is the time when the associate's clinical and "people skills" are evaluated, along with the professional relationship between the owner and the associate. The associate's maturity, communication skills, and experience level have a lot to do with how smoothly this phase goes and how quickly the associate begins the process of practice-building. Though some practice owners have an overflow of patients to provide an associate, it's normally necessary for the associate to build his or her practice from within the owner's (in conjunction with bringing in new patients).

Commitment to the practice also is measured during this time. It will be helpful to ask yourself the following questions:

- Is the Associate motivated to bring new patients into the practice?

- Is the associate joining local clubs, organizations, churches, and so forth in an effort to meet prospective patients?

- Is the associate interested in checking hygiene patients, even though he or she is not receiving any of the hygiene income (other than perhaps an extra fee)?

- Is the associate willing to cover practice emergencies on evenings and weekends?

- As the owner, how willing are you (and/or can you afford) to funnel some existing new-patient flow to the associate?

- Will the associate be allowed to check hygiene patients (when possible) to enhance his or her exposure to patients?

Duration. The trial period generally lasts from six months to one year. During this phase, the two dentists determine if they are right for each other and if the arrangement is what each dentist individually wants. Most dentists who take this process seriously will know if they have made the right choice within three to four months. If the two dentists don't have a good "gut feeling" about the relationship at this point, it's best to end it, so each can pursue a new direction. In the long run, both parties will be happier with this decision. (Figure 4.3)

THE TRIAL PERIOD
DURATION: SIX MONTHS TO ONE YEAR
EVALUATION OF ASSOCIATE'S: • **CLINICAL ABILITIES** • **COMMUNICATION SKILLS** • **COMMITMENT LEVEL**

Fig. 4.3

Phase II:
The Post-Trial Period

Once the trial period is completed, the owner and associate enter the phase appropriately referred to as the post-trial period. During this time, associates continue developing their clinical and managerial skills, because both will be necessary to become a successful co-owner in the practice. During this time, the associate's ability to build a practice and an income stream necessary to buy in should become clearer.

It is imperative for a production target to be established for the associate. This target is determined from an initial practice analysis (the practice co-ownership format). It should be sufficient for the associate to make co-ownership payments while still maintaining a satisfactory lifestyle. (Figure 4.4)

Two things represent the delineation between the trial period and the post-trial period: an associate noncompete agreement and creation of a "good faith" deposit fund.

1. Noncompete agreement. This provision (also referred to as a restrictive covenant) is absolutely essential to have in place in an associateship leading to co-ownership. The noncompete agreement is an associate's commitment not to compete with the owner-dentist during

THE POST-TRIAL PERIOD

FURTHER DEVELOPMENT OF:
- **CLINICAL, MANAGERIAL & LEADERSHIP SKILLS**
- **INCOME STREAM FOR BUY-IN**

COMMENCEMENT OF:
- **NONCOMPETE AGREEMENT**
- **GOOD FAITH DEPOSIT FUND**

Fig. 4.4

or upon termination of their relationship. This protects the practice against unfair competition and allows the owner to comfortably refer more patients to the associate without the fear of patient loss.

Noncompete agreements involve both time and distance. Typically, the associate agrees not to practice within a specific geographic radius of the practice for a specified period of time, if and when the associate discontinues working in the host practice. Some practice owners want the noncompete agreement to be in place from the associate's first day in practice, but I don't feel this is always necessary.

Since the idea behind such a covenant is to protect the owner's practice from competition, there may not be a need to have such a provision in place from the first day of the associate's employment. For example, should either or both parties decide to terminate the relationship after three months, it probably would be an overly protective move to then restrict the associate from practicing in the area for one to two years afterwards. By using a three-to-six month "window" (during which either party could terminate the arrangement without any restrictions being placed on the associate), a more palatable situation would exist.

Few patients will readily bond to an associate in that short period of time, particularly enough to follow him or her out of the practice. The question thus becomes, "Is it really necessary to restrict the associate from practicing in the area if the relationship terminates prior to three to six months?" For the associate who has moved his or her family to join the owner'' practice, an unnecessary hardship would be placed on the individual who might choose to stay in the area. (Please consult a knowledgeable attorney in your state about the enforceability of a deferred noncompete provision without some form of consideration given at the time of enforcement.)

There *are* situations, however, in which a noncompete agreement is necessary from the associate's first day in practice. Two such situations include specialty practices and small-town general practices. The lifeblood of a specialty practice is in the referring dentist base. A new associate-specialist quickly could be exposed to the entire referral base within a matter of weeks. This same process in a general practice (i.e., an associate meeting all of the *patients* of the practice) would take many years to occur. Once the associate-specialist is introduced to this referral base, the associate could damage the owner upon termination if only one or two of the referral sources gravitated toward the new associate.

In addition, the overall likelihood of an associate specialist staying in the same area after termination usually is greater than in the case of a general dentistry associate. Knowing this, few owner-specialists wish to be directly responsible for inviting a competitors into the area. This holds true for the general practitioner practicing in a small town.

The process of patient transfer from owner to associate often is impeded by the absence of a noncompete agreement. Why should the owner-dentist freely transfer patients if there is no protection against losing the patients should the associate later set up a separate practice in the area? Owner-dentists who are reluctant to ask for or who don't understand the importance of a noncompete agreement probably will join the majority of dentists whose well-intentioned associate arrangements were short-lived.

2. *Noncompete buy-out provisions.* I speak with many associate candidates who fear these noncompete agreements. The thought of signing one is particularly difficult for those who are moving back to their hometown from dental school, or those who are migrating to some new area, perhaps for the rest of their lives. This is why, in some circumstances, a fair buy-out mechanism of the noncompete agreement should be considered.

Noncompete buy-out agreements can be constructed several ways. The amount paid by the associate to "buy-out" this noncompete provision usually is based on some fixed, graduated amount, which depends on the length of time the associate has been in the office. It also may be a percentage of the associate's collections for the one-year period prior to the time the associate decides to leave or is terminated. Every practice situation is different, so don't take this as a blanket recommendation, but as a point to consider. (See Chapter 8, "Structuring Your Agreements.")

Good Faith Deposit. I believe the associate should start making a financial commitment toward buying in early in the relationship. I generally recommend that this begin at the commencement of the post-trial period, using earnings that have been retained from the associate's compensation.

These retained (after-tax) earnings are applied toward a pre-agreed price for the Co-ownership, based either on a fixed percentage of the associate's total after-tax earnings or a percentage of the associate's earnings over and above an agreed-upon threshold amount.

The associate retains an amount earned short of this threshold to maintain some minimal lifestyle; earnings above it are subjected to deductions that will go toward building the good faith deposit. This way, the associate agrees to make a financial commitment, but has the assurance of knowing that a reasonable lifestyle can be maintained in the process. The percentage used in the first option typically would be higher than the percentage used in the second option.

In the first method, a fixed percentage of the associate's earnings are retained after a given point in time (usually at the six-month mark). In the second method, a larger percentage of earnings are retained after a minimal threshold income has been achieved. I typically use 10% of all earnings in the first method, and 50% or greater in the second (Figure 4-5).

GOOD FAITH DEPOSIT EXAMPLE	
Option #1	
Associate Monthly After-Tax Earnings	$6,000
Good Faith Deposit Retained (10%)	$600
Net Earnings To Associate	$5,400
Option #2	
Associate Monthly After-Tax Earnings	$6,000
Associate *Threshold* Earnings	$4,000
Excess Over Threshold	$2,000
Good Faith Deposit Retained (50%)	$1,000
Net Earnings To Associate	$5,100

Fig. 4.5

Phase III:
The Buy-In

It's been my experience that most associates are ready for co-ownership one to two years from their initial date of employment. By that time, the owner-dentist should know if he has a suitable "match" for his practice. The right associate is eager for the buy-in to occur as soon as possible and will not be happy with a prolonged period of time before becoming a co-owner. Once you've found the right individual for your practice, let the actual buy-in occur as soon as it is financially possible.

If your practice co-ownership agreements were well thought out and designed in advance, the buy-in should occur automatically. There should be no need to go back to the drawing board to negotiate the price, terms, and other structural components—it's already been done. The actual date that the buy-in occurs will be based either on a specific date that was agreed upon upfront, or upon the associate reaching a minimal gross-production level. The agreement then triggers the event to occur any time on or before that date, with the mutual consent of both dentists. (Figure 4.6)

Figure 4.7 offers an example of what a typical buy-in looks like. In this scenario, the entire practice had been valued at $400,000. The valuation was done prior to the associate's entry into the practice, so the buy-in price and down payment are clear. The associate purchased a 50% interest in the practice for $200,000. A $50,000 down payment was made and the balance was financed, most often at 1% to 2% over prime. The associate on a monthly basis then pays the principal and interest payments to the seller (unless cash is paid).

Financing the Down Payment. Historically, associates have had difficulty borrowing money for the purpose of buying in or purchasing a

THE BUY-IN
• **OCCURS IN 1-2 YEARS**
TRIGGER EVENTS
a) **PRE-SET DATE** *OR*
b) **PRODUCTION GOAL**
• **ESTABLISHES CO-OWNERSHIP**
• **PARTNER-LEVEL INCOME COMMENCES**

Fig. 4.6

BUY-IN EXAMPLE	
TOTAL PRACTICE VALUE	$400,000
BUY-IN (50%)	$200,000
DOWN PAYMENT	$50,000
BALANCE	$160,000

Balance: Seller-Financed 60 Months at 1-2% over prime.

Fig. 4.7

practice. They're typically loaded down with dental school debt, making it a pipe dream (on the part of an owner-dentist) to find an associate with large amounts of cash or access to cash through family or some other source. Traditionally, associates have borrowed $25,000 to $50,000 for co-ownership down payments from traditional lending institutions, with the seller financing the balance of the co-ownership. These lending institutions have almost always required the co-signature of someone with adequate collateral (i.e., parents, relatives, and oftentimes the owner of the practice). Occasionally, the loan is approved provided the owner of the practice is willing to subordinate his or her interest in the collateral of the practice for such a loan (which, in my mind, is not much different than co-signing).

But there is good news! A tremendous shift has occurred in the marketplace in the last few years regarding available financing for dental practice buy-in and outright purchase. New lending institutions have emerged (such as the Matsco Companies) to meet the needs of dentists in need of loans for buy-in opportunities. This can be of great benefit to both parties, but it's especially helpful to the buyer who is usually anxious to buy-in and become a co-owner. I highly recommend checking out such new loan services as sources of financing. They know the process, they service the loans quickly, and they understand the needs of dentists.

Although there are tax considerations to consider when receiving the entire buy-in price in cash, for some owner-dentists, this still will be the preferred route.

Seller-Financed Balance. In those situations where the seller prefers to finance the balance of the buy-in price (or where no other alternative exists), this typically is done over a five-year period. This payout period can vary based on what the dentist buying in can afford to pay out of earnings while still trying to make a reasonable living. Allowing a flexible payout period (such as extending the payment period from five years to seven years or longer) may in some situations be the difference between a successful co-ownership and a failure.

The interest rate that a seller normally charges on the balance is generally one to two points above the existing prime rate at the time of the co-ownership and usually is fixed at that rate for the duration of the pay-out. Payments of principal and interest to the owner usually are in one of two forms: amortized payments made directly from the associate to the owner or a salary reduction (differential) method of payment. Let's examine these two payout methods.

1. Amortized payments from buyer to seller. In the first option, payments are made similar to any other type of mortgage or installment payment. The associate writes a check for payment to the owner on an agreed-upon day each month. From a tax perspective, the associate deducts the cost of the co-ownership through normal interest deductions, as well as depreciation of the assets being purchased. These assets would include things such as equipment, furniture, fixtures, supplies, goodwill, and so forth.

2. Salary differential (also referred to as salary reduction or salary shifting). The salary differential method is another payment method commonly used. Here, an amount equal to the amortized payment is deducted from the associate's earnings and shifted to the owner's salary. Many advisors justify this difference in salary based on management and other duties that the senior co-owner has in the practice.

This salary-reduction method is extremely beneficial to the dentist buying in, as the payment is all "pre-tax." The automatic payment also eliminates the senior co-owner from ever having to ask for the payment, because it works like an automatic payroll deduction. Although this pre-tax method of buying in is ideal for the associate, it can present a problem to the senior co-owner, because it usually is taxed as ordinary income. Many financial advisors have reduced the effects of this tax impact through tax-sheltered, defined-benefit plans and other methods. Others simply adjust the selling price up to help offset the additional tax that the owner-seller is paying. I have my own concerns about this approach—it really doesn't look like an actual sale has occurred and it almost looks as if it's been disguised. This is why I prefer the purchase of assets approach. This way, it's all "above board." The associate gets to depreciate the assets being purchased over a prescribed period of time, and the owner-dentist is able to have capital gain treatment on many of the assets being sold.

Note: Consult with your tax advisors about these buy-in payment methods, as well as all tax implications involved in this process.

Adjustments to the Buy-In Price. Certain situations may arise in which the buy-in price will need to be adjusted. Here are some of the most common of them.

Buy-in price should be adjusted upwards based on the purchase of any major assets for the practice after the practice valuation was performed. I've found that the following is the easiest way to handle these purchases:

- If buy-in occurs less than 18 months following the purchase of these assets, I recommend adding the full invoice amount to the practice value.

- For any period of time beyond 18 months, the amount added should be based on a 10% reduction of "useful life" for each year owned. For example, in two years, 20% of the original price is deducted off the original purchase price.

- Another approach is to purchase the assets through a five-to-seven-year loan. At the time of the buy-in, the new co-ownership "entity" assumes the loan in addition to the agreed-upon buy-in price. This way, the associate is paying for half of the residual value in addition to the previously agreed upon buy-in price.

Another common situation adjusts the purchase price in the event that the owner-dentist purchases a second practice, after the original valuation, and prior to the buy-in. Normally, the practice value would be increased by a minimum of the practice purchase price. I suggest that the practice be revalued at the buy-in date, deducting out the goodwill value of the associate's gross collections at that time (or by merely excluding the associate's collections from the valuation calculation).

This allows the associate the benefit of *earned equity*; at the same time, the owner can recoup the price of the purchased practice and any equity expansion created by the owner.

Downward Adjustments. The buy-in price can be adjusted downward in the event that any major equipment or other assets of the practice were sold after the valuation of the practice was completed. Although few dentists sell off assets this way—without replacing them with similar, newer assets—consideration should be given when any assets have been disposed of.

Deferring the Buy-In Date. There are situations in which the proposed buy-in should be legitimately deferred to a later date. Some of these situations might include insufficient production by the associate for the buy-in to be economically feasible, and lack of desire by either party to follow through with the buy-in at that particular time.

Obviously, if there were not sufficient production on the part of the associate, neither party would want to proceed with the buy-in. (An economic failure for the associate eventually would be an economic failure for the owner.) If a proper analysis of the practice is done in the pre-associateship phase, both parties should have a clear picture of the gross income the associate must attain prior to the buy-in.

I often encounter situations in which an associate is brought in to potentially buy into two practices (usually a solo dentist's main office and satellite office). The owner wants to lessen the burden of running both of them and the associate buy-in route looks ideal. Occasionally, the owner subsequently decides that it's best to sell one of the offices to the associate through an outright sale. This situation (i.e., two practice locations) can provide an excellent "back door" through which one of the two dentists can exit the joint-purchase arrangement if need be. If you are faced with such a situation, make sure this contingency plan is clearly spelled out in your agreements.

The Equal Owner Concept. Some legal advisors have a great deal of concern over their clients selling an equal-ownership interest in their practices. These dentists often are counseled to maintain a 51% ownership position, so that their client has a controlling "edge" over the junior doctor. Long term, this environment creates psychological barriers between the two dentists, with the junior co-owner always feeling second-class. It is understandable that most senior doctors want to maintain control, but at some point, all co-owners want to feel equal.

Even though unequal ownership situations are common in other businesses, it tends to create animosity in the dental practice arena. However, if desired by both parties, I recommend a 49/51% ratio be maintained between the dentists for five years, or throughout the buy-in payout period, whichever period is the longest. Then, the ownership should become i.e. 50/50—it's certainly what you would want if you were the junior person. Safeguards can be incorporated into your agreement, helping to protect the senior co-owner from any problems that the advisors may be concerned about.

In maintaining the philosophy of "equal owners," I recommend always selling equal shares—50% interest, in the case of two dentists; a one-third interest, in the case of three dentists; and so on. New partners purchase an equal interest in the practice from all existing co-owners. Every co-owner then feels equal.

Practice Co-Ownership Entity. When the associate buys in, the two dentists are most often partners or shareholders, depending upon whether the new entity created continues as a partnership or corporation. Although from a consultant's perspective, the results are identical, various advisors recommend different entities for different reasons. Be sure to consult your own legal and tax advisors for their suggestions.

Phase IV:
The Buy-Out

Most dentists would like the eventual buy-out of their remaining interest in the practice to be secured. The best security available is through an equitable buy-out arrangement with existing co-owners of the practice. Without this security, senior co-owners have anxiety about how they will sell their interest in the practice.

A buy-out will occur under several circumstances—including death, disability, relocation, or retirement. Some dentists will want to sell and retire from practice at this point. Others will sell their remaining equity to existing and/or to new co-owners and continue working in the practice after the sale. (See Chapter 3, "Successful Sales Strategies.")

Buy-Out Option Vs. Obligation. For a successful buy-out to occur, it's important that your agreements address the obligation of all junior-level co-owners to buy out senior-level co-owners. All dentists entering the practice know that it is a two-way street, and all new co-owners entering the practice have the same obligation: to buy out co-owners who are chronologically ahead of them in the practice. Every co-owner then has the security of knowing his/her interest in the practice will be purchased at some point in the future. You are taking a great risk (of potentially tens or hundreds of thousands of dollars) if you bring someone into your practice that does not have a clear understanding of the obligation to buy-in and buy out senior co-owners.

Co-ownership Compensation

This section deals with various options available for distributing the profits of the practice to all co-owners.

Profit distribution should act as compensation for each dentist's clinical roles, and where mutually agreed, their managerial roles as well as their financial investment as owners. There are three basic options for the distribution of co-ownership profits. (Figure 4.8)

Ownership Distribution. The first method of income distribution is referred to as ownership compensation. In this case, net income is distributed solely on the ratio of ownership interest between the partners.

In this scenario, 50/50 co-owners divide the net income of the practice equally, irrespective of their varying degrees of productivity.

CO-OWNER COMPENSATION OPTIONS

- OWNERSHIP DISTRIBUTION

  Equal Owners Receive Equal Compensation

- PRODUCTIVITY COMPENSATION

  Compensation Based on Individual Productivity

- OWNERSHIP & PRODUCTIVITY COMPENSATION

  A *Blending* Of Ownership & Productivity

Fig. 4.8

Although this approach may work well in some businesses, it can discourage individual productivity in the typical dental-practice setting. In an ideal world, this might not become an issue, but most dentists prefer a direct reward system for their production efforts. The chances of two individual dentists being equally productive in a co-ownership setting are unlikely. The co-owner who is capable of producing more than the other may hold back on productivity, feeling that once there's no financial incentive, why work beyond a certain production level? In addition, it's difficult to determine what to do when one co-owner decreases his or her number of days or weeks in the practice because of hobbies, family commitments, or illness. It sets up an inequity, with the more productive partner feeling penalized.

There is no doubt that the ownership distribution method is simple, but it lacks one ingredient essential in any good co-ownership agreement: a productivity incentive. (Figure 4.9)

Productivity Distribution. Another method of income distribution is productivity distribution, which distributes net income solely on the productivity ratios between the parties.

OWNERSHIP COMPENSATION

PRACTICE GROSS INCOME	**$600,000**
• **OVERHEAD (65%)**	**$390,000**
NET PROFIT	**$210,000**

DR. A AND DR. B ARE 50/50 PARTNERS

DR. A COMPENSATION = $ 105,000
DR. B COMPENSATION = $ 105,000

THE PROFITS ABOVE HAVE BEEN DIVIDED BASED ON OWNERSHIP RATIOS

Fig. 4.9

In this situation, if Dr. A produced $360,000 and Dr. B produced $240,000, the productivity ratio is 60/40%. In a 35% net profit situation, the profit of $210,000 is divided 60/40% (Figure 4-10).

The co-owners could take as a salary a draw of 25% of their collections on an ongoing basis. Any remaining profit would be distributed based on the partners' productivity ratios (60/40%). This distribution could be performed monthly, quarterly, semi-annually, or annually.

This is by far the most common income distribution method used in dental practices, and, for most dentists, it makes more sense than distributing income based solely on ownership. This method, however, gives no recognition to ownership interest that, I believe, should be part of any compensation plan for the owner of any business, including a dental practice. This income stream also becomes part of the long-term incentive for an associate to buy into the practice.

The productivity-distribution method also discourages reduction in personal workload on the part of any co-owner, which of course is contrary to the desire many dentists have as they approach late career. This disincentive makes it difficult for late-career dentists to enjoy various quality-of-life pursuits, and, as a result, may impede the growth of any junior-level co-owners, who may want access to the senior co-owner's patient base at some point. Because the productivity only compensation model creates no income on a passive basis, dentists often invest in other businesses to create such a benefit.

Dentistry vs. "Worm Farms": A Story

We've all heard stories about business ventures that have gone bad. We listen with particular interest to those stories that involve dentists. Sometimes, these ventures defy logic and we say, "What could these intelligent individuals have been thinking? It was obvious that the venture was bound to fail."

About 15 years ago, I heard a dentist tell a story about his own failure, and it's stuck with me because it could have been avoided. I heard the story during a long drive with a dentist friend. At one point, he started talking about losing his life savings in—of all things—a worm farm. It seems that he borrowed money to start his worm farm, believing the venture had potential, both because of a demand for the product and the fact that other people could work the farm for him, while he continued to practice dentistry.

PRODUCTIVITY COMPENSATION

PRACTICE GROSS INCOME	**$600,000**
• **OVERHEAD (65%)**	**$390,000**
NET PROFIT	**$210,000**
DR. A COLLECTIONS (60%)	**$360,000**
DR. B COLLECTIONS (40%)	**$240,000**
DR. A COMPENSATION =	**$126,000**
DR. B COMPENSATION =	**$84,000**

**THE PROFITS ABOVE WOULD BE
DIVIDED BASED ON PRODUCTION
RATIOS**

Fig. 4.10

My friend's real motivation was to create a passive-income stream. He had a vision of going out to look at his worms now and then, checking in with his employees, and waiting for the checks to roll in. Well, the year he started the farm happened to be one of the rainiest in the area's history. Apparently, worms don't like that much rain and they either crawled away to drier ground or they died. He lost his entire savings in the process.

Sad, but curious, I asked my friend what was so exciting about worm farming that he dumped his life savings into the business and borrowed money to boot. Without missing a beat, he said, "I wanted income from a business that didn't need me to be there, day in and day out. I looked forward to being an absentee owner, just like many of my business-owner friends are. Since I couldn't do that in dentistry, I began to feel trapped, like I was missing out on something other people seemed to create quite easily. Why can't we do something like this in dentistry? Why don't we restructure the way we do things?"

These questions are even more critical today. My friend was correct to wonder why so many health-care professionals invest in businesses they know nothing about (but are reluctant to invest the same dollars in their practices, where they have great expertise). My point is that associateship to co-ownership arrangements is one way to begin creating the passive income most dentists want.

When you think about it, too many dentists go whole hog into some high-risk venture, but pay little attention to low-risk options within their own industry. My erstwhile worm-farmer friend sure wished he'd thought twice about it, before he jumped in and risked everything. He could have been cultivating young dentists to whom he could have sold shares of his practice, instead.

Ownership and Productivity Compensation

By and large, dentistry has been a solo business throughout most of its history. Therefore, most dentists view net income as a function of what they personally produce and collect (with the exception of what net income is produced from the hygiene department and associates). This mindset has unfortunately made its way into the practice co-ownership arena, with dentists still compensating themselves from a solo mentality.

So, another method of net-income distribution involves blending the previous methods of ownership and productivity into a combination that includes the best of both.

My philosophy is that dentists in co-ownership arrangements should consider compensating themselves differently—perhaps by looking at the way some other businesses do it. By properly blending both ownership and productivity, we are rewarding the co-owners in the practice, based on different levels of responsibility, liability, and investment within the practice.

Ideally, compensation should consider the following: initial financial investment; subsequent financial investment made through buy-ins or asset purchases; personal productivity; management responsibilities, and marketing expertise.

Ideally, compensation should consider the following:

- Initial Financial Investment

- Subsequent Financial Investment Made Through Buy-Ins or Asset Purchases

- Personal Productivity

- Management Responsibilities

- Marketing Expertise

- Enhancement of External Referral Sources

Enhancement of External Referral Sources

After paying agreed-upon and reasonable salaries to the owners (based on productivity), the remaining profit is distributed to the co-owners, based on their respective ownership interest in the practice. Most companies establish yearly budgets that include normal and necessary salaries and/or bonuses for any owner-employees. This way, the company always can have "true profits" to distribute to the owners, so that both ownership and productivity are rewarded. (Figure 4.11a)

I always have thought that in co-ownership situations, it is important to have profit remaining in the practice to distribute, based strictly on recognizing ownership, for the following reasons:

- *All co-owners in the practice will benefit collectively from the efforts of the entire practice.* This increases the incentive to build the

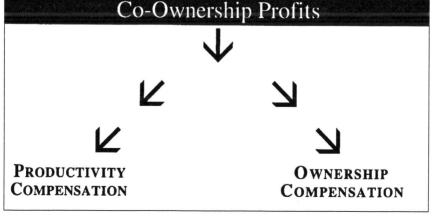

Fig. 4.11a

practice as a team, rather than as independent practices sharing space. It also enhances internal referrals that might be better treated by a fellow co-owner, because everyone profits from some of every dollar produced in the practice.

- *It establishes additional incentive for dentists to want to buy into this practice.* This passive income, based on ownership, creates an income stream that can be enjoyed by the co-owners, even in their absence from the practice. Although this benefit is available to all co-owners, senior co-owners often take advantage of the quality-of-life aspects of this benefit sooner than the junior-level co-owners. By providing senior co-owners with incentive to take time away (at a time in their life when they believe they deserve it), it enhances the production income of all junior co-owners, because the production income represents the lion's share of the total net income.

How does one determine how much of the practice income should be distributed based strictly on ownership? How is the amount calculated and guaranteed? There are a number of approaches to consider. Among them: Using the practice's total gross or total net income or the net income generated strictly from the hygiene department.

Distribution Based on Gross Collections. I recommend using a percentage of the gross collections of the practice, as this amount is easy to determine at any given time. (Figure 4-11b, page 89). In this example, 10% ($60,000) of the total gross income was divided equally (5% to each) with that amount deducted from the total profits of the practice ($210,000). The remaining profits ($150,000) were then distributed based on the productivity ratios of the co-owners, which in turn is based on the co-owners' individual collections.

In this example, Dr. Junior's personal collections represent 30% of the total and Dr. Senior's, 70%. Thus, the profits that remained after distributing co-ownership profits was allocated based on a 70/30 ratio. As you can see, the lion's share of the total practice profit is distributed to the highest producing co-owner.

Distribution Based on Net Collections. One can also distribute ownership profits based on the total net income of the practice (Figure 4-11c, page 90). In this example, 25% ($52,500) of the total net income of the

OWNERSHIP AND PRODUCTIVITY COMPENSATION			
Practice Gross	**$600,000**	**Dr. Senior**	**Dr. Junior**
Production Ratios		**70%**	**30%**
Practice Net 35%	**$210,000**		
10% Gross Divided Equally	**$60,000**	**$30,000**	**$30,000**
Balance on Productivity	**$150,000**	**$105,000**	**$45,000**
Total Compensation		**$135,000**	**$75,000**

Fig. 4.11b

practice (equal to 35% of the gross income) was divided equally between the co-owners. That amount then was deducted from the total profits ($210,000), leaving $157,000 to distribute based on the productivity ratios of the co-owners (the previously calculated 70/30 ratio). Again, the major portion of the total practice profit is distributed to the highest producing co-owner.

Distribution Based on Hygiene Net Income. One can also distribute ownership profits based on the net income generated strictly from the practice's hygiene department. (Figure 4-11d, page 91). In this example, the hygiene net is equal to $30,000, calculated by multiplying the hygiene gross collections ($120,000, equal to 20% of total gross collections) times a profit factor of 25% (which will differ from practice to practice). The hygiene net was divided equally between the co-owners and then deducted from the total profits, leaving $180,000 to distribute based on the 70/30-productivity ratio.

Special Circumstances and Considerations

Associate's Earned Equity

Transferring ownership inevitably brings out self-interest, which is just part of human nature. Many owners believe their practice is

OWNERSHIP AND PRODUCTIVITY COMPENSATION			
Practice Gross	**$600,000**	**Dr. Senior**	**Dr. Junior**
Production Ratios		**70%**	**30%**
Practice Net 35%	**$210,000**		
25% Net Divided Equally	**$52,500**	**$26,250**	**$26,250**
Balance on Productivity	**$157,500**	**$110,250**	**$47,250**
Total Compensation		**$136,500**	**$73,500**

Fig. 4.11c

worth more than the typical buyer thinks is legitimate. Associates might also believe that when they buy in to a practice in which they've been working, they're paying, in part, for what they've built. This is especially true if the value of the practice was determined after the associate had been in the practice for some time. The owner often feels that the associate has only "built" what he or she was given by the owner, and if it were not for him or her, the opportunity would not have existed.

Here's a way to settle the problem: after the practice has been valued, determine what is to be done with the "sweat" or "earned equity" earned by the associate. Ask yourself these questions:

If the practice grows between the time the associate entered and the time of the buy- in, who is credited for this increase in value?

If the equity credit is given to the associate, how will we measure this without knowing what the value of the practice was prior to the associate entering into the practice?

If the credit is given to the owner, how will the associate feel about paying a higher price than was determined up front?

This means that, in certain situations, the practice buy-in needs to be handled differently. For example, should the host dentist continue to work in an aggressive growth mode after the entrance of the associate, he or she may need to revalue the practice at the time of the buy-in. Normally, after bringing in an associate, the host dentist levels off production, thereby allowing the associate to build a practice within the owner's practice. This prevents the host and associate dentists from competing with each other for new patients, especially in the first two to three years of their association.

OWNERSHIP AND PRODUCTIVITY COMPENSATION			
Practice Gross	**$600,000**	**Dr. Senior**	**Dr. Junior**
Production Ratios		**70%**	**30%**
Practice Net 35%	**$210,000**		
Hygiene Gross 20%	**$120,000**		
Hygiene Net 25%	**$30,000**		
Divided Equally		**$15,000**	**$15,000**
Balance on Productivity		**$126,000**	**$54,000**
Total Compensation		**$141,000**	**$69,000**

Fig. 4.11d

In practices that can support two dentists who are both in a rapid-growth mode, there are different considerations. In this case, I would suggest the following:

Step One: Determine Practice Value. First, determine the value of the practice (as previously prescribed) before the associate enters the practice. This will establish a benchmark number for the associate, who then knows that the buy-in price will be based on a total practice value of no less than this figure. Financial projections then can be constructed showing the basics of what the buy-in would look like, based on the existing value of the practice.

Step Two: Revalue the Practice on the Buy-In. Just prior to the buy-in date, the practice should be revalued by similar methods used in the first valuation.

Step Three: Deduct the Value of the Associate's Goodwill. Deduct the value of the associate's production (goodwill) from the total value.

The same could be accomplished by merely excluding the associate's production from the valuation process.

The associate's goodwill value can be calculated by using a gross-income multiplier times the most recent 12-month gross collections of the associate. This usually is a range of 20% to 30% of the associate's collections, averaged over the one- to three-year period prior to the co-ownership.

Some owner-dentists may believe that additional production may exist in the practice, in the form of potential that merely needs to be tapped. Although this thinking may appear logical, the bottom line is this: if the associate knows he/she must pay for the value of his/her own production at some point (regardless of where it comes from), it may negatively impact the proposed co-ownership arrangement.

The big picture on which the owner needs to focus is how much more profitable the practice becomes with the combined production of the two dentists. This is where the real profitability windfall comes from—not from the buy- in price, but from enhanced profitability that the practice will enjoy for years to come.

Selling Less Than Half Your Practice

I'm often asked about selling the practice in increments over a period of time, such as 10% a year. The question arises because:

- The owner wants to maintain as much as control as possible, (although all he or she would have to do is maintain a 51/49% ownership ratio).

- The associate and/or the owner each thinks that, by buying 10% at a time, the practice is more affordable.

I understand this logic. But if one uses the combined ownership-productivity compensation model—that the more someone buys, the more someone profits—then it might seem more logical to approach the buy-in from the perspective I've outlined in this chapter. It doesn't require a mathematician to figure out the higher the associate's net income (which hopefully will include profits based on ownership, as well as productivity), the higher the payment an associate can make. Frequently, this increased payment is offset by additional profits made by buying an additional interest in the practice. The owner-dentist also receives a higher payment, so he or she benefits, too.

Remember, this is all part of a fair exchange—the greater the risk, the higher the payment, the greater the reward. In exchange for a higher payment, it's true the owner is giving up some potential profits; but, the idea is that, collectively, the two dentists together create a combined practice that is much more profitable than the two parties would have been separately.

Remember too, together the buyer and seller are expanding equity, so both have something to sell in the future.

Associate to Co-ownership: Managing the Transition

Though entirely separate books have been written to cover the associate recruitment and transition management, the following checklist contains the most important items to consider in an associateship to co-ownership transition.

Recruiting.

- Ask about previous work experience and background. Do they like being helpers? Ask what they're looking for in an associateship position.

- Look for an associate with the right attitude. Aptitude can be trained and instilled over time.

- Before reviewing your practice information with them, have them sign a confidentiality agreement. You should, in turn, ask them for a personal financial statement and recent credit report.

Transition Management.

- Try to thoroughly acquaint the associate with the history of the practice as well as the office systems before he or she begins treating patients.

- Endorsement of the associate from the owner-dentist and staff is important. Whenever possible, include the staff in the process. Patients in the practice often ask the hygienist about the new dentist; he or she needs to convey the fact that the staff went through a process to select the associate.

- Whenever possible, the associate and owner-doctor should work the same hours so they can begin to develop professional camaraderie, particularly during the associate's orientation period.

Many owner-dentists desiring an associateship leading to so-ownership scenario share a common concern: uncertainty as to whether they have enough patients to support the arrangement. Acquiring the practice of a transitioning dentist in the same area often is the answer to this dilemma. In the next chapter, you'll read about how to go about the process of merging. Here, you'll see how to enhance your proposed (or existing) associateship to co-ownership arrangement, as well as learn about the many other reasons to consider a practice merger.

5

PRACTICE MERGERS: A LOGICAL, PROFITABLE OPTION FOR JOINING PRACTICES

On the second Tuesday of every month, they met. Several dentists, practicing in a medium-sized town, voicing their concerns over the future of fee-for-service dentistry. Each had a list of pressing issues. Some were concerned about the growing complexities of patient/staff communication. Others were worried about the challenges of OSHA, governmental agencies, and insurance companies now invading their practices. Underlying all this, there remained growing concern about the rapid expansion of managed care.

In their small-town atmosphere, the job market consisted of middle-class workers who included a number of government employees and a large staff base from a major university system. The previous five to eight years reflected a time in which a significant segment of the area population had chosen managed care. This dramatic conversion to the managed-care delivery system was of major concern to the traditional dental practitioner in the community. Many practitioners, fearing patient loss, were beginning to feel pressured to join this new network of providers in hopes of maintaining their own patient bases.

As a transition specialist, I knew most of these dentists. I began to research possible solutions for their growing dilemma. One solution kept coming to mind. I had previously experienced a positive end-result in the joining of two practices to form one practice entity. I was convinced that by utilizing the same concept, these dentists could benefit from this unique model (commonly called *practice merging*). Since the group consisted of dentists of varying age levels, it made perfect sense to look at combining the practices of dentists nearing retirement with younger dentists who desperately needed to continue the practice-building mode. The benefits were promising and a gradual transition could be exhilarating for all parties.

I was excited. I began spreading the word about practice mergers. Armed with numerous successful case studies in which I had been involved over the years, I initiated discussions with each dentist. After talking about the general concepts and specific benefits of practice mergers, I made recommendations about opportunities in their area.

I was amazed by their responses. Growth-oriented dentists, in early and late career, expressed their feelings:

- "What an interesting concept ... I hadn't thought about merging my practice as a way of expanding my patient base."

- "I'd certainly be interested in merging if I could do it with the right person ... especially if the numbers made sense."

- "I've heard of practice mergers before. Sounds like a great idea—how can I start looking for a merger opportunity?"

There also were responses from dentists who needed more information.

- "How can you join two entirely different practices without creating total chaos?"

- "How can you combine two practices into one facility?"

- "Can the seller-dentist really let go enough to no longer be the boss?"

- "Wouldn't it be very expensive to remodel or move out of my existing office, just to merge practices with someone?"

- "Is it wise to incur all that debt in order to increase my patient base?"

- "Do these mergers really work? How do you deal with delicate staff issues and scheduling problems in these scenarios?"

- "If someone in my area is selling, wouldn't I stand a chance of some patient transfer? Why should I buy a practice if I might receive some of the patients anyway?"

Initially, I was discouraged and surprised by these questions. I couldn't understand why this kind of negativity was coming from dentists who desperately needed new patients. These were the same dentists who could benefit most from such a transition.

Next, I discussed these ideas with dentists in the group who were two to three years from their target retirement dates. They responded with questions like:

- "Selling my practice to someone who is already practicing in my area is certainly an avenue I hadn't considered—how would that work?"

- "Gosh, I already know a perfect candidate for this type of arrangement. He moved into the area a few years ago and I'm sure that he needs to increase his patient base."

These questions were followed by concerns from others:

- "I'm not sure about the idea of merging with another dentist. Shouldn't I just sell my practice the normal way—to a new dentist looking at the area?"

- "Wouldn't it be better to recruit a new graduate or a dentist who has been in the military to buy my practice? Besides, this way I can 'mold' him or her to fit my philosophy and style."

With this age group, the responses to the idea of merging were mixed. In the end, some members of the group were still unable to recognize the benefits of this type of endeavor. Surprisingly, it appeared that none were taking advantage of the opportunity to greatly expand their practices.

The dentists in the group continued with business as usual. In an effort to attract more new patients, many paid for large, expensive Yellow Page ads. One dentist decided to establish a second practice location—miles away from his existing office. When opening the new location, he failed to remember the financial advantage of purchasing an already-existing patient base and completely ignored a merger opportunity only minutes away from his existing practice. He soon felt the effects of significantly increased overhead costs. The daily pressures of operating two facilities caused him to quickly grow weary of the unsuccessful solution he had chosen. He, like other members of the group, continued to struggle.

During this same time frame, a young dentist moved into town. He had minimal practice experience and no patient base. After looking at various opportunities, he decided to purchase a well-established, existing practice. And, eventually he found a practice ... one that had been on the market for some time. The financial projections of the practice looked good. He closed on the sale and began to establish himself in the community. In less that a year, this young dentist created a very profitable practice with excellent new-patient flow.

He later heard about the concept of practice mergers. He recognized this would be the fastest way to expand his patient base. He knew, in some respects, he simply would need to repeat a few of the same steps he had taken less than a year before, when he initially purchased an existing practice.

He contacted me to discuss practice-merger opportunities in his area. After developing a personalized, comprehensive transition plan to meet his goals, we soon found an ideal practice-merger situation. He first purchased an additional pre-existing practice. He then combined his already-established practice with the newly purchased practice.

Significant overhead costs of operating two separate facilities were immediately eliminated.

Throughout this process, he worked closely with transition consultants at The Transition Group. Personalized letters were developed to inform the patients of this new "association." Management systems were refined and simplified. Communications skills were taught to assure patient retention. The staff became encouraged and motivated to take risks. The entire team dedicated its efforts to protecting the transition investment and everyone was excited about making this venture successful. As a result of the immediate growth in profitability, the young dentist experienced a marked increase in net income.

This practice merger worked extremely well. In fact, it worked so well that by his fifth year of practice, he had purchased three additional practices. After successfully merging these practice into one practice entity, he built and paid for a large, modern facility. He easily continued to make the payments on the practice mergers, still benefiting from the profits of the mergers.

The transition-action plan included: practice expansion through practice mergers; insured patient retention thought transition management provided by specialized consultants; and increased profits through team-building efforts including training, motivation, and incentives for the staff.

The end results? Increased profitability; increased practice value; a beautiful new facility; an efficiently run practice with excellent management systems; enhanced quality of life for the doctors and staff; peace of mind; and a satisfied patient base.

All of the above contributed to the true sense of accomplishment felt by this young buyer-dentist. And, what about the seller-dentists? The first seller-dentist represented a traditional retiring-dentist profile. His hopes of transitioning into retirement within a short period of time perfectly fit the goals of the young buyer-dentist.

The second seller wanted to sell his practice early and continue working for the buyer for two to three years. His plan was to gently glide into retirement, relinquishing the day-to-day management responsibilities of owning a practice. Again, this worked well for the young buyer-dentist who now needed the support of an associate to care for the increased patient base.

The third seller-dentist was a mid-career practitioner who planned to continue practicing for another 10 to 15 years. She had decided that the management responsibilities of recruiting, training, and retaining staff, combined with the overall overhead pressures of practice ownership, were no longer enjoyable. She wanted to dedicate the rest of her career to the clinical aspect of practicing dentistry, leaving managerial and ownership responsibilities behind. She was excited about the opportunity to sell her practice and still have the ability to continue working in a fully functioning practice. At last, she could begin plans to have children. As an added bonus, her patients never even knew about the transfer in ownership.

The merger of the three practices provided the buyer-dentist with an excellent opportunity to continue in the practice-building mode and increase profitability. The successful planning and smooth transition of these opportunities soon allowed the young man to afford the luxury of practicing only 24 hours per week. Profitability in his practice now greatly surpassed the profitability of all the other practices in the area. Viewing the success of this young entrepreneur, others realized the unfortunate "missed opportunities" that caused distress for many members of the small group, those dentists who chose not to explore the magic of a merger-economics."

It came as no surprise when this young dentist-entrepreneur became economically independent in his late thirties. What a great story for the dentist open to the practice-merger concept!

The point of this story is simple. Whether you are in a practice-building mode seeking new patients, transitioning-out-of-practice modes, or searching for an associateship to co-ownership opportunity, look first in your own backyard. You might just find an outstanding opportunity, often times practically on your doorstep.

As with any successful transition, you get what you plan for. Throughout the remainder of this chapter, you'll be introduced to the practice-merger concept model. As you learn the true definition of this unique transition option, we'll explore the merger-economics of this model. Let's begin by looking at important factors to consider when choosing this solution.

The Practice-Merger Model

A merger joins two separate practices into one single, practice entity. In one of the merger models we'll be reviewing, one dentist actually purchases the practice of the other. In the second merger model, two dentists merge to become co-owners, similar to the scenario described in Chapter 4, "Creating 'Win-Win' Associateship to Co-

Ownership Arrangements." In either situation, a single practice entity is formed in the process.

At some point during the process, the two practices are merged into one single facility, and the seller-dentist becomes an employee-dentist of the newly established practice entity. This option allows the seller-dentist to continue practicing for a preplanned period of time, while also allowing the buyer-dentist the advantage of the seller as an associate to care for the needs of the expanded patient base. The unique purchase-sale feature of the practice-merger concept differentiates this model from more common forms of joining practices, such as group practice, solo group, and various other space-sharing arrangements.

A Historical Perspective of Practice Mergers

In the past, dentists attempted several different approaches to practice-merging. Due to concerns with rising overhead costs, they approached the practice-merger concept from a shared overhead point of view. This type of merger more appropriately represented a space-sharing arrangement. Other concepts of office-sharing such as group practice, solo group, and cluster groups became popular. Only recently have dentists begun to recognize practice mergers as an ideal approach to immediate practice expansion. For dentists within five years of retirement considering a future practice sale, the practice-merger model provides an excellent, phased exit-solution. In the late 1970s and early 1980s, transition specialists actively promoted the benefits of practice mergers. At that time, much of the information seemed to fall on deaf ears. However, the response today and in the future appears to be quite different. Dentistry now has entered an era where practice mergers are becoming very common.

Practice Merger Models

There are two types of merger models to explore: the merger acquisition and the co-ownership merger (Figure 5.1, page 102)

By taking a closer look at the merger models, we will begin to see the benefits of each. This chapter will concentrate primarily on the merger-acquisition model, as it is the most commonly implemented type of merger. In a merger-acquisition, there is a clear differentiation of ownership between the two dentists and the length of the relationship is shorter as compared to the co-ownership merger.

The Merger-Acquisition. A typical merger-acquisition involves joining two dental practices with the following profiles: The Buyer's Profile: Dr. A is a positioned-for-growth dentist wishing to purchase a practice. The Seller's Profile: Dr. B is a transitioning-out-of-practice dentist (Figure 5.2, page 103). The purchasing dentist wishes to expand his or her practice, while the selling dentist wishes to sell and retire now or in the near future.

Dr. A, practicing in a suburban area, was in a quandary over his declining new patient flow. He had watched several new dentists move into his area over the past few years. Some started practices from scratch. Others purchased practices from retiring dentists. These new dentists, eager to build successful practices, looked for ways to quickly create an active flow of new patients. Due to the fact that attracting new patients was becoming more difficult, many joined managed-care programs and committed to expensive Yellow Page ads.

Dr. A feared that he was losing patients to these new practitioners. He did not approve of actively marketing or accepting managed-care plans. These approaches, in his mind, were "gimmicks" and bordered on unprofessionalism. Dr. A decided to offset his declining productivity by increasing fees. Through this method, he could maintain the same gross production and continue to cover rising overhead costs. This plan seemed to work; however, he still no longer felt the security of practice growth.

Dr. A began to question his own philosophies and look for any possible solutions. Like the new dentists in his area, would he almost be forced to sign up for some type of managed-care plan? Should he begin paying for a patient referral service? What type of reflection would aggressively marketing through direct mail have on his reputation? What impression would he make to the new patients by offering coupons for free prophies and X-rays? Would the investment in a large Yellow Page ad attract the quality of patient he desired to treat?

PRACTICE MERGERS

Two Separate Practices ⇒ Single Practice Entity

- **The Acquisition Merger**
- **The Co-Ownership Merger**

Fig. 5.1

THE MERGER-ACQUISITION

- **One Dentist *Purchases* The Other's Practice**
- **They Merge Into One Facility**
- **Seller Works for Purchaser**

Fig. 5.2

Dr. A desperately struggled with these types of solutions. However, he wondered if perhaps even choosing one of these options might improve his situation. He questioned if "doing nothing" would prove to be a bigger mistake. Were the "good old days" of treating people right and doing good dentistry gone? Would the future growth and survival of his practice depend upon some nontraditional method of marketing or a managed-care agreement? His pending decision and lack of ideal solutions saddened him and he didn't know where to turn.

Meanwhile, Dr. B (a late-career dentist whose practice was located less than a block from Dr. A's), was within two years of making retirement plans. As he approached this critical time in his life and career, he also was concerned about his options. He had heard stories about other dentists who had retired. Were they satisfied with their end results? Were they happy after retirement? How difficult was it to just wake up one day and no longer have a practice?

Like other dentists he knew, he was uncomfortable discussing his future transition plans with his colleagues in the community. He feared that rumors about his retirement would surface. What if patients began to hear these rumors? Would they start looking for another dentist? What if the staff found out? Would they feel their job security could be in jeopardy? Perhaps they would start looking for other positions. This wasn't the time for staff turnover or patient loss. While fear-induced emotions caused Dr. B to bring an abrupt halt to his decision-making process, his heart told him to face the future.

His mind continued to fill with questions. How could he go about quietly selling his practice? Who would be the right buyer for his practice? How could he find that person? Should he run blind ads in the various dental journals and other periodicals? Should he begin contacting nearby dental schools? How could he discretely talk to possible buyers? When would he even have time to show the practice? Even if he located a prospective buyer, would he be placed in an uncertain position of owner financing? Perhaps he could require the buyer to acquire the necessary financing. Would lending institutions require a comprehensive appraisal of the practice prior to lending such a large sum of money? How could he know he would receive the "true" value of his practice? Knowing that financial institutions find the "rule-of-thumb" methods of valuing a practice unacceptable, who could he trust to place a fair market value on his life-long endeavor? Was there anyone who could help him develop a strategic-transition plan? What a relief it would be to find someone who specialized in the entire transition process, from start to finish.

Familiar with the situations of both Dr. A, and Dr. B, I arranged for the two to meet. While introducing the idea of merging their practices, I encouraged both doctors to look at the logistics of this solution. They had complementary situations—Dr. A, in practice-building mode, was very interested in new patient growth; Dr. B planned to eventually sell and wanted to gradually transition-out over the next few years. By combining the two practices through a practice merger, a new practice entity would be formed to meet the needs of both parties. Why should Dr. B have to look for a buyer when Dr. A (actively seeking new patients) was right down the street?

For a moment, Dr. A and Dr. B seemed stunned. Within a few short minutes, a sigh of relief appeared on the faces of both doctors. Could this be the solution they were both desperately looking for? Would the practice merger also provide each of them the highest level of emotional satisfaction (not to mention the most financially rewarding possibilities) available during this rapidly changing dental marketplace? The answer was clear. We agreed to schedule another consultation. The meeting ended. Fortunately, this story has a happy ending.

A strategic-transition plan was designed to meet the needs of both parties. As "win-win" agreements were constructed, the negotiation process was simplified. Comprehensive agreements (already in place) were sent to the financial and legal counsels of both doctors. Surprisingly, minimal review time was required as their advisors quickly gave their stamps of approval. The entire process, saving Dr. A and Dr. B thousands of dollars in legal and accounting fees, added to the positive feelings about the future.

Through the direction of specialized transition-management consultants, Dr. A and Dr. B effectively merged their practices. With skillfully constructed transition letters, combined with enhanced communication skills learned by the doctors and staff, patient retention was excellent. The renewed energy of the team created a practice atmosphere that easily encouraged patient referrals. Dr. A purchased the practice of Dr. B, who was appreciative of the advantages of having an established-practitioner purchase his practice. Dr. B became an employee-dentist, working with Dr. A during the phase-out arrangement. Dr. B was excited about the opportunity to gracefully glide into retirement and continued to practice for three years after the sale. The practice merger instantly increased Dr. A's patient base, followed by rapid growth in practice profitability.

Who Prospers From an Acquisition-Merger?

The Buyer-Dentist Prospers

The merger of two practices dramatically expands the size of the buyer-dentist's patient base and literally increases profitability overnight. This increase in profitability is illustrated in (Figure 5.3, on page 106).

Profit From the Seller's Production

The first reason profits increase is obvious. In most mergers, the seller remains in the practice providing clinical services, generating passive income for the buyer. It's true that some of the seller's profits go toward paying for the cost of the practice, as well as direct compensation to the seller for providing clinical services. (This compensation usually is based on a percentage of the seller's collections.) If the terms and conditions of the merger have been structured properly (and the practice's purchase price has been verified by appraisal), profit will remain after paying the price of the practice and compensation to the seller for providing clinical services.

Profit From the Expanded Hygiene Department

Another source of profits from the merger comes from the expansion of the buyer's hygiene department. This becomes another form of passive income. In some situations, the profit generated from the hygiene department alone can pay for the price of the practice being purchased and merged.

Profit From an Associate's Production

As discussed in Chapter 4, "Creating 'Win-Win' Associateship to Co-Ownership Arrangements," a merger-acquisition is often a consid-

PROFITING FROM A MERGER A PURCHASER'S PERPECTIVE
• **PASSIVE PROFITS FROM** **SELLER** **HYGIENE** **ASSOCIATE(S)** • **INCREASED PURCHASER PRODUCTION** **INCREASED TOTAL NET** **INCREASED NET PERCENTAGE**

Fig. 5.3

eration prior to bringing in an associate. The enhanced size of the patient base goes a long way toward insuring the economic success of the future co-ownership arrangement. It also relieves the buyer from turning over his or her existing patients to the associate.

With an associate adding additional production (from the seller's practice), we have another source of passive profits. This profit is similar to the profit generated from the seller's personal production.

Profit from the Buyer's Additional Production

In some merger-acquisitions, the buyer plans on acquiring all of the seller's production for him or herself. Therefore, upon the preplanned exit of the seller, the buyer enjoys the combined profits from both practices. This profit is not only active and additive, but to a certain extent, passive. The additive component is clear—there is profit added due to the direct efforts of the buyer. The passive component of this profit comes from the increased net percentage of profit created by the consolidation of the two practices into one facility.

In the process of merging, the fixed overhead expenses of one practice are eliminated. (Even when a new facility is required for a merger, the cost is generally much less than that of two facilities.) Although the overall combined production of the two practices may remain the same as before, the total net income will increase due to lower fixed overhead expenses. Example: Two practices, each netting $100,000, could show a total net of $250,000 (or more) once they are merged.

The Selling Dentist Prospers

For the selling dentist, a merger-sale creates an opportunity to secure practice value prior to approaching late career or retirement. By becoming a provider of services for the buyer-dentist, the seller is freed from day-to-day management and overhead responsibilities, while gradually phasing into retirement. Having an option to continue practicing after selling has proven a popular choice for many transitioning dentists.

Early- and Mid-Career Dentists Prosper

Early- and mid-career dentists with an established patient base should consider the practice-enhancement benefits of merger. Over the last two decades, mergers have proved to be extremely efficient for the practitioner to expand an existing patient base and increase profitability. Unlike other methods used to reach these same goals, practice-merging can bring overnight results. In fact, the specific economic viability and benefits of practice mergers are quite astonishing. In addition, a merger converts the once existing competitor into a team member.

Early-career dentists looking for associateship opportunities find recently completed practice mergers ideal situations to explore. The owner's expanded patient base greatly encourages short- and long-term economic viability for the owner, as well as associates. An ample supply of patients appears to provide the most successful results of an associateship leading to co-ownership arrangement. A practice merger generally creates patient expansion. Why not look for practice-merger opportunities prior to bringing in an associate? This is certainly an approach many dentists should think about.

Additional Benefits of Practice Mergers

Practice mergers can benefit dentists of all career levels. The specific benefits enjoyed will depend upon the career stage of the dentist. Advanced planning is a key element in determining the magnitude of such benefits. Here are a few specific benefits to consider in a practice merger:

Security of an Experienced Buyer: The practice merger model provides the seller with the security of a buyer who is already an established, experienced practitioner. Many late-career dentists find mergers the preferred method of selling their practice and often use this approach when selling prior to retirement.

Many seller-dentists prefer their patient base be taken over by an experienced dentist. All things being equal, the buyer with the greater amount of experience is more likely to create a success from the transaction. With most dentists, practices have been built on relationships. Dentists want to leave their patients in good hands, and they find it difficult to pass the torch to inexperienced dentists (there are many practices where this would be impossible). In the eyes of the seller, the trust and confidence factor is lower with a new graduate. With no experience in private practice, clinical and managerial abilities of the new dentist have not been truly proven and formed. For this reason, the seller-dentist is often reluctant to sell to a practitioner in the initial stage of private practice.

Continued Clinical Practice: The ability to provide clinical services after a practice sale is a great benefit to a seller-dentist who would like to continue to practice. This is often not an option for the seller in a traditional practice sale. Even in pre-retirement sale scenarios (See Chapter 3, "Successful Sales Strategies"), the post-sale working arrangement between seller and buyer often is limited when the buyer is not adding an existing patient base to the equation. Merging two practices creates a sufficient patient base in which the seller and buyer can combine and continue their efforts. This is generally not possible when the buyer is a new graduate. Often, a new practitioner must quickly take over the seller's patient base in order to meet cash-flow demands.

In typical practice-sale scenarios, the seller exits quickly following the sale—not because he or she wants to, but because that was the only choice. In a practice merger, the seller often can work for an extended period of time in the buyer's practice. Most selling dentists enjoy phasing out of practice on a gradual basis. However, if he or she attempts a phase-out without a successor in place, profit margins are squeezed as production levels drop. When it comes time to sell the practice, the numbers are not attractive to a potential buyer. In a practice merger, the retiring dentist actually can enjoy a high quality life and ease out of dentistry.

Financial Security: The financial security of a practice merger is obvious—it benefits the seller and the buyer. Commonly, the selling price of a merger is financed by the seller due to the extremely low default history of this type of transaction. (Having participated in more than 2,000 such transactions since 1981, I only have seen two defaults.) Lending institutions tend to favor proven track records. Sellers are generally less at risk when selling to an established dentist. This is particularly true when the seller is financing any part of the sale. The fact that the buyer already has an established patient base increases economic security.

Expanded Income Potential: Two incomes are better than one. The cash flow generated from the buyer's patient base added to the cash flow generated from the seller's patient base creates increased net income for the buyer. (Figures 5.4 and 5.5)

Common Concerns Surrounding Practice Mergers

New concepts often are viewed with initial skepticism. Many things we today regard as truth initially went through three phases: a stage of total rejection, followed by a period of skepticism, followed by acceptance of the fact as truth. Practice mergers are no exception. When I first began speaking on the topic in 1981, most dentists felt it violated the "too good to be true" rule. Consequently, it was ignored for many years.

Objectivity is essential, and as dentists, we often are our own worst enemies. We fail to realize when our doubts and fears create blocks to prevent us from acting in our own best interest. There are still reasons why some dentists are hesitant to explore practice mergers. Some feel their facility would not accommodate a merger. This is a legitimate concern. Prior to saying "no" to a future merger, ask yourself the following questions:

- "Could my existing facility be expanded and/or could the hours of the practice be staggered to accommodate the merger?"

- "Is there additional space in my area that could be used for the merger?"

- "Would the merger be profitable enough to justify either an expansion or relocation?"

- "Is it possible that the seller's facility could accommodate a merger?" (If the seller is unknown at this time, then this certainly would leave open a possibility.)

Some dentists have a difficult time seeing themselves as selling

---

**PRACTICE MERGERS
PURCHASER BENEFITS**

- **Expanded Patient-Base**
- **Enhanced Profitability**
- **Passive Income**
- **Creates Associateship-Buy-In Opportunity**

Fig. 5.4

their practice to (or purchasing a practice from) another dentist in their area. These dentists are competitors, and some dentists feel more strongly about this fact than others. Some have negative feelings about other dentists in their area, while others are concerned about exposing their transition plans to their local colleagues. The stumbling block that many dentists have on this issue involves the same element that makes it successful—familiarity.

Often, dentists in the same area have only a cordial professional relationship and are not personally close. Friendships often flourish between dentists who practice hundreds or even thousands of miles away. These dentists are certainly no threat of competition. Because dentists are familiar with their competitors, many are hesitant to even think about talking with one of their "neighbors" about a future merger. Due to these fears, they are often left with little choice but to find a stranger to buy their practice. Selling a practice to an unknown can be successful, but it just makes good sense to consider the possibility of selling to a local candidate first. (Dentists who become aware of the benefits to merging with a practitioner in the same area share a new insight: they turn former competitors into compatible "transition-partners.")

When it comes time to sell, dentists should try to be more objective in their thinking about an ideal buyer-candidate profile. There are just too many advantages to practice mergers to ignore them as an option. Are these ventures profitable? Let's look at some basic merger-economics.

Practice-Merger Economics

The specific numbers involved in a practice merger are interesting from the perspective of both parties. Despite the almost foolproof economics involved in a merger, conservative financial projections

PRACTICE MERGER SELLER BENEFITS
• **Experienced Purchaser** • **Allows Continued Practice** • **Financial Security** • **Secures Practice Value** • **No Management & Overhead Responsibilities**

Fig. 5.5

should always precede the final stages of the transaction. This step helps both parties determine the overall viability and proper timing of the merger.

Details of the transaction depend on the financial projections of the proposed merger. From these projections, the purchase price of the seller-dentist's practice can be established/evaluated and the terms of the purchase can be defined. The terms are equally, if not more, important than the selling price. Terms might include information such as down payment amounts, interest rates on any seller-financed amounts, and payment periods. (Be sure to check with lending institutions that specialize in loaning money for this type of transaction.) Other considerations stated in the terms could include the number of hours per week the seller has agreed to work in the buyer's practice, as well as the seller's total compensation package. Since the buyer will now incur these costs, they must be identified upfront and made part of the overall financial projections.

Buying and selling dentists need different types of financial projections. The buyer obviously needs an awareness of specific overhead costs. These costs include the normal fixed and production-related expenses as well as some new, less familiar expenses. One such expense is the *debt service* on the seller's practice, which is equal to the total of the monthly or yearly payments due from the purchase of the practice. This includes payments to lending institutions, the selling dentist, or, in some cases, a combination of the two.

Two areas of merger economics should be established prior to a practice merger.

• determine merger expenses and

• determine the total debt amount on the institutional or owner financing of the practice down payment and payout.

Expenses normally associated with additional production are "production-related" as opposed to "fixed" expenses. Expenses directly related to production are increased proportionately. Since the buyer is responsible for these expenses, he or she will no doubt be interested in determining these costs prior to a practice purchase. In general, you will find increased expenses in the following areas: dental supplies (5% to 8%); office supplies (1% to 2%); and laboratory expense (8% to 12%). Depending on available financing, the debt service will average 12% to 20% of the selling dentist's gross collections.

Once these additional expenses have been deducted from the additional gross collections, the remaining net income is then added to the buyer's existing net income, minus the debt service. Determine the total monthly payment amount due for financing of down payment and practice purchase. Generally speaking, debt service should be a manageable sum when paid on a monthly basis, allowing a comfortable margin of net income for the buying dentist. As discussed earlier, the debt service often can be covered with the additional hygiene profit generated by the merger.

Should the seller become an "employee-dentist" for the buyer, the cost of this compensation package must be determined in advance. The payment structure for the seller should be designed on a production/collection-based system. In some cases, the seller is paid a fixed percentage of personal productivity/collections, excluding fees generated by the hygienist. The buyer usually pays all expenses of the practice, with the seller's laboratory bill taken "off the top." (Figure 5.6)

MERGER-ECONOMICS
BUYER EXPENSES

- **DEBT SERVICE**
- **PRODUCTION-RELATED EXPENSES**
- **FIXED EXPENSES?**
- **SELLER COMPENSATION**

Fig. 5.6

In most mergers, the buyer's fixed expenses are not increased. This assumes that the seller is moving into the purchaser's facility and that the staff costs become "production-related" (i.e., rise and fall as a function of the production from the merger). Should the purchaser move into the seller's facility instead, the net result is the same (except for any differences in rent).

As we discussed earlier, much of the income stream enjoyed by a buyer is passive; it represents income generated without any additional production on the part of the buyer. Obviously, mergers offer a profitable option to consider in a practice expansion and transition plan.

In looking at the merger approach, ask yourself the following questions: Without actually having to produce the clinical dentistry, how many mergers would it take to create a marked increase in net income? The results of a practice merger seem almost too good to be true. Why haven't more dentists considered practice mergers?

Eight Facts Making Practice Mergers Advantageous

Opportunities to Consider

Fact One: Wealth and Security. Acquiring practices for merger can create a great deal of wealth and income security. Much of this income can be generated passively if an arrangement is made for the seller to work for the purchasing dentist for a period of time after the sale.

Fact Two: Eliminates Competitors. The buying dentist has eliminated a competitor in the area, which probably prevents a more aggressive competitor from moving into the area and buying the same practice (and then competing with the buyer for the next 15 to 20 years). If corporations are buying up practices, why shouldn't we as a profession consider buying some of them ourselves?

Fact Three: Hygiene Production Often Pays for the Investment. The debt can be serviced by only a small percentage of the additional gross income generated from the merged practice. In fact, many dentists who have purchased and merged practices have found the hygiene production alone more than pays for the additional expenses involved, including the purchase price of the practice.

Fact Four: Buy Low/Sell High. Depending upon the type of practice purchased and the age of the practitioner, it's common to find practices grossing $200,000 that have the potential of being converted into $400,000 practices within a couple of years. In other words, it's very easy to buy low and end up high, by tapping into the dormant potential in these practices.

Fact Five: Patient Base Expansion. Dentists have devised many ways to attract new patients. Coupons, Yellow Page ads, neighborhood networking, public relations strategies, and so forth are expenses that often seem necessary to keep new patients coming through the door. However, when the expenses of a merger are examined, the total cost may be less than all other methods combined. Merging with a dentist who has had a successful practice for 20 to 30 years is one of the easiest ways to maintain patient flow—it's certainly easier than devising a series of promotional strategies whose outcome can't be accurately predicted anyway.

Fact Six: Reduced Additional Overhead and Increased Profit. As previously discussed, the greater gross dollars come in at a tremendously reduced overhead. In many cases, this allows the buyer to work fewer hours while making the same income as before. The seller also is able to work fewer hours and make the same net income because the practice equity has been converted into an additional cash flow stream.

Fact Seven: Expanded Hours and Services. Expanded hours and services can be accomplished through a merger and this can happen in several ways. The buyer and seller can stagger their hours to allow each greater access to the treatment rooms. This opens the schedule and allows patients to schedule appointments earlier or later than they could with only one practitioner. Expansion eventually allows the buyer to bring in an associate to accommodate the workload. Associates are almost always willing to work staggered hours because it increases their opportunity to meet patients. Many patients are willing to schedule appointments with a new associate, precisely because appointment hours are more convenient.

Dentists involved in this merger, including associates, will inevitably create a situation to expand services as well as hours. For example, many young associates can provide excellent specialty services (depending upon their experience and skills) that have been traditionally referred out by the practice. The seller may have skills in some areas that the buyer doesn't, or the opposite may be true. Either way, the patients and practice clearly benefit. In today's economic climate, keeping services in-house makes a lot of sense and goes a long way toward maintaining an economically viable practice.

Fact Eight: Facilitates Associateship to Buy-In Arrangements. As discussed in Chapter 4, "Creating 'Win-Win' Associateship to Co-Ownership Arrangements," an inadequate number of patients is a leading cause of failure in associate to co-ownership arrangements. Although it may appear that there are other problems, most are economic—the dentists were not making enough money because there weren't enough patients for both to treat. A merger can eliminate this problem. Greatly expanding the patient base prior to (or in conjunction with) bringing in an associate expands current profitability for the buyer, expands the hours and services provided by the practice, and "jump starts" an associate's practice. Many dentists spend decades trying to build their practices large enough to be economically comfortable and support an associate. With a practice merger, this could happen overnight. Why not do yourself a favor and reach your goal as soon as possible?

Now that you've taken a look at a comprehensive view of the practice-merger model, let's talk about what a merger is *not*. A merger does not mean simply sharing space. I feel it is important to include information about space-sharing concepts in the practice merger chapter of this book. Why? Because far too many dentists are unaware of the fact that many space-sharing arrangements don't work. Many practitioners also are not aware of some of the transition-obstacles that space-sharing arrangements present. Dentists enter space-sharing arrangements for various reasons. Most often, it revolves around the central theme of sharing overhead. In addition, most dentists hope to achieve other things in the process, such as office coverage in each other's absence, professional camaraderie, and bulk-purchasing abilities. (Figure 5.7)

The most common space-sharing profile generally consists of two or more established dentists who decide to practice in a single facility. These arrangements must be carefully designed in order to be profitable. They must also be approached with great caution in order to protect practice value in the anticipation of any future transitions. If you are considering space-sharing, take note of the following: To further illustrate the do's and don'ts of space-sharing, the following story is a classic example of a group of dentists who decided that space-sharing was the way to go.

A Space-Sharing Saga

It was 1981. I was in the thick of my first year as a transition consultant. A group of four dentists (who had been in a space-sharing arrangement for five years) asked me to help them dissolve their space-sharing arrangement on an equitable and nonadversarial basis. (They also wanted to avoid any lengthy and adversarial legal battles.) For various reasons, they no longer wanted to practice together. After listening to each dentist's viewpoint, I agreed that it was time for him or her to dissolve their relationship and go back to independent locations.

Each dentist voiced the same basic concerns. All members of the group were working just as hard as before, but were making less money. (The main reason for their original space-sharing arrangement was to save overhead costs and increase their profit margins.) Having given up their independence without financial gain, they were all frustrated. The camaraderie they had once relied upon had turned to bickering. Even small day-to-day issues became obstacles as they attempted to reach agreements.

At one time or another, they all posed the same question, "Why can't four dentists seem to agree about anything?" Being employed to help them through their situation, it was important to understand what had gone wrong and how to help others avoid similar problems. In further discussions with the dentists, I discovered the following facts about their individual practices, prior to entering the space-sharing arrangement: each dentist had been in practice three to five years; each dentist had three treatment rooms and one hygiene room (approximately 1,200 square feet); each dentist had one assistant, one person at the front desk, and one hygienist; and each dentist was working 32 to 36 hours per week.

They had started from similar circumstances. Initially, everything looked good. In order to keep everything the same, they built a new office space (4,800 square feet) to accommodate all four doctors and staff.

SPACE-SHARING DESIRED BENEFITS

- **SHARED OVERHEAD → HIGHER PROFIT**
- **BULK-PURCHASING ABILITY**
- **OFFICE COVERAGE**
- **PROFESSIONAL CAMARADERIE**

Fig. 5.7

Why didn't this work out be a win-win situation for everyone? In looking at the true cost effectiveness of this venture, the findings were astonishing.

Staff overhead remains unchanged. Each dentist had his own assistant (total of four), his own front desk person (total of four), and, of course, his own dental hygienists (total of four). Since each dentist wanted to maintain an independent base of employees, the situation did not allow the opportunity to share any staff-overhead expenses. No cost savings here.

Facility costs were up. The rent costs for the facility had escalated to an average of $5.00 per square foot more than the cost of the prior facilities. No cost savings here.

Supply costs didn't decrease. Each dentist reserved the right to choose his own materials. So, the group maintained individual supply inventories, sharing only some common disposable items. The only savings they ever achieved were by ordering disposables in bulk. These savings were marginal to say the least. No real cost savings here.

Utility costs increased. Their beautiful new palace had high ceilings. Amazing how much more they now had to pay to heat and cool their offices. The actual prorated share of utilities for each practitioner increased significantly compared to individual costs prior to forming the group. Again, increased expenses.

Insurance, telephone, and other fixed costs remained the same. The dentists were unable to share any of these costs, resulting in no real cost savings.

Equipment purchases and maintenance remained the same. Since they didn't share treatment rooms, each dentist continued individual equipment purchases and maintenance costs. The only shared equipment cost they could show was a Panoramic X-ray machine. Only minor savings here.

Other expenses, such as continuing education, dues and subscriptions, etc., were the same.

After analyzing their total expenses, the only true cost-sharing among them was their joint use of the dark room and their Panoramic machine. The obvious question: "Was the small cost savings worth all the new challenges they faced while trying to work together?" Coupled with the necessity to make joint decisions on numerous day-to-day issues, the end result was frequent fighting amongst all four members of the group and their staffs. Were projected cost savings of the new group calculated before formation? Had they made false assumptions, based on misinformation about group practices and other similar space-sharing arrangements?

The Challenges of Space-Sharing

Minimal Overhead Savings. Above, we looked at a classic example of entering into a group practice with no cost savings. We've seen how easily costs can increase in such a situation. Unless hours truly are staggered, with all dentists essentially using the same space and equipment, a true cost savings is difficult to achieve.

Unclear Practice Ownership. Sharing space creates another problem, often invisible to the dentist entering into this type of agreement—perception of ownership. Will one large practice model be created? Or, are we actually looking at building several independent practices? Patients going to dentists in space-sharing situations often assume that the dentists are "partners" of some sort. Likewise, potential buyers also find it difficult to identify ownership as it relates to the transfer of patients once a transition has occurred.

Unclear ownership within a group greatly complicates the future sale of the practice. In some situations, the possibility of a sale is completely destroyed. Since much of the true practice value is based on goodwill, potential buyers often are fearful. Will patient loyalty transfer to other dentists in the group rather than to the buyer? Although this sometimes represents distorted thinking, it is true that patients often view the doctors as partners. The potential for patient loss does exist. In these cases, the new name and face of the buyer presents little security to the patient.

The lack of clarity around ownership, combined with the uncertainty surrounding the transfer of patients, often prevents the possibility of a successful sale. In almost all space-sharing situations, the final selling price is affected.

Competitive Environment. Dentists in the practice-building mode consistently strive to increase new-patient flow. Inevitably, competition surfaces within groups practices. There is no easy way around this issue; it is just a fact to be aware of.

Separate-Camp Mentality. When multiple staffs are combined and practice from one facility, the possibility of separate-camp mentality significantly increases. In the shared space situations, the following comments often are heard: "Dr. Smith's staff always leaves the lab in a mess. We're constantly having to pick up after Dr. Jones' staff. Would you please have a talk with him about that? Dr. Harris sure uses a lot of disposable supplies—much more than we do—is it fair for us to equally share the cost? Dr. Smith's staff just received a raise, I think we should, too. Dr. Jones took all his staff to Disney World last year, why don't we ever have team retreats?" The list goes on and on. This is the essence of a separate-camp mentality—one practice vs. another.

The doctors also develop a separate-camp mentality, as they discover differences in their management and treatment philosophies. Day-to-day management decisions can be tough, causing alliances to form that often exclude one or more members of the group. The goal of camaraderie is lost as the intended group cohesiveness becomes an illusion. Sadly enough, most of these problems exist as a result of bad planning.

Lack of Internal Buy-Out Plans. A serious complication of most space-sharing models is the lack of an agreed-upon, buy-out arrangement among the members. With the exception of the purchase of a "key-man" insurance plan, most practices in space-sharing arrangements remain unprotected in the buy-out phase. In the event of retirement and/or disability, lack of planning can literally cost thousands of dollars. The true awakening for the senior doctor with no buy-out plan begins when he or she discovers that his or her practice is not easy to sell due to the space-sharing arrangement environment.

The retirement nightmares faced by many dentists in space-sharing arrangements come late in the transition cycle. Unfortunately, late-career dentists in these types of arrangements have sad stories to tell (Figure 5-8).

A True Retirement Nightmare Story

A few years ago, a dentist in his early 60s contacted me to talk about selling his practice. He first wanted to have the practice valued. He then planned to present the price and terms to his buyer. I congratulated him for locating a buyer so quickly and told him how lucky he was to have a built-in buyer in hand. He explained it had not been difficult to find a buyer, as he had shared space with this person for 15 years. Although they had never really talked about what would happen upon his retirement, he was sure his friend and practicing companion of 15 years would buy his practice. My heart sank and I got that same bad feeling in my gut that I always get when I hear situations like this. Sadly, I know what usually lies ahead. After completing the practice valuation and accompanying practice-sale format, I forwarded the package to the seller and arranged to discuss the information with his "buyer."

The potential buyer was quite surprised when approached for such a purchase, strongly stating that he was quite busy in his own practice with no need for additional patients. In reviewing the advantages and benefits of adding this additional patient base, it was easy to see that such a purchase would not only strengthen his practice, but also allow for a future associate. By preventing his "partner" from selling his practice to an outside buyer, he could prevent the possibility of having to share the same space with a complete stranger in the future. Unable to see the benefits of buying the practice, he unfortunately decided against a purchase.

Several months went by. The selling dentist became more and more anxious about the situation. He just couldn't believe that the person he considered his partner was not interested in buying his practice. He began looking for an outside buyer on the open market.

In each case, prospective buyers were concerned about the transfer of the patients. A few of the thoughts haunting potential buyers included: the seller-dentist's younger partner had seen many of these patients on an emergency basis. He often checked them for routine hygiene visits. He covered the seller's practice when he attended continuing education course. He kept the practice going when the seller-dentist took vacations. He was always available to the seller-dentist in the case of other absences.

SPACE-SHARING CHALLENGES

- **MINIMAL OVERHEAD SAVINGS (IF ANY)**
- **UNCLEAR PRACTICE OWNERSHIP**
- **COMPETITIVE ENVIRONMENT**
- **SEPARATE-CAMP MENTALITY**
- **NO BUY-OUT STRUCTURE**

Fig. 5.8

It was clear that all the patients believed the two were true partners. This made prospective buyers quite nervous (rightfully so). How can you buy a practice without having some assurance that the patients are going to transfer to you?

Eventually, a buyer was located. Unfortunately, the buyer was only willing to pay only 50% of the fair-market value. Accepting this type of offer represented a loss of more than $200,000, a loss the seller couldn't afford. Nearing retirement, he needed every dollar he could get.

The seller then was faced with exploring other options. He struggled without knowing what to do. He could sell at a drastically reduced price to an outside buyer; go back and try to renegotiate some rock-bottom price with his existing partner; or move his practice to another location for a couple of years in order to overcome the current obstacles of patient transfer. Unfortunately, he owned the building. It made no sense to consider relocation.

In the end, the seller-dentist eventually sold his practice to his existing partner for $150,000 less than market value. Even then, the buyer-dentist believed he was doing the seller-dentist a favor. As a result, deep resentment grew between the parties and their relationship gradually deteriorated.

Who would have known that sharing space without a structured plan could lead to such a huge financial loss for the seller-dentist? Would either dentist ever have thought of destroying the relationship between two friends? The seller retired a very disappointed man.

A Note on Making
Space-Sharing Arrangements Work

With a structured plan in place, space-sharing arrangements can create a high degree of success. Here are some suggestions:

- *Staggered hours:* By utilizing the facility to its maximum potential through staggered working hours, dentists in a space-sharing situation can enjoy spending less hours in the office. With proper planning, production goals are easily attainable. The expanded hours almost always increase patient satisfaction and attract new patients.

- *Age-staggering:* Consider age staggering when constructing space-sharing groups. Maintaining (where possible) an age separation of 10 or more years between the dentists in the group creates a more conducive environment for the buy-out of senior-level doctors as they approach retirement. When the individuals in the group are approximately the same age, retirement plans become difficult. This often creates problems and negates many of the advantages dentists look for when forming a group.

- *Secure an internal buy-out plan:* The assurance of having an equitable buy-out plan for all group members can save dentists hundreds of thousands of dollars. The plan should include the terms, approximate time frame, and price of the future buy-out. A well-designed plan will protect all members of the group in the case of death, disability, and/or retirement.

- *Separate reception areas:* When an internal buy-out plan can not be agreed upon between the members of the group, each individual should be prepared for the sale of his or her practice to an outside party at some point. Where possible, each dentist should have his or her own separate reception areas. This will at least give the impression (to the public) of totally separate practices, making the future sale of the practice to an outside party more easily accomplished.

The Co-Ownership Merger

A second type of practice merger was mentioned in the beginning of this chapter. It is known as the co-ownership merger. It differs from an acquisition-merger in that it involves co-ownership of the practice once formed (as opposed to ownership by only one of the dentists).

This type of merger typically involves two dental practices with the following profiles: Dr. Mid-Career owns a growth-mode practice. Although his patient base is manageable, having another dentist in the practice would help with the eventual overflow of practice growth and reduce overall overhead. Dr. Early-Career has a small patient base and practices near Dr. Mid-Career.

Dr. Mid-Career presents Dr. Early-Career with the opportunity to move his or her patient base to Dr. Mid-Career's facility. Dr. Early-Career merges with Dr. Mid-Career and practices initially as an associate. Dr. Early-Career covers the gradual overflow of Dr. Mid-Career's practice. The resulting growth of Dr. Mid-Career's practice allows the opportunity for Dr. Early-Career to buy-in. In this model, the buy-in usually occurs within three to six months of the merger. A precalculated formula to buy-in for this type of model is required.

The following is an example of how a co-ownership merger formula might be designed for Dr. Mid-Career and Dr. Early-Career:

Co-Ownership Merger Buy-In Formula
Dr. Mid-Career's Practice Value = $250,000
Dr. Early-Career's Practice Value = $50,000
Combined Practice Value = $300,000

We now have a combined practice value of $300,000. To create a 50% co-ownership model (which is the usual desire of two dentists), Dr. Early-Career will need to buy-in to half of the total value (or buy-in to the "middle") by paying Dr. Mid-Career $100,000. The end result is that Dr. Early-Career and Dr. Mid-Career each now own half of a $300,000 practice.

Dr. Early-Career's Buy-In Price
Total Practice Value = $300,000
50% Buy-In = $150,000
Dr. Early-Career's Practice Value = $50,000.
Resulting Buy-In Price = $100,000

In Closing: Thoughts on Practice Mergers

Whatever the merger opportunity, be sure to plan carefully and seek the advice of a transition specialist. A practice merger reflects one of the most profitable options available in dentistry. This model has been tried and tested. A sure bet, it proves true almost every time. With strategic-transition planning including appropriate means of informing patients and staff training, practice mergers will continue to provide solutions to dentists of all career levels.

Many dentists today are selling and merging their practices and starting new practices in other areas (often as smaller versions of their previous practices). The merger approach allows this "new start-up" to be economically viable (i.e., having the security of continued income from the practice he or she has built and sold, while gradually giving birth to a new practice in another area).

The next chapter, "New Practice Establishment," will shed some light on this new and exciting option being pursued by dentists across the country. It also gives sound advice for dentists setting up from "scratch" for the first time.

6

NEW PRACTICE ESTABLISHMENT: STARTING A PRACTICE FROM "SCRATCH"

Dr. Smith has been in private practice for more than 22 years. He is a very quality-oriented clinician who managed to establish a most respectable practice over the course of his career. Having invested in a progressive practice-management program five years ago, he is proud of the well-trained and motivated team he developed to support his practice goals. Together, they've implemented effective systems to manage patient information, and treatment acceptance is near 100%.

In growing the practice, he created staff incentives and shared the profits. He rarely has staff turnover. His patients pay for their treatment with gratitude and appreciation and he enjoys his time at the office.

The practice has evolved into a well-organized and profitable business. He currently is producing more than $500,000 per year on a four-day workweek. He enjoys practicing dentistry and is not interested in retirement for at least 10 years.

Then why has Dr. Smith decided to sell his practice and start another practice from "scratch"— only to repeat the process and start over?

Good question! The answer: several reasons.

Dr. Smith is concerned about the future growth of the practice. Over the years, the area in which he originally established his practice has changed. The average income level in the area is low and the population is transient.

Dr. Smith would like the opportunity to cash-in his practice value at its peak. With his practice value being at its highest point ever, he has made the decision to sell. In negotiation with a perspective buyer, a very attractive purchase offer on the practice has been received.

Dr. Smith has enjoyed the journey. In fact, he is so excited about how things have turned out, he'd like to try it again. He plans to sell his practice and work part-time for the buyer for one year. During his commitment as an "employee-dentist," he will make plans for a new practice venture.

Dr. Smith has strategically planned to protect his retirement. While he continues to practice with the buyer of his current practice, he will start a new practice 30 miles away. Utilizing the funds of his practice sale, he will cash in a high practice value and protect his retirement. Since he has planned well and is financially stable, he is willing to risk new-practice establishment without a patient base.

Dr. Smith would like to practice closer to his home. He lives 25 miles away from his current practice. He and his wife have built a wonderful home near a nice country club. Over the years, many of his friends at the club and in the community have expressed their desire to become patients "if only his practice were nearby." Dr. Smith would like to take more time off with less concern for practice overhead. In building the new practice, Dr. Smith plans to build a very small, efficient and well-run office. Dr. Smith's wife will retire at a young age from her career in education. Their plans are to travel while they are both young enough to enjoy it. He plans to later retire and enjoy his golf game.

Dr. Smith is not afraid of starting a practice from "scratch." The truth is, he is excited about the new venture. With the new-patient flow of friends and neighbors, Dr. Smith plans to start small and grow slowly. Immediately, Dr. Smith will be relieved from the demanding practice-management pressures of the past. As his practice grows, he plans on bringing an associate into the practice to become the future buyer. Again, Dr. Smith will be capitalizing on cashing-in practice value.

The projections for Dr. Smith's transition plan look excellent. As we've discussed, there is a growing number of older and much more experienced dentists now pursuing new practice establishment. As this interesting new trend in practice establishment develops, many dentists in their early to mid-50s may begin to look at selling their established practices and starting over. Uncertain about the future value of their practices, well-established dentists are already becoming interested in "cashing-in" practice value early while peak numbers are strong.

Being far from retirement, these practitioners have the physical and financial strength to better insure the success of a new practice venture. Some established practitioners, having built large practices requiring extensive management efforts, simply are hoping to reduce management responsibilities and look at the possibilities of downsizing career lifestyles and goals.

This trend, common in today's business world, is now starting to create excitement in the dental industry. Although we understand that new practice establishment without an established patient base is not a risk-free venture, future trends may show a resurgence of new practice establishment for the seasoned professional like Dr. Smith.

New Practice Establishment for the New Practitioner: Approach with Caution

Why do we continue to hear warnings in regard to new practice start-ups? It's true that the days of setting up practice from "scratch" with little planning (almost anywhere you want to) are gone. (When I set up practice from scratch just outside of Atlanta, Georgia, in 1975, I thought about it for a couple of days, went to the bank the third day, and opened the doors the week after.) Today, there are high growth areas that can support a new dentist—especially those areas where no established practices exist to purchase.

Despite this, I still urge beginners to proceed with caution. Starting a practice from "scratch" is an option requiring insight, some significant form of financial security and, most of all, strategic planning.

For the newly graduated dentist, new-practice establishment comes with a much higher price tag. Setting up a practice from "scratch" has no built-in safety net. Few hours of dental training and education are spent focusing on practice establishment or practice management. Programs to educate dentists on all the aspects of setting up a practice from scratch are difficult to find.

New graduates should be very cautious of this option. Several years ago, I received a call from a dynamic young dentist seeking advice about setting up a practice. Having spent his early twenties struggling financially in an unrewarding career, he made some life-changing decisions at the age of 34.

In his mid-30s, he decided to earn a college degree. With the added responsibilities of a family, his college years were difficult. Upon his graduation with honors, he was accepted into a dental school program. Life created even greater challenges.

Determined to succeed, he began his first year in dental school. Taking part-time jobs to make ends meet, he earned enough money to survive and actually juggled things quite well.

When he graduated from dental school at 42 years of age, his family stood proud as he received his degree. He had accomplished more than anyone had thought possible during his early years of life. His goals had been met. He had done his job well.

He soon found a temporary position as an associate in a small town, never giving up his dreams of some day owning his own practice. Only two short months after his temporary associateship ended, he decided to start his own practice.

Soon afterwards, he called me back. By this time, he had found an area where he wanted to practice, located a rental space, designed an office, leased equipment, and hired an office manager.

In his haste to begin practicing, he hired a friend of the family as his office manager. She and her husband were more than happy to loan him the initial start-up capital for his new venture. Although he did not have a patient base and knew practically no one in the community, he had chosen a growing area in which to practice. He felt sure that he was doing things right, especially now that he had decided to employ a consultant (somewhat after the fact) to advise him on how to get started.

My initial response to his course of action was concern. Knowing very well what obstacles might lie ahead for this energetic young practitioner, there were a *few* questions we needed to discuss. Later realizing the need for a strategic-action plan to protect his investment, he began to see things more clearly.

Fortunately, in the end, things seemed to fall into place. His dynamic personality, his active involvement in the community, and his drive for success greatly contributed to the large numbers of new patients he was able to attract in his first year.

His numbers grew quickly. During the first six months of practice, his Profit and Loss Statement reflected enough stability for a local banker to willingly take a risk and loan him operating capital. Since the tension of "friendships" at the front desk were growing daily, he appreciatively repaid his initial loan to the office manager in order to earn the right to "redirect" her career. Surprisingly, the family ties were not broken.

Years later, he now laughs at his first attempt at practice establishment. Now a successful businessman, he recently became the buyer of two very profitable practice-merger opportunities in his area.

The beginning of this story represents only a brief introduction to "The 10 Biggest Mistakes Dentists Make in New Practice Establishment" (a fictitious book that could easily be written by compiling our own horror stories of the past). Sadly enough, all new business ventures don't end the same way.

The point of this story is to encourage you to look seriously at the basic steps to new practice establishment. Ask yourself the right questions; diligently search for the correct answers. Carefully seek the advice of trained transition specialists to guide you through the process.

Structuring a Plan for New-Practice Establishment

There are several important areas to review prior to structuring your plan for new-practice establishment. As you review each of these points, make notes along the way where you will need to do additional research. Review your information carefully and cover all your bases. Try not to leave any stone unturned in developing your guidelines for new-practice establishment. Seek the advice of trained specialists in every category of this checklist. Their experience and expertise comes with a much lower price tag than will the crucial mistakes you will make on your own. If you are unable to find someone to help you, ask your colleagues for names of dependable professionals in the area. The point: Get help somewhere!

Develop your plan and stick to it. Believe in yourself along the way. Don't give in to the "things gone wrong" syndrome. Take the time to do your homework; it saves time and money (not to mention headaches.) Let's look at 10 basic steps to follow in new-practice establishment:

Geographic Area

One of the first things to consider is in which geographic area you (and your family) wish to live. Explore all your personal and financial reasons for choosing your location. Some geographic areas are enjoying more growth than others are, and this certainly should be a consideration. Some areas have a greater number of retirees with discretionary income than others, and this also may influence your decision.

What type of climate do you enjoy? Do you prefer the coast or the mountains, or areas where you can have both? Have you always wanted to live where the weather was warm year-round, or do you prefer a change of seasons? Although nothing prevents you from moving to another geographic area in the future, it's certainly better to start out practicing exactly where you want to be.

Specific Location. "Location, location, location!" is a popular phrase used in the real estate industry, and it certainly holds true for determining the geographic area as well as specific location of your practice.

What type of community do you want to live in? Will your spouse be happy in the area? Do you have children? Do you thrive on the excitement of city life or do you long for the peace and quiet of the country?

When first starting out, office exposure is especially important. When possible, locate your office in a high traffic area where people can see your sign. I had one client who got a real "jump start" when he opened an office near the drive-in window of the local McDonald's. With the number of people stopping there each day, they couldn't help but see his sign while waiting for their food.

Determining the location to best suit your needs is a personal decision that only you can make. Many factors affect this decision, some emotional, some financial, and others based on timing and space availability. Limited only by your own requirements and licenses, enjoy your exploration of the possibilities that are overall most attractive to you.

Once you have narrowed your search to a specific area, do your research. Meet with advisors from the local Chamber of Commerce. Network with other professionals in the area. Dental specialists are an especially good source of information, as they often know how the general dentists in the area are doing economically. Look at your competition. Scan the area Yellow Pages—see how many other dentists there are in the same are. Review demographic studies of the area. Evaluate the average household-income statistics of the area. Talk with dental-sales representatives. Get a feel for the obstacles others in the area are facing. How many other new dentists are considering coming to the same area that you are considering? (You don't want to get caught in a situation where a new dentist sets up in the same area at the same time.)

A myriad of situations should be explored in choosing the right area for your practice. Choosing the best location to meet your personal needs is the first step in building a solid foundation for your future happiness in the practice. Choosing a location to best suit your patients' needs may very well be the first step in building a secure patient base for the future. Consideration in both these areas is your best bet for success.

A word of warning. Do not make your decision on location based solely upon your personal and emotional desires. Although this is an important part of the equation, adequate growth in the area and other economic factors must be evaluated.

Location Factors. Climate. Metropolitan vs. Small Community. Growth Potential and Demographics. Chamber of Commerce. Yellow Pages. Dentists and Specialists in the Area. Dental Sales Representatives.

A couple of years ago, I worked with a stately gentleman dentist who, in his late 40s, had chosen a beautiful vintage town in Florida in which to establish and grow a practice. He and his wife loved the area. With the peacefulness of a quiet country flavor and the accessibility of a major airport only an hour and a half away, this small town looked like a great place to later sell a practice and retire.

Over the course of the past 10 years, he had managed to grow the practice into a million-dollar-per-year operation. He was sure that with all the activity of new and experienced dentists looking for practices in Florida, he easily would secure his retirement with his practice sale.

Unfortunately, he had not considered that this hidden area was three hours from the nearest beach, had low potential for business development and offered out-of-state buyers little of the Florida "allure" that they were seeking.

His reasons for choosing this location were purely emotional. His business logic in assuming this would be an excellent resale area was incorrect. He failed to plan carefully for retirement, making the mistake of relying heavily upon the future sale of his practice to provide for future needs. He is 62 now years old, still practicing in the same area. Unable to retire, his practice has been on the market for more than two years.

It takes a lot to make it in the business world these days. Your location plays a vital part in your success. Make your decision about your location carefully and intelligently. Consider the overall picture.

Facility Type and Size

What's the best type of facility to go into? Freestanding building? Corporate high-rise? Medical complex? Strip shopping center? Old Victorian residential conversion? What are the different factors to consider?

Investment in space. Buy, build, or lease? Are there advantages to leasing vs. owning, and what are the tax considerations? These are all-important considerations in determining what type of facility you should invest in.

In the end, your final decision in choosing your ideal facility location and space may be limited by money supply and availability of suitable space. Do a financial analysis of the pros and cons to leasing vs. owning a facility. Look at the projected leasehold improvement costs vs. the investment of designing and owning your own building. Consider the importance of patient convenience and accessibility factors for growth potential.

Once you've decided on a facility location, determine the amount of space you will need. There is no ideal size for a facility. Your work style and professional goals will determine your initial plans for the size of your facility.

The perfect size of a dental practice has been in question for years. The dentist who saved thousands on facility costs by only utilizing 800 square feet may have never recognized the lost potential due to the productivity limitations of the same facility. The "ego-palaces" of the '80s cost dentists literally hundreds of thousands of dollars, with many never recouping from the enormous emotional roller coaster of month-to-month financial pressures.

Design with efficiency and sensibility. That's not to say that you should cut every corner, leaving your personal tastes and desires behind. Let's face it, much of our time is spent at the office. The environment of your office should reflect *you* as a person. Create an atmosphere that will make your life easier and make you happy. Spend some time touring other dental offices and talking with representatives who can give you ideas. Interview business managers who understand the daily functions and flow of the business systems prior to designing your front office. Research the psychological aspects of patient care before you invest heavily in reception room decor, furnishings, and design. Seek the advice of trained dental-space design specialists to assist you in the process.

Equipment. Should you purchase equipment or lease it? Are there tax considerations to consider? Prior to even beginning this process, you may want to make your life a lot easier by choosing a reputable equipment-sale professional to guide you in your equipment purchases or leases.

In a desperate attempt to save money on equipment, many dentists try to accomplish this task on their own. There are many trustworthy professionals who can help you with equipment purchases and installation. From the full-service, supply-house representative to the reliable independent contractor, search out references on these individuals.

Together, make a checklist of all your equipment needs and costs. Look at options for new and used equipment. Weigh the costs of purchasing vs. leasing. Develop a plan for purchasing, installing, and maintaining equipment.

Supplies. Whether you choose to purchase your supplies in bulk through mail order or work with a local dental supply company, shop for prices. Mail order services often represent lower prices on supplies. However, it is not uncommon to see local supply dealers match those prices in return for your business. The services of your local supply dealer in setting up a practice from "scratch" often are very beneficial. Through the use of computerized inventory-control systems, your entire supply inventory can be developed and monitored on a regular basis. Most often, this is service offered at no charge.

Financing. The rapidly changing face of the banking industry has brought new challenges to today's newly establishing dentist. In the "good old days," the DDS/DMD after our names easily put a smile on the face of the local banker. Having established a reputation of success in the business world, dentistry as a profession was viewed as a favorable lending venture. Because we were medical professionals, we were trusted.

As with other professionals, we now join the ranks of the thousands of small business owners who must meet the requirements of tighter restrictions in the lending process. The banks have long considered dentists as commercial risks, like any other business venture, and have evaluated us likewise.

New lending institutions have emerged. The good news is that we are beginning to see a shift in the areas where monies for dental-practice opportunities can be funded. New lending institutions have emerged (such as The Matsco Companies) that understand the needs of dentists and are willing to lend money for new practice start-ups as well as for the purchase of established practices.

Financial Business Plan/Budget. A financial budget and business plan are essential in structuring any new business. Structuring a realistic budget and financial plan can be a most important building block in your practice-establishment foundation.

Realize the importance of knowing where you are financially at all times. Begin this process early in your decision-making process. Knowing the numbers will "set you free" from the emotional anxiety that often exists from the unknown.

Choose trained financial advisors and accountants who have knowledge and experience in the dental industry. Check their references. Most reliable professionals are eager to supply you with names of clients who they've serviced over the years.

Don't rely on your advisors to take care of all your financial considerations. Use their services wisely. Ask for their help in educating you on how to truly understand and read your Profit and Loss Statements. Monitor your overheads daily. Read your monthly accounting reports and evaluate them for accuracy.

Not knowing, understanding, and being involved with the numbers of your practice are deadly mistakes. Lack of involvement in this area is no different than writing checks without ever knowing the balance in your checkbook. Unless you have the luxury of no concerns in the financial-security department, the financial aspect of your practice will be a primary driving force in your career.

Staffing. One of your most valuable assets in new-practice establishment will be the team you design to assist you in your endeavor. Attracting, training, and retaining quality staff members are a must in all phases of practice transition. These are the people who hold the key to your dreams and goals. Interesting enough, most of us assume that salary is the most important issue to a staff member. Think again. National surveys have proven that although money is a very important issue to today's employee, appreciation rates number one.

Many dentists become discouraged in the recruiting process. Concepts such as advertising for "nondental" employees often are never considered by dentists. We have come to the conclusion that we need to hire staff with previous dental training and experience. Well, how well were they trained and by whom?

We've seen many successful practices benefit from the professional efforts of a nondental employee. Former bank employees and insurance representatives often become great front desk coordinators; they have been trained to communicate well, deal with the security and emotional aspects of client finances, have been screened for honesty, and are often underpaid for their efforts. Former LPNs and medical technicians have the potential to become excellent dental assistants; most have extensive training in sterilization techniques and OSHA regulations, and again the salary structures for these positions usually are far below the cost of a trained dental assistant.

Obviously, in most states, your dental hygienist must be trained and licensed. Your investment in a quality-oriented professional who meets your standard of excellence will prove to be a great asset to your practice.

Where do you find these individuals? Your location often will dictate availability and salary requirements of qualified candidates. There are several ways to recruit staff. Should you attempt this process on your own, begin by networking in your community. Talk with banking and medical colleagues. Contact local civic organizations, clubs and churches. Advertise in the local newspaper. Invest in a quality ad to attract the type of individual you would like to represent your practice. Saving money by placing short, generic ads almost always costs more in the end. Consider employing a professional writer to design your ad. List your ad in the medical section (you'll be surprised at the increased responses you'll receive). Advertise for one day only—Sunday. With the busy lifestyle of the general public, most of your candidates will look first in the weekend classifieds. Your opportunity to save hundreds of dollars often can be found in one-time ads.

Keep in mind that agencies normally require a percentage of salary as payment for their services. If you decide to use an agency, make sure that your representative is willing to take the time to meet with you, see your office, and understand your goals in the hiring process. Too often, valuable time is wasted interviewing candidates who would never meet the qualifications for the job. As a return on your investment, be sure that the agency has properly screened and interviewed the candidates.

Other avenues to consider in recruiting staff are employment agencies and dental-management consultants. Professional management consultants often are your safest bet in the recruiting process. Their years of training in communication skills and employee evaluations will give you an added edge in the hiring and training process. Quality staff, trained in management programs, frequently relies on consultants for job placement. For this reason, management consultants have a network of potential candidates at their fingertips. Your investment in hiring a quality management consultant can save you valuable time and protect you in the process.

Prior to beginning the interview process, be sure you are clear on your goals for your practice. Employees are desperately searching for leadership. A clear vision of the road ahead will be most attractive to a potential candidate. Provide your candidates with a written job description and employee manual. Answer all questions and make all commitments upfront. Summarize your agreement in writing.

Again, with all the "employer" legal requirements and regulations we face today, it certainly helps to know that you can depend on the advise of a professional who specializes in this area.

Business Equipment/Supplies. Your business equipment will include such items as computers, fax machines, telephone systems, inter-office communication systems, calculators, answering services, and much more. Office supplies are dependent upon your specific needs. Charting systems, appointment books, recall systems, and tickler files are only a few of the business systems to put in place for the new office. Relying on the efforts of the front desk staff always helps in this area. Management consultants often can simplify this process and protect the future of the business by making sure you have "cross-checks" in place before you begin.

Practice-Management Business Plan. Develop a business-management plan before you open your doors. This will not only help you in the future, but will allow you to clearly define your goals and design your action plan. Set up trend indicators to monitor the growth and progress of the practice. Set goals and implement systems. Make checklists and review them. Write a mission statement for your practice. Seek the advice of a management consultant to help you complete your plan. Rely on the expertise of your accountant for added information. Research your local library for books written on this topic. Your time and research in this area should serve you well in the future.

Marketing Plan. A strategic-marketing plan should be a requirement for new practice establishment. Starting up from "scratch" brings no guarantee of actually having patients walk in the doors. Marketing involves more than advertising. As a group, many dental and medical professionals still question the ethics of advertising services. A strategic-marketing plan doesn't always mean advertising. A comprehensive-marketing plan should include an overall approach to attracting new patients to your location.

There are many areas to address in this type of marketing plan. From the announcements you place in the local paper to the information you distribute in the community, potential patients constantly will judge your efforts. Your logo, business cards, stationary, and brochure should reflect the image of your practice. The image projected by the appearance and communication skills of your staff is a measuring tool for patient acceptance. Patients often judge the quality of care upon the external and internal presentation of the facility (modern, clean, and up-to-date).

Develop a marketing plan that matches your philosophy of practice. Make sure you implement your plan carefully. Employ the efforts of your staff.

I once heard a story about a business card given out by a staff member to a young college student on the subway. Apparently the dentist had been uncomfortable with the staff member handing out business cards and promoting the practice. He felt it was unprofessional to "solicit" patients. He had relied only on patient referrals for new patient growth.

Some years later, at a year-end staff meeting, the results of the new patient monitor were surprising. The statistics showed that approximately $250,000 of their total productivity was generated from the referrals of patients employed by a local law firm.

In evaluating the origin of these referrals, they found that the senior partner in the law firm had been the young man on the subway. Having been impressed with receiving a business card from an enthusiastic staff member, he became a patient in his last year of college. He later completed law school and became a successful attorney. Upon making ownership in the firm, he referred every new lawyer in the firm to his dentist.

Isn't it interesting to note how the marketing efforts of one staff member handing out a business card could result in more than $250,000 in income for the practice? Never underestimate the efforts of your plan.

Monitor your results. Know what works and evaluate what doesn't. Continue to be creative. Practice growth relies heavily on the efforts of a well-designed marketing plan.

Here is a checklist of some options to consider for externally marketing for new patients. (Figures 6.1, 6.2, and 6.3)

As you can see, there are many important things to consider when structuring a plan for a new-practice startup. Let's take a moment to review the key points in a new practice establishment.

- A practice startup is sensitive to some important factors. For example, the growth in the area and the number of dentists in it will impact it, especially in the beginning.

- Determine the number of dentists in the area you are considering and the community's dentist-population ratio. The national average is one dentist to approximately 1,600-1,700 people. If the community you are considering has a better ratio than this, it may warrant closer inspection.

- Also, try to find out if other dentists are planning on starting a practice in the same area. You don't want to get caught in a situation in which more than one dentist is starting a new practice in the same area at the same time!

Direct Advertising

- Yellow Pages
- Cable TV
- Local Newspapers
- Mailed Coupons
- Flyers & Church Bulletins
- Welcome Wagon
- Team Sponsorship

Fig. 6.1

Miscellaneous Things To Consider
• Stationery & Logo • Business Cards & Signage • Newsletters & Brochures

Fig. 6.2

- Consider the local employers and what dental benefits they offer their employees. Also, find out the number of retired persons living in the community and their levels of discretionary income.

- New graduates should get at least a year's experience prior to establishing a new practice. There are dentists seeking temporary associates, allowing the new dentist to develop and enhance both clinical and managerial skills before venturing into ownership.

- Make sure the practice is located in a desirable geographic area, one that especially suits you. Also, look for a high-exposure location and make sure you have adequate signage.

- Begin by fully equipping two operatories and allowing for eventual expansion to four. Ideally, look for space that was occupied by a dentist, as this can save thousands of dollars in construction costs. Be sure to retain the services of a licensed contractor.

- Be postured and poised for potential rapid-growth options that may become available in the future, such as merging your practice with that of a retiring dentist in the area.

- Compare the total costs of leasing vs. purchasing equipment.

- Make sure to prepare an initial budget and business plan. Knowing the numbers will set you free from the anxiety that often is caused by the unknown. Seek the advice of trained specialists in the area. Their experience and expertise can save you a tremendous amount of stress as well as thousands of dollars.

COMMUNITY INVOLVEMENT
• Join Organizations • Seminars On Dental Procedures • Newspaper Column • Sponsor A Career Day

Fig. 6.3

- Regarding financing, traditional banks may not be very receptive to loaning money for a practice startup, so consider specialized lending institutions like The Matsco Companies. They understand the needs of dentists and are willing to lend money for new ventures as well as the purchase of established practices.

Conclusion

In closing this chapter, let me emphasis a few points. By no means was this chapter intended to give you all the information necessary to start your own practice. The new-practice establishment option is the least favored option in today's marketplace. With the exception of the resurgence of experienced professionals choosing this option, I strongly encourage all dentists to first look at other options prior to their initial venture into practice ownership. In choosing the best transition option available to you, your next step in the transition cycle is to begin building practice value. After all, the future success of your practice-transition option is determined by the true value of your practice.

In looking at future or current practice ownership, it is important to understand how practice value is established and determined. Through the course of the next chapter, "Determining the Value of Your Practice," you'll have a clearer insight as to how a practice should be appraised and valued by learning the techniques used by professional practice appraisers.

7

DETERMINING THE VALUE OF YOUR PRACTICE: IDENTIFY, MAXIMIZE, AND PRESERVE YOUR INVESTMENT

We've talked about the numerous transition options available to dentists at all career levels during the life cycle of a practice. At this point, we're faced with the task of finding the bottom-line answer to the question asked by dentists, and heard over and over by transition specialists everywhere: "What's the market value of my practice?"

If you're a practice owner, the education you'll receive in this chapter will help you to identify, as well as protect, your practice value for a lifetime. Whether you're a newly established practitioner or an established dentist looking to merge with or purchase an existing practice, you'll find invaluable guidelines and checklists within these pages, to assist you in your pursuit of new practice ventures.

We'll discuss in detail why you should know the market value of your practice at all times during your practice life cycle; why dental practice value is so fragile; and we'll show you ways to protect the value in your practice by avoiding practice-value destroyers.

As we study the intense process required to determine practice value, we'll review this information in five parts:

- Part One: Understanding Practice Value;

- Part Two: A User's Guide to a Comprehensive Practice Appraisal;

- Part Three: Breaking Down Your Profit and Loss Statement;

- Part Four: Preserving Practice Value by Avoiding Practice-Value Destroyers; and

- Part Five: Knowing When to Have Your Practice Appraised and Establishing a Secure Plan for the Future.

Part One: Understanding Practice-Value

A Historical View of Practice Value

In years past, dental practices had little value beyond the used equipment and supplies. Because it was relatively easy to set up a practice and become established in a short period of time, there was basically no value attributed to the accumulation of goodwill.

Increased competition among dentists made setting up a practice from "scratch" more difficult. As fewer dentists chose the option of new-practice establishment, the components of practice value began to reverse. Today, the majority of practice value is attributed to goodwill— a practice-value component that was almost worthless two decades ago.

In the early 1970s, few dental school students thought about purchasing or buying into established practices. Most new graduates directly went into business for themselves. Others practiced as associates (on a temporary basis) until they were ready to go solo. New graduates often felt invulnerable and rarely considered the risks involved in new-practice establishment. There was little demand for established practices and they simply did not sell during this time. Occasionally, we'd hear about a colleague purchasing a retiring dentist's used equipment and supplies; however, the thought of purchasing a patient base and goodwill was rarely considered.

During this time, it was common for associates to practice for only six months or so prior to setting up their own practices (usually in new, growing areas). They soon became quite busy and were well on their way to building successful practices, many with exceptionally good cash flow. A decade later, however, it became more and more difficult for other dentists to duplicate that process.

Suddenly, there was a dentist on every corner. With supply exceeding demand, some dentists began experiencing financial difficulty. They were shocked by stories of colleagues filing for bankruptcy. After years of training and schooling, a tragedy now faced our profession.

A new methodology evolved from that period: dentists began to purchase established practices. Many sold for far more than the customary "used equipment value" of their equipment. Within 10 years, a dramatic metamorphosis occurred within the dental marketplace; the dental practice—in the past an asset worth little to nothing— now had a substantial market value.

Dentists can continue to expect to invest increasingly large sums of money to establish a new practice. Until newly established practices become productive and show significant profits, it will be difficult for most new owner-dentists to net even a very small base salary for their efforts.

For these reasons, dentists are seeking practice-transition opportunities that offer immediate, positive cash flow. In turn, this trend has dramatically driven up the value of established dental practices. For the established practitioner, the increased demand for practices with existing cash flow makes market conditions ripe for selling part or all of the value of their practices. Often viewing this period as an ideal time to cash in practice equity, dentists with mature practices were becoming very interested in understanding the truth about practice value.

Since our profession has placed little focus on this practice value in years past, the established practitioner often does not have a clear understanding of how to determine practice value. Lacking a driving reason to sell part or all of their practices until very near retirement, many "old ideas" about practice value developed. The carry-over of these "old ideas" has led many dentists to unknowingly lose a large portion of their practice value in mid- and late career. This lack of understanding also has caused many dentists to miss out on the opportunity to cash in part of their practice value years in advance of retirement through practice buy-in arrangements.

There are many factors that lead to loss in practice value. As dentists reach the late-career stages of the transition cycle, they often reduce practice production levels without a plan to transfer production (and its value) to a successor. Another complicating factor for the established dentist is a loosely structured associate arrangement. Often, value is lost to associates or to space-sharing dentists without clear and equitable written agreements outlining a plan of transition. In many cases, disagreements cause the revolving-door syndrome of associateships. This syndrome has a negative impact on practice value, not to mention its impact on staff and patients.

Later in this chapter, a section entitled, "Practice Value Destroyers" will give you a broad overview of additional situations and circumstances that can lead you to loss in practice value.

This sudden burst of energy and interest in practice value is easy to understand. The dental practice quickly is becoming a valuable asset in the financial blueprint of most dentists. Knowing and understanding the potential value locked inside many dental practices will be a true key to success for dentists choosing to take advantage of future practice-transition opportunities.

Your Practice-Value—
Perhaps One of Your Most Valuable Assets

The potential value that lies within a dental practice is a powerful one affecting every practice expansion and transition opportunity a dentist will consider during the course of his or her career.

Unlike the value of many other small businesses, the bulk of practice value for most dentists remains in a "locked" position until retirement. Making advance preparations to successfully transfer practice value can enhance the reward received by the seller-dentist. As dentists begin to learn how to "unlock" practice value, they will learn how to protect it in the process.

Because dentists now are interested in capturing this "locked-in" value, many are exploring new transition options. Creating, maximizing, preserving, and cashing in practice value is becoming a high-priority mission for dentists at every career level.

Practice value represents a substantial component of most dentists' total net worth. It's frequently second only to the value of a home and helps to determine quality of life issues for the owner-dentist. The sad reality is that few dentists understand how to preserve and/or maximize this value and rarely convert it into a cash-flow stream.

Fragile—Handle With Care! Dental-practice value is fragile because the close personal relationship between the dentist and the patient is at its heart. This relationship generally is not present in other businesses. Why do we so often see dentists holding on to their practices, long past the best time to sell, until the right person comes along to buy? How many owners in other small businesses are willing to forego lucrative cash offers in order to feel good about the person who purchases the business?

This stems from the fact that dentists continue to feel responsible for the overall dental health and care of the patients they have treated over the years. The relationships they've built with patients have always been a high priority. They're proud of the fact that they care about the individuals they treat. They take pride in the quality of service they provide to their patients. In fact, they place so much emphasis on the relationship aspect of dentistry, they often leave themselves out when it comes time to sell. Until there is a plan to transfer this relationship (actually the goodwill value of the practice) to another dentist, practice value always will remain fragile.

The "Perishability" Factor. Practice value stays in a perishable state until the practice is sold and transferred to a successor. For this reason, it is crucial that dentists plan in advance for cashing in this value.

The actual process of cashing in practice equity may differ from one dentist to another. Some will choose to cash in equity in increments and at multiple pivot points throughout their career; others will wait to reap the rewards of practice value by completing only one sale transaction, shortly before, or upon, retirement. What's common among them: dentists who fail to plan carefully for this process may suffer the severely diminished value of the practices they've taken decades to build.

Maximize/Preserve Practice Value. Maximizing and preserving practice value is an important process for dentists at all career levels.

Most dentists anticipate the option of cashing in this value at some future point during their career. For some, this will represent the sale of practice value that was established from "scratch" when they first opened the doors and hung out the "shingle." For other dentists, it will be the sale of practice value derived from an initial practice purchase which was expanded over a period of time. This expansion typically is a part of the normal growth pattern of a practice, perhaps accentuated by mergers and various other practice co-ownership arrangements.

As we begin to understand the importance of practice value, we naturally begin to wonder what the market value of our practices may be. How much could we sell it for today? The answer to this question lies within the pages of a comprehensive practice valuation.

A comprehensive practice valuation, provided by a trained transition specialist, is an investment that protects dentists at every level. Whether planning for the future or desiring to sell immediately, a comprehensive valuation provides dentists with a guide as well as an insurance policy for the transition plan. For the buyer-dentist, practice valuation establishes the true market value of the practice and uncovers areas of practice potential. Lending institutions prior to guaranteeing funds for practice transitions often require the comprehensive valuation. In providing lenders with a professional practice valuation and Proforma (future income projections), the seller and the buyer assume less adversarial positions from which to negotiate.

Part Two:
A User's Guide to a
Comprehensive Practice Valuation

The Practice Valuation Process

Many theories and methods address practice-value determination. Your choice of a valuation method and how you structure the terms of the transition based on that valuation are two components which most dramatically affect the final selling price. Choosing the correct valuation method (and purchase terms) and blending those choices with market knowledge of actual practice sales throughout the country may well be the most important part of the valuation process.

Once the value has been determined, maximizing and preserving this value, along with various methods of "cashing-in" this value, can be explored.

Practice-Valuation Methods

Some common practice-valuation methods used in the industry today are included in Figure 7.1. Although these methods are important keys to the practice-valuation process, they always should be balanced with real market knowledge. Real market knowledge allows for consideration of factors such as the actual selling prices of dental practices in the marketplace; the terms (down payment, interest rate, etc.) commonly seen in dental practice sales; and how cash vs. seller financing, allocations of the price for tax purposes, outright sale vs. buy-in, and any post-sale working relationship with the seller impacts the market price. (Figure 7.2)

Note: In years past, the general non-availability of institutional financing for practice purchases required that sellers finance these transactions. However, new lending institutions today are eager to make such loans.

Competent real estate appraisers tell us their opinions often are based largely on comparable sales. The same holds true for dental practice appraisals.

With this information in mind, let's take a look at what steps these various practice-valuation methods actually involve.

Capitalization of Earnings. In the capitalization (or capitalized earnings) method of valuation, the value is based on the projected future

---

COMMON PRACTICE VALUATION METHODS

- **CAPITALIZATION OF EARNINGS**

- **ASSET SUMMATION**

- **GROSS & NET INCOME MULTIPLIERS**

Fig. 7.1

THE "REAL MARKET": IMPORTANT APPRAISED FACTORS

- Current Selling Prices of Comparable Practices
- The Normal Terms Involved
    - Seller Financing?
    - Down Payment
    - Interest Rate
    - Interest-Only Period
- Cash Price vs. Seller Financing
- Will the Seller Continue Practicing?
- Outright Sale or Buy-In?

Fig. 7.2

earnings of the buyer-dentist. In this approach, the buyer-dentist looks at how quickly profits generated from the practice can pay off the purchase price. The appraiser determines a capitalization rate based on the overall relative risk of purchasing the practice as compared to the risk of purchasing other investments. This method converts the income stream of the practice into a current lump-sum amount. (This lump-sum amount becomes the practice value.)

The owner's pre-tax earnings (net profit) are determined first. This is calculated by subtracting all normal and required expenses from the gross income of the practice. An expense to be included is the amount considered as reasonable compensation to a dentist who could be hired by the owner to provide clinical services (30% of collections was the compensation chosen in the example that follows this paragraph). The remaining net income then is divided by an appropriate capitalization rate. (The capitalization rate for most dental practices ranges between 20%-35%.) Figure 7.3 (page 149) shows an example of one way of approaching the Capitalization of Earnings method.

Asset Summation. In the asset-summation approach, the overall value of the practice is established by first determining the independent values of all the various assets of the practice and then adding them togeth-

CAPITALIZATION METHOD

PRACTICE GROSS INCOME	$500,000
OPERATING EXPENSES	$300,000
NET PROFIT	$200,000
DENTIST COMPENSATION*	$120,000
REMAINING NET INCOME	$80,000

*Gross Income - Hygiene (20%) = $400,000 = Dentist Production

Dentist Compensation = 30% X $400,000 = $120,000

Capitalization Rate = .23 (or 23%)

Net Income/Capitalization Rate = Practice Value
$80,000/.23 = $347,826

PRACTICE VALUE = $347,826

Fig. 7.3

er. Some of these assets include dental and laboratory equipment, clinical and office supplies, and leasehold improvements (where transferable), as well as the value attributed to the seller's goodwill, patient records, and noncompete agreements (restrictive covenant). This noncompete agreement essentially protects the goodwill being sold. An example of the Asset Summation Approach is shown in Figure 7.4 (page150). This approach assumes that the market value of the practice can be determined by merely totaling the value of various assets.

For example, a newly started practice (with new equipment) might have an equipment value greater than the actual market value that the practice would sell for. With little or no established patient base, the equipment and location in a new practice such as this might sell for only 20 cents on the dollar (based on original costs), and in some situations, may not sell at all. (There is little demand today for practice "locations.")

By comparison, the asset-summation method would probably not work well in the valuation process of real estate (i.e., the market value of a house could differ greatly from the total sum of the house "parts").

Rule-of-Thumb Formulas. Dentists frequently look for "rule-of-thumb" formulas to determine practice value. I hesitate to recommend

ASSET-SUMMATION METHOD	
Dental & Office Equipment	*$ 65,000*
Laboratory Equipment	*$ 10,000*
Dental & Office Supplies	*$ 10,000*
Leasehold Improvements	*$ 25,000*
Goodwill & Patient Records	*$100,000*
Noncompete Agreement	*$ 50,000*
Total Value	**$260,000**
PRACTICE VALUE = $260,000	

Fig. 7.4

their use because these approaches are of limited value in many practice situations. However, for the owner-dentist with no sound knowledge as to the value of his practice, this approach can suggest a possible value range.

Rule-of-thumb formulas first became popular years ago, when dentists were seeking simple methods for determining practice value. Each of these method types present unique challenges and dentists should be extremely careful when using them. Never rely on a rule-of-thumb method to assure practice value when entering a serious transaction. Consult with a skilled professional in the field of practice valuation to verify the results of the method used.

Here are a few of the general rule-of-thumb approaches we see used to determine practice value. Practice value is equal to:

- Tangible assets + 25%-50% of one year's gross collections

- 50%-80% of one year's gross collections

- One and one-quarter to two times the "true practice net"

For many years, a popular rule-of-thumb method for practice valuation calculated one-year's gross collections based upon the most recent year's collections. This figure was thought to adequately represent the value of most dental practices. However, the specific conditions associated with that valuation method were confusing. Many questions arose in the process, such as, what did the price include? Did it include accounts receivable? Was the price based on a no-interest payout, or on an installment basis with amortized interest and principal? Was the price fixed, and did the buyer-dentist produce the method of payout based on a percentage of gross collections? Was the price based on the seller-dentist remaining in the practice during the transition for a reasonable period of time following the closing?

It's easy to see how confusion can surface when using a "rule-of-thumb" method for practice valuation. For the dentist who simply wants some idea of what his practice is worth, an explanation of the common rule-of-thumb formulas (listed above) might be helpful. (Figure 7.5) For example, Rule of Thumb Formula #1 says that practice value equals tangible assets value + 25% to 50% of one year's gross collections.

This rule-of-thumb method is fairly straightforward and has probably been around longer than other such methods. Even today, many dental supply dealers continue to use it. This method assumes the value of the practice is equal to the sum of the value of the tangible assets, plus a chosen multiplier (or multiplier range) times the most recent year's gross collections. (This income-multiplier times gross collections is used for measuring the goodwill value in the practice.) As you can see, a multiplier is selected from within a range, and an appraiser using this method will choose a specific multiplier based on a number of subjective variables that will be largely based on the appraiser's knowledge of the market.

One of the first challenges in using this formula is determining the value of the used equipment. To do so, it's best to use a market value (representing what the equipment would realistically sell for). A local supply dealer can provide this. It's better than using an accountant's depreciation schedule, which may not reflect the equipment's true resale value. You also can use the method described in the section "Appraising Hard Assets on page 157."

RULE OF THUMB FORMULA #1

Practice Value Equals

Tangible Assets Value + 25 - 50%
of One Year's Gross Collections

Fig. 7.5

Note: Much of the value of equipment drops during the first one to three years after purchase, with a more gradual reduction following that period. In addition, certain equipment develops functional obsolescence over time, with little or no value retained a year or two after its purchase. (Just look at the value of a used computer.)

The greater challenge of using this formula is determining what number (within the 25% to 50% gross income range) should be used for the particular practice being valued. A significant variation of ranges is to be expected.

Once these independent values have been determined and combined, a rough value for the practice is established. In using this method, it is preferable to use an average of the most recent three years' gross collections and "weigh" them (as described later in the section, "Using Weighted Averages"). (Figure 7.6) This Rule-of-Thumb Formula says that practice value equals 50% to 80% of one year's gross collections.

Gross Income Multiplier

This next rule-of-thumb method is simple and one of the most commonly used. It requires no valuation of the equipment and other hard assets of the practice. In addition, it does not require an analysis of the practice profit-and-loss statements or any information about marketplace value. Again, we are dealing with a multiplier range, with the final value dependent upon the marketplace. (Figure 7.7, page 152) Rule-of-Thumb Formula #3 says that practice value equals one and one-quarter to two times the "true practice net."

RULE OF THUMB FORMULA #2

Practice Value Equals

50 - 80%
of One Year's Gross Collections

Fig. 7.6

Net-Income Multiplier

This method, focusing on the net income of the practice, probably makes more sense than of any of the other rule-of-thumb approaches. After all, buyers and their advisors inevitably base their decision to purchase on the net income the practice generates.

To consider the practice a viable investment, the buyer must first believe it will generate net income sufficient to pay the existing overhead. There must remain net income to pay the debt service on the purchase price. In the final analysis, remaining net income must meet the buyer's minimal needs while paying off the practice debt. Most buyers hold minimum income expectations when purchasing a practice, as compared to income levels experienced as an associate.

Dentists choosing to sell their practices to associates must be aware that few of them will be happy with less income than earned in their present arrangement. (i.e., few associates want to make less money after they buy into or purchase a practice than they are making as an employee of the seller). This is another important reason to review the projections of the purchase or buy-in prior to the associate entering the practice. At this point, initial associate compensation, as well as the terms of the buy-in or purchase, can be adjusted accordingly to prevent this from happening.

Using Weighted Averages

In using rule-of-thumb methods, a weighted average should be considered in the calculation. This is determined by averaging the gross collections of the most recent three-year period and placing the greatest emphasis (referred to as "weighting") on the most recent year. (An

---

RULE OF THUMB FORMULA #3

Practice Value Equals

1.25 - 2 Times
the "True Practice Net"

Fig. 7.7

example of this method is listed below.) In this example, the previous three years' gross collections were multiplied in sequence by a factor of one, two, and three respectively. The final number arrived at by this factoring process was then averaged by the total of the combined factors (six).

Examples of using weighted averages (based on gross collections):

- Two Years Prior $150,000 X 1 = $150,000

- One Year Prior $200,000 X 2 = $400,000

- Most Recent Year $250,000 X 3 = $750,000

- Total = $1,300,000

- $1,300,000 divided by 6 = weighted average = $216,666

Now that we have explored various methods of determining practice value, let's look at the components that make up practice value.

Practice-Value Components. We will look at two basic components: the tangible assets (hard assets) and the intangible assets (often referred to as the cash-flow-value component) of practice value. (Figure 7.8)

Tangible (Hard) Assets Value. The tangible component of your practice value includes assets you can put your hands on and clearly identify. These would include equipment, furniture and fixtures, supplies, and leasehold improvements.

The tangible-assets category also may include any cash assets of the practice that the seller-dentist plans to transfer to the buyer-dentist as part of the sale. These cash assets include available cash funds of the practice, combined with any collectable accounts receivable as well as contracts receivable (common to orthodontic practice) owned by the

PRACTICE–VALUE COMPONENTS
• **Tangible Assets (Hard Assets)**
• **Intangible (Cash-Flow Component)**

Fig. 7.8

practice at the time of the sale. Though not normally included in a valuation, any value placed on accounts receivable must take into consideration the collectable amount minus any costs involved in the actual collection process. Cash-on-hand (i.e., balances in any of the practice bank accounts) also is not normally included in a valuation. In a practice sale or buy-in, this cash typically is used by the seller to pay previous practice bills—laboratory costs, supplies, and other expenses that the practice incurred prior to the transaction. Any remaining cash funds usually are distributed to the seller as income. (Figure 7.9)

As previously mentioned, accounts receivable usually are excluded from the valuation. In a sale, the buyer usually collects these funds on behalf of the seller. When collected by the buyer, continuity (between old and new) is established in the eyes of the patients. This helps the seller collect accounts that might be more difficult to have collected, particularly after the seller's retirement. However, in some cases, they're collected directly by the seller separate from the new practice accounts. If the accounts receivable are to be included in the sale, they usually are factored (discounted) to arrive at a current value. Figure 7-10 (page156) shows one method by which the value of the accounts receivable can be determined in this way.

Appraising Hard Assets. A price range for dental equipment usually can be obtained from a local supply dealer. In lieu of such an appraisal, the next best approach is using *straight-line depreciation*.

Depreciating the assets by 10% of their original value each year helps you to arrive at a reasonable value figure. In addition, I apply a

---

PRACTICE-VALUE COMPONENTS
THE TANGIBLE ASSETS

- EQUIPMENT
  - DENTAL
  - LABORATORY
  - COMPUTER AND OFFICE
- FURNITURE AND FIXTURES
- PRACTICE CASH ASSETS
  - ACCOUNTS RECEIVABLE
  - CONTRACTS RECEIVABLE
  - CASH ON HAND

Fig. 7.9

Accounts Receivable Valuation Factoring	
Accounts Receivable Age	**% of Face Value**
0- 30 days	90%
31- 60 days	80%
61- 90 days	70%
90-120 days	60%
Over 120 days	Negotiable

Fig. 7.10

residual value of at least 15% of original cost to reflect the "real" marketplace—that is, the assets would be no less than 15% of original value even after 10 years, unless obsolete. (Be careful of certain "obsolete" assets such as dental equipment made by companies no longer in business, old computers, etc.) The following is an example of straight-line depreciation, with a residual. (Figure 7.11, page 157)

Most lending institutions are accustomed to loaning money to potential buyer-dentists for a conservative estimate of the tangible-assets value. In years past, this value was all a seller-dentist could get for the sale of the entire practice. Specialized new lending institutions (such as The Matsco Companies) now make practice loans based on goodwill value as well as the tangible assets of the practice. The influx of loan approvals for practice purchases and buy-ins has been a refreshing turnaround from the past, when few institutions would loan any money for goodwill.

Intangible or Cash-Flow Value Assets. Cash-flow value in most dental practices now is worth significantly more than the value of the tangible assets, which is a total reversal of what existed a decade or so ago. The cash-flow value of a practice is determined by several methods. Regardless of the approach used, it's fundamentally based on the income that the practice has generated over its prior financial history (usually the previous three years). This financial history allows the buyer to anticipate potential income in the future.

Unlike the relatively stable value of the tangible assets, the value of the intangible assets is very unstable. The intangibles can rapidly dis-

DETERMINING EQUIPMENT VALUE

Straight-Line Depreciation (10% per year/15% residual) 15% Residual = $675	
New Dental Chair	$4500
Value At End of Year 1	$4050
Value At End of Year 2	$3600
Value At End of Year 3	$3150
Value At End of Year 4	$2700
Value At End of Year 5	$2250
Value At End of Year 6	$1800
Value At End of Year 7	$1350
Value At End of Year 8	$900
15% Residual	$675

Fig. 7.11

integrate unless the owner gives careful attention to maintaining and preserving them. For this reason, it is crucial for today's dentists to plan ahead for the eventual transfer of these perishable assets to a successor. Otherwise, tens, or even hundreds, of thousands of dollars could be lost.

The terms goodwill, going-concern value and patient-record value frequently are used synonymously. The "goodwill" that exists in the patient base is transferred along with the patient record and creates value to the business as a "going concern." Goodwill and going-concern value usually are measured by some multiplier of the gross and/or net income (or by some capitalization factor) produced in the practice on an annual basis. Patient records frequently are treated in the same way and are sometimes assigned a value of a certain dollar amount per chart. They also can be lumped together in a single sum, based on the most current yearly practice production. When patient records alone are purchased in a practice sale, often the amount paid is based on the number of patients that transfer or a percentage of collections received by the buyer on patients that transferred. (See the section on goodwill-only sales in Chapter 3, "Successful Sales Strategies.")

What Your Practice Valuation Should Include. When you invest in a comprehensive practice valuation, it's important to understandwhat you're paying for. Following is a list of components often found in a professional practice valuation. (Figure 7.12, page 159) Although most components of a professional practice valuation are self-explanatory, it may be beneficial to clearly define certain categories.

Practice Buy-Out Formats. If the purpose of the valuation is for the planning and structuring of a practice buy-in or sale (as opposed to an outright sale), more than just a valuation will be necessary. Once the practice valuation has been completed, the next step is structuring a format for the transition being considered—that is, an outline of the strategic plan leading the parties through the proposed buy-in arrangement. It's a guide for both owner and associate, taking them through all of the steps and stages of their relationship—initial trial period, post-trial period, the actual buy-in culminating with the eventual buy-out. (See Chapter 4, "Creating 'Win-Win' Associateship to Buy-In Arrangements.")

A practice buy-in format should contain economic projections for the various stages, leading from associateship to buy-in. It should show the compensation of the associate prior to, as well as during, the buy-in. It also should show the net income remaining after making payments to the owner and/or fulfilling the loan for the buy-in price. It's similar to the Proforma provided to a buyer-dentist who considers the outright purchase of a practice, based on a given set of terms and conditions. This Proforma is one of the most valuable tools used in the practice valuation process. It gives both the owner and the associate an economic forecast and helps to explain the overall value of the practice, as opposed to focusing on just the price. Similar formats should be constructed for all transition options, including deferred sale, pre-retirement sale, practice merger, and so forth.

If the purpose of the valuation is for the planning and structuring of an outright sale, then as part of the valuation, a practice buy-out (or practice sale) format should be included. A practice buy-out format is an outline of the strategic plan leading you through the proposed sale arrangement. A practice buy-out format should contain economic projections for both parties, and should show the net income remaining after making payments to the owner and/or to any lending institutions involved.

COMPONENTS OF A COMPREHENSIVE PRACTICE VALUATION

- Financial History of the Practice
- The Suggested "Market" Value of the Practice
- The "True" Net Income of the Practice
- Valuation Methods Used
- Explanation of Why Certain Methods Were Used
- How the Value is Impacted By a Buy-In or Earned Equity
- Qualifications and Experience Level of the Appraiser

Fig. 7.12

Important Factors Affecting the Practice Valuation Process.

The areas of consideration listed below will not be found in any valuation "formula." They will, however, represent important consideration factors in a comprehensive practice valuation. Blending these factors together to arrive at a final value will almost always require the services of an experienced transition consultant. (Figure 7.13, page 160)

Area Desirability. The importance of location relates closely to the value of a dental practice. Dental practice sales are much like the real estate sales in this one area: the more desirable the location, the higher the price. In real estate, two identical properties can sell for drastically different prices, based on location. Dentists often accept this information as fact when they're buying real estate, but choose to ignore such statistics when they're trying to sell practices.

Practices located in desirable locations sell very quickly. Location drives up the market value in good areas and drives down the market value in less-desirable areas. Time also is a factor to consider here: in less desirable areas, the sale process can take months or even years.

I recently spoke with a dentist practicing in a small town approximately 200 miles away from any major metropolitan area. He had been

PRACTICE VALUE DETERMINATION: IMPORTANT FACTORS

- Area Desirability
- Comparable Practice Sales
- New-Patient Flow (Fee-for-Service)
- Financing Terms
- Perceived Transferability
- Specialty Versus General Practice
- Death or Disability
- Tax Allocations

Fig. 7.13

trying to sell his practice for years and finally contacted me for help. He just couldn't understand why his practice wouldn't sell. After all, he was using a "cookbook" formula for selling it.

It became obvious to me that, based on his location, he was asking too much for his practice. His misconceptions regarding practice value had caused him to miss out on several viable opportunities to sell to potential buyers who had looked at his practice in the past. Based on the formulas he was using, these potential buyers were not willing to pay the price he was asking. He was unaware that, based on location, "identical" practices may differ greatly in price. He didn't understand why practices in small towns often sell for less than practices in larger cities. Despite the higher quality of life to which people living in small towns attest, the market demand for practices in metropolitan areas is greater.

Comparable Practice Sales. Comparable sales (a common term in real estate) offers data to document the final selling price brought by practices similar in productivity, design, and location. A dental practice valuation should take into consideration what "similar" practices are selling for in the marketplace.

Regardless of the actual appraisal method used to determine real estate value, appraisers always weight their final value statement on the selling price of other like properties in the area. Utilizing the "comps," an adjustment process structures comparable properties to the subject property.

Lending institutions base their loans on this data. Few banking institutions lend more than what they believe the resale value of the property to be, and there's probably no truer indication of the real market value of a practice than comparable sales data. In legal disputes, judges frequently throw out "formula-driven valuations" in favor of value based on real-market data received from experts in the business of selling dental or medical practices.

Fee-for-Service Patient Flow. All things being equal, the greater the number of fee-for-service patients entering the practice (as opposed to managed-care patients), the more desirable the practice becomes. This growth, in turn, drives up the value. Some practice appraisers even use this as a "back up" practice-valuation method—multiplying the number of fee-for-service patient records in the practice times a per-record value. This per-record value methodology sometimes uncovers untapped potential within the practice, particularly when the per-record value is much greater than the value arrived at by "normal" valuation methods.

Financing Terms. The availability and cost of institutional and seller financing also may influence the final selling price of a practice.

Most buyers have little (if any) access to cash funds for the purchase of a practice. Obviously, the lower the cost and the more flexible the financing, the greater the possibility that the seller-dentist will receive full price.

In the not too distant past, the seller-dentist who wanted "all cash" was likely to receive a discounted price when compared to market price. However, some new lending institutions have emerged that are willing to loan up to 100% of the purchase price and at reasonable terms. In this way, both seller and buyer can "win."

Perceived Transferability. Another important factor affecting practice value is perceived transferability. Will the typical buyer believe the seller's patients will transfer? If so, to what degree will they remain with the new buyer? After all, this is the intangible goodwill portion of the practice, which often represents the greatest portion of the overall value. It's important that a potential buyer believe there is a high rate of patient transfer. The single biggest fear that buyers have in a transition is that large numbers of patients may leave the practice after the sale. Without a feeling of security in this area, few buyers will pay more than the value of the equipment and leasehold improvements of the practice.

A 'Global' Patient Base. In discussing the area of transferability, I recall an appointment I had years ago, with one of my first clients, to confidentially discuss the sale of his practice. As I walked through the reception room, I noticed two large maps on the wall—one of the United States and another displaying countries throughout the world. Colored pins marked cities and countries across the world. As I took a moment to glance over the maps, I assumed that these were probably places he had traveled. I found it interesting that he probably enjoyed showing his patients all the places he had visited.

During our meeting, we discussed his plans to retire within the following six months and mapped out a solid transition plan for the sale to occur. As I was leaving, I again glanced at the maps and said, "Just out of curiosity, what's the story behind the maps?" A proud smile appeared on his face as he remarked, "Oh, that's where all my patients are coming from." I looked back at the map and said, "You have patients coming from all over the world?" He replied, "Yes, many of my patients travel thousands of miles to see me."

Looking more closely at the map, I noticed a manifold of pins located in cities literally all over the United States. I saw a pin in Brazil and several throughout Italy, Greece, England, and elsewhere. The twinkle in his eye told me he really was proud of the maps.

I now was concerned for the dentist who might take over the practice. How would a potential buyer feel about the great distances these patients were coming from? Obviously, there were certainly many dentists who would be more geographically desirable for these patients. Would the patients continue traveling this far if their dentist was no longer there?

In the end, I discovered that the maps represented only about 30 to 45 patients in the practice. Most of the patient base lived only a short distance from the office. Although this practitioner was proud of the fact that his patients came from all over the world to see him, he quickly understood how a potential buyer might be skeptical of the display.

The point is that when you're selling your practice, it's extremely important for the buyer to have the perception of a satisfactory transfer of the patient base. This perception, of course, is greatly dependent upon the individual confidence level of a buying dentist. It's important for the seller to keep in mind that many buyer-dentists have been out of school five years or less and their confidence and skill levels are far different. In the seller's mind, the "ideal" buyer is often the person he or she sees in the mirror each day. The more charismatic the seller, the more difficult patient transfer likely will be. Highly skilled dentists who have "niché-"type practices should begin the process of searching for a buyer two or more years before their desired sale date. As always, be realistic when it comes to the face you put on a potential buyer and try to understand his or her perception of patient transferability.

Perceived Transferability in Practice Buy-Ins. Perceived transferability plays a lesser role when only a part of the practice is being purchased.

In most buy-in arrangements, a long-term relationship between the buyer and the seller is established. Therefore, there is a much longer transition time, resulting in less fear surrounding the transfer of patients to the new "partner" and only minor problems involving patient transferability.

Specialty vs. General Practice. In outright practice sales (particularly retirement sales), you'll often see general practices sell for a higher ratio of price to gross than specialty practices. Why? Because general practices have an ongoing base of repeat "customers" not dependant upon referrals from a second professional. The reinforcement of continuing-care programs, not found in most specialty practices, almost always guarantees an ongoing income stream. (Exceptions, of course, are pediatric and periodontal practices.) This income guarantee will inevitably support a higher selling price than practices without such programs.

On the other hand, orthodontic practices present a unique situation in determining practice value. Because orthodontic practices have "contracts receivable," they often generate greater sale amounts than general practices. These "contracts receivable" represent another form of guaranteed income to a buyer–perhaps, more so than the recare program in a general practice.

Specialists will enhance the total selling price of their practices by selling in increments over a period of time. This is most often accomplished through associateship leading to co-ownership arrangements. Through proper planning, the final value received can be much greater than the original appraised value of the practice. (See Chapter 4, "Creating 'Win-Win' Associateship to Co-Ownership Arrangements.")

Death or Disability. Death or disability of a dentist can result in a substantial reduction in the market value of a dental practice. In the event of a dentist's death, the value of the practice initially plummets and continues to decline rapidly on a daily basis thereafter. Tragically, in most cases, 30 to 60 days after a dentist's death, little or no residual value remains in the practice.

With disability, the impact is less severe, particularly when the patients perceive that their dentist will return to practice within a reasonable period of time. However, when extended time off due to disability is required, the impact on practice value can be almost as severe as what occurs with a death.

The dramatic reduction of practice value resulting from death or disability is extremely important to keep in mind during the valuation process. Valuation methods must be modified to take these situations into consideration. It's also a good reason to consider the possibility of incorporating a built-in buyer for the practice in the form of an associate/co-owner. With properly structured agreements in place prior to a death or disability, the owner and surviving spouse need never worry about locating a buyer-dentist in time of need. This one step could save a tremendous amount of stress and money in the future.

Tax Allocations. Taxation on the proceeds of a dental practice sale also may alter the final selling price of the practice. The way in which the purchase price is broken down ("tax allocations") has varying effects on the buyer and the seller, and will impact the transaction in the following ways:

- The actual after-tax proceeds received by the seller.

- How *quickly* the buyer can deduct the purchase price of the practice.

- How *much* of the total purchase price the buyer can deduct.

In a transaction of this nature, it's important to fully understand tax issues affecting both sides of the transition. Let's take a closer look at the typical tax goals and desires of the buyer and seller in a sale transaction.

The buyer's tax-allocation goals are:

- To deduct as much of the purchase price as possible, preferably 100%.

- To deduct the purchase price as quickly as possible.

The seller's tax-allocation goals are:

- To pay as little tax as possible on the sale proceeds. The greater the after-tax proceeds received by the seller, the higher the price the seller actually has received. Under current tax guidelines, this goal is accomplished by allocating as much of the purchase price as possible toward assets that will allow the seller the use of capital gains.

- To receive enough funds at closing to offset the amount referred to as "recapture of depreciation," in which taxes become due on an entire amount allocated, regardless of the amount of down payment applied to the sale.

It's also important to consider if the seller-dentist is incorporated. If so, it's possible that the sale of certain assets will be "double-taxed"— once at the corporate level and again at the personal level. (Subchapter S corporations are treated differently. Please check all tax issues with your tax advisor.) This double taxation obviously will reduce the net after-tax proceeds of the sale for the seller-dentist.

An experienced transition consultant can suggest "win-win" guidelines for allocating the purchase price of a practice sale or buy-in. (In other words, there always is a "fair" way to achieve the end result!) This aid can eliminate the thousands of dollars spent on adversary negotiations.

Having given you the information on how a comprehensive practice valuation is constructed, and shown you the practice value components, you now are ready to take a closer look at your own practice. We will start by evaluating your Profit and Loss Statement—an essential part of understanding the true value of your practice. Time after time, I see dentists who begin the transition process, look at their Profit and Loss Statement, and get discouraged with what appears to be their net income (which is a crucial part of the valuation process).

Why? In many cases, the neatly compiled packages received from accountants each month continue to collect dust on the bookshelves of some practice owners. Over the years, accountants have encouraged us to take advantage of tax savings in every aspect of the practice. Having done that, many of us have a tendency to forget how "creative" we have become in this process. Before you try to determine your practice's true worth—perhaps becoming discouraged in the process—let's look at your overall profit margin. We begin by breaking down your Profit and Loss Statement to determine the "true" profit of your practice. After that, we'll look at important factors affecting practice value.

Part Three:
Breaking Down Your Profit
and Loss Statement

Some time ago, a mid-career dentist contacted me about selling his practice. He said he was "burned-out" and tired of the rat race, and explained that the primary reason he wanted to sell was due to the fact that his overhead was high and that his net only was 15% to 20%.

I was concerned that this young dentist obviously was considering throwing in the towel at only 42 years of age. After exploring many other transition options with him (including selling his practice and working for someone in order to increase his net income), I discovered his true overhead might be lower than he perceived it to be.

I reviewed his most recent year-end income and expense statements. As he had said, the report reflected a net profit of only 19.5%. Based on the fact that he was using this information to guide his decision, I certainly could understand his dilemma. It appeared that his advisors had been legitimately creative in handling his practice expenses, as many nontraditional expenses appeared on the report.

In reviewing his numbers, we noticed that his overall expenses definitely seemed "out of line." A large portion seemed to be more "creative and elective" than "normal and necessary" for running a dental practice. As a result, we added these expenses back into the net income figure shown on the dentist's income statement, as they represented other forms of non-cash owner compensation. After doing so, his net profit jumped to a comfortable 42%. By truly understanding his overhead-expense categories and properly breaking down his profit and losses, he quickly realized the value of keeping his practice and staying in dentistry.

The point: If you think your practice is not generating the income you deserve, it may be wise to invest some time in determining the "true net" of your practice. Who knows, you may be pleasantly surprised.

Determining True Practice Net

"True net" represents the total economic return received by a practice owner. For dentists, it reveals the complete compensation package (including all of the fringes).

By taking advantage of tax deductions, many dentists have discovered ways of using pre-tax dollars to increase non-cash owner compensation. Without properly tracking these various creative and elective expenses, the Income and Expense Statement will reflect what appears to be a lower net income of the practice. Obviously, the owner's net income affects practice value. Without a proper analysis of the income and expenses, combined with subsequent adjustments to the bottom line, the value of the practice could easily be discounted in the eyes of a buyer.

So, how do you determine "true net"? To begin, let's look at the breakdown of practice expenses. We typically look at them separated into four groups: practice expense breakdown; operational expenses; non-operational income and expenses; owner's cash compensation expenses; and owner's non-cash compensation expenses.

To better assess this subject, the following material is reprinted from the "Management Income Statement" of the Pankey Institute for Advanced Dental Education (used with permission).

The category of operational expenses is the only category that reflects its "true" overhead expense. As we define each expense category, you'll begin to see how the true net picture of a practice unfolds.

Definitions of Group Expenses

Group One: Operational Expenses: Operational expenses are broken down into several categories:

- Variable operational expenses;

- Production-related expenses. Variable production-related expenses include clinical supplies and laboratory fees;

- Associate salary and benefits. This category represents the total amount of salary paid to any associates in the practice, including payroll taxes, unemployment, retirement, health and other insurance, uniform allowance, continuing education, profit-sharing, and any other associate benefits; and

- Hygiene salary and benefits. This category is represented in the exact same form of the associate structure.

Fixed operational expenses. Administrative and clinical salaries and benefits include total amounts paid to staff in salaries, including payroll taxes, unemployment, retirement plan, health and other insurance, uniform allowance, continuing education, profit-sharing, and any miscellaneous staff expenses such as casual or contract labor expenses.

- Facility expenses. This category represents the total amount paid in rent, repairs, maintenance, utilities, office decor/design, property taxes, property insurance, and any property association fees.

- Administrative expenses and supplies. These are the usual and customary fixed expenses required to adequately run the practice. Items such as bank/credit card charges and fees, dues and subscriptions, insurance, laundry, office supplies, postage, accounting and legal fees, consulting, telephone, business taxes and license fees, printing, contributions, practice promotion, computer supplies, and other miscellaneous expenses are shown in this area.

Group Two: Non-Operational Income and Expenses: Non-operational income and expenses are broken down into the following categories:

- Other income. Funds received by the practice other than production/collection-related fees.

- Other expenses. Any other expenses required by the practice unrelated to expenses shown above.

- Interest expense. Interest-due expenses on loans, credit cards, late fees, etc.

- Capital equipment leases. Owner leases to the business for depreciation purposes.

- Depreciation expenses. Time depreciated-asset expenses and direct equipment write-off expenses.

Group Three: Owner's Cash Compensation: This includes the principal's salary and benefits. Total amount paid in salary to the owner, including payroll taxes, unemployment, and retirement benefits.

Group Four: Owner's Non-Cash Compensation: This category includes:

- Continuing education. Total amount paid in expenses for continuing education for doctor and spouse only. (Spouse is included in the category only if he/she is not employed with the practice; otherwise, this is a legitimate staff overhead cost and does not represent non-cash compensation.)

- Travel expenses. Expenses paid for travel for events such as continuing education, meetings, speaking engagements, etc.

- Automobile expense. Expenses paid for owner auto.

- Uniform allowance. Expenses paid for owner/spouse clothing/laundry allowances.

- Personal related owner-insurance expenses. Owner's life, disability, major medical, and family insurance coverage.

- Other officer perks. Personal owner-related tax savings and expenses run through the business.

- Officer profit-sharing. Fees paid to owner's portion of profit-sharing expenses.

- Other officer-related expenses. Any other expenses paid to practice resulting in owner non-cash compensation.

Once the Profit and Loss Statement has been broken down into these categories and true numbers assigned to each, we can begin to review the practice Net Worth Statement.

You can begin to see how some items listed in owner non-cash compensation, owner compensation, non-operational income, and expenses are added back to the net profit of the business in order to show the "true" net of the practice. In reviewing these items, the following information will provide you with a more in-depth understanding of why these categories are added back to the net. (These items are often referred to as "add-backs," Figure 7.14, page 171).

Dentist's Salary. In incorporated practices, the owner-dentist's salary often is shown as an expense. It usually is called officer salary or doctor's salary. This obviously is the first item to add back to the net.

Depreciation. Depreciation is a way of expensing out the useful life of certain hard assets purchased for the practice. Depreciation, reflected as an expense on Profit and Loss Statements, is not a true cash expense. Since the owner does not actually write a check for depreciation, as he does for other expenses (such as rent and utilities), this amount always is added back to the practice "bottom line."

Travel and Entertainment. Though some travel and entertainment expenses are necessary in a dental practice, much of it is considered creative or elective.

As part of an overall marketing plan, dental specialists often entertain referral sources. Their expenses often can be quite costly. In these cases, expenses are considered legitimate. However, many dentists, expense out personal entertainment and it must be added back to the net.

Pension Plan Expense. Pension-plan contributions on the doctor's behalf actually are considered net income to the owner. Earmarked to be cashed in later on a deferred basis, this income currently is not taxed. Contributions made for the owner, as well as for any family members not actually employed in the practice, should be added back to the bottom line.

Auto-Vehicle Expense. Vehicular expense rarely is a true expense in dental practices. Dentists providing services at multiple locations, or

DETERMINING TRUE PRACTICE NET "ADDBACKS"

- **Dentist Salary (if incorporated)**
- **Depreciation**
- **Travel and Entertainment**
- **Pension**
- **Vehicle Expenses**
- **Continuing Education (Use Allowance)**
- **Premises Rent (+ or -)**

Fig. 7.14

making frequent trips to local hospitals, who can justify some automobile expenses generally are the only exceptions to this rule. However, writing off an automobile at 100% is truly stretching the deduction in this category. Add back all vehicular expenses, unless they were absolutely necessary for the operation of the practice.

Continuing Education. These costs are a necessary expense. Depending on your specialty or area of focus, a normal yearly allowance for continuing education could range from $1,000 to $5,000. However, many dentists use the continuing education expense category for vacations in disguise. Trips, combined with various courses, technically allow the vacation to be the true focus and the course to be secondary. Add back all travel and hotel expenses for courses that could have been taken locally (as opposed to the courses taken in Maui). If the course expenses were, in fact, legitimate, add back any incurred costs that were not absolutely essential.

Premises Rent. Dentists who own their own facilities have a unique situation. To determine how this impacts true net, the following questions should be asked: Does the practice actually pay rent to the owner-dentist? Is a check actually written and shown as an expense? If the answer is yes, move on to the next question.

If the answer is no, a normal fair-market rent must be deducted from the owner's net income. It is obvious that a buyer would have to pay rent, so this must be shown as an expense. For facility owner-dentists not paying themselves rent, the total amount of rent that would have been paid should be deducted from the net profits of the practice.

Dentists who are paying themselves rent should look at the monthly rental amount to see if the amount being paid is in line with the fair-market price for the area. Is the amount paid higher or lower rent than what it should be? Any difference between fair-market rent value and actual rent paid should be deducted from the net (if the rent is less than fair-market value) or added to the practice net (if the rent is greater than fair-market value.)

Dentists who own their own facilities often show an inflated net income. Potential buyers in these situations need to beware. There have been cases where a seller's strategic-marketing focus was the fact that his practice net was 52%. As suspected, the seller owned the facility and was not paying himself any rent on the facility. Normal market rent for the area might have been $14 to $16 per square foot. After making the necessary adjustments for the rent, the net income of the practice would be reduced to 42%—although still quite good, it was not exactly the net figure the seller was claiming.

Part Four:
Preserving Practice Value

Practice-Value Destroyers

Few of a dentist's assets are more perishable than the value of the practice. Collectively, many millions of dollars of practice value are lost each year. These losses are caused by a wide array of events and circumstances. Some are apparent, while others are not. Even though most practice-value destroyers are preventable, the only way to stop this "bleeding" is to look at prevention.

As dentists become aware of these destroyers, their view of the transition process changes drastically. As a result, they often begin looking for a much different type of candidate when considering potential associates, co-owners, or buyers for their practices. Some find it necessary, though painful, to re-examine proposed arrangements with existing candidates, while for others, it may require restructuring or even dissolving current practice relationships that have been in place for many years.

Preventing Practice-Value Loss

Most owner-dentists fail to recognize the decline of practice value until it's too late to reverse the process. When buyer-dentists take over practices in serious states of decline or under questionable circumstances, they also lose.

As we've previously discussed, there are logical steps to take and definite situations to avoid in order to protect practice value. The first step is the awareness that the problem exists. Dentists always should focus on the "big picture" and plan well in advance for the eventual transfer of their practices to a successor. With a secure transition plan in place, practices are much less vulnerable to the events, circumstances, and conditions collectively referred to as practice-value destroyers. I encourage dentists to do three things to prevent practice-value loss:

- Construct a plan of transition,

- Learn to identify practice-value destroyers, and

- Then, avoid them at all costs!

Let's look at some of the more common practice-value destroyers.

Death. Nothing destroys the value of a practice more quickly than the untimely death of the owner-dentist. Compared to its pre-death value, we often see an immediate 50% drop in the market value of the practice when the owner dies. (I have handled the estate sales of many practices over the years. It frequently has been a struggle to receive even a 50% figure—sad situation considering the years spent building the practice, only to watch its value quickly vanish.)

With the owner-dentist no longer available to assist in the proper transition of the patients, concerns arise from the buyer. The perceived transferability of the practice now becomes a major factor in determining a final selling price. In this situation, most buyers believe that the successful transfer of patients in this situation is doubtful. They often ask questions like, "After hearing of Dr. Smith's death, how many patients have already left the practice?" "What guarantees do I have that the patients will come to me, especially since Dr. Smith never knew me?" "How many of the staff members will be staying? How many are already looking for another job?"

As the daily decline of practice value continues, the search for a buyer who would be willing to pay market value under these questionable circumstances becomes more difficult. As you might guess, buyers often are attracted to this type of sale for one primary reason—they hope for a drastically reduced selling price inherent in a "death sale" and feel that a fire-sale price will offset any patient loss that might have occurred.

This rapid decline in value makes it essential for the deceased dentist's practice to be sold as quickly as possible. In most cases, surviving family members look to the support of personal, professional, and family advisors (including practice attorneys, accountants, and colleagues). Unfortunately, many of these willing advisors build up an enormous amount of billable hourly time providing a "service" in which they rarely have had any experience. This, combined with the quickly vanishing value of the practice, leaves little chance for family members to receive much for the practice. A "fair price" is not possible with death.

Example: The Death of a Dentist. Dr. A had set up his practice from scratch. After only a few years in practice, he was killed in a plane crash. Upon hearing of Dr. A's death, Dr. B was very interested in the possibility of taking over the practice. Since the two offices were within walking distance of one another, it seemed logical to buy the practice, merge it with his own, and transfer patients. He thought it would a "win-win" situation for all parties concerned.

When Dr. B contacted Dr. A's widow, he was referred to Dr. A's previous accountant and attorney, who were handling the estate. They believed Dr. A's practice should bring a good price, since it was located in a rapidly growing area. They informed Dr. B that they were in the process of doing an in-depth inventory and analysis of the practice in order to determine the exact value of the practice, and that this analysis would take quite some time.

Dr. B was, in fact, ready to make a very reasonable offer for Dr. A's practice and he was concerned the patient retention would be lower as time passed. As the weeks passed, he continued to contact Dr. A's advisors; repeatedly, he was told that the inventory of the practice was still in process and that, until they were through, they would not be ready to accept bids on the practice.

During this time, many of Dr. A's patients transferred to other dentists in the community. Several patients even began seeing Dr. B. Except for bargain hunters hoping to get a good deal, few dentists continued to inquire about the practice. Soon, potential buyers were only interested in the deceased dentist's space and the "salvage" value of the equipment.

Dr. B was extremely upset with the way the situation had been handled and eventually gave up on the idea of purchasing Dr. A's practice. Justifiably, he was convinced that the bulk of the patient base had already transferred to other dentists. In the end, Mrs. A lost several hundred thousand dollars in practice value when it was finally sold. She was also burdened with substantial legal and accounting fees for the valuation and practice-analysis process. This is a sad, but true story of how a practice-value destroyer easily could have been avoided had the advisors called in an expert who actually had experience in selling dental practices.

Establish a secure plan in the event of your death. It's hard to believe that a situation like this could happen. However, over the course of my consulting career, I've seen this scenario repeat itself. I can't overemphasize how important it is to put in place a secure plan for the sale of your practice upon your death. This is absolutely necessary if you want your spouse or estate to receive *anything* from the practice.

To ensure that competent people handle the sale, attach specific instructions (often referred to as a *co-de-cil*) to your will. This insures that your advisors have a plan to follow. Be sure to designate a specific individual or organization that you trust to handle the sale of the practice upon your death. The individual or organization you choose need not necessarily be in your immediate area. With today's advanced communications and networking among practice brokers nationally, many practices are located and purchased through the Internet. You can choose someone you trust anywhere in the country. (If you are uncertain whom to designate, search thoroughly for a reputable transition specialist.) Colleagues who have bought or sold practices usually will have recommendations. Do not put this task on the shoulders of your spouse and don't rely on advisors who have little or no experience in the area of selling dental practices.

Disability. In situations involving disability, the value is not negatively impacted to the same extent as in the event of a death. Practice continuity is easier when disability occurs, making this a far more stable situation. Unless patients sense that the nature of the disability is serious enough to keep their dentist from ever returning to practice, few patients leave it.

Should the disability be prolonged and require the sale of the practice, there is at least the opportunity for the disabled dentist to "hand-pick" the buyer. In addition, the disabled dentist often can encourage and reinforce the transfer of the patient base through introducing the new dentist through personal letters to the patients.

A word of caution regarding office coverage: Dentists need to be very careful in choosing other dentists to provide office coverage for the practice in the event of a death or disability. Although choosing a nearby dentist seems logical, it's risky. It's possible that patients may like the new dentist and, depending on the circumstances, decide to transfer. Potential buyers are correct in being concerned about the fact that other dentists are covering the practice. For these reasons, follow this cardinal rule: Hire dentists from outside the area to support the practice in the event of death or disability. It reduces the risk of patient loss. If you're part of a practice coverage group (dentists who have chosen to provide practice coverage in such circumstances), make sure the services are provided by member dentists who practice outside the deceased or disabled dentist's area.

Casually Constructed Associateships ("No-Agreement" Associateship). As the marketplace makes it riskier to set up from scratch, associateships are becoming more common. Unfortunately, many owner-dentists still view these associations as benign arrangements. They sense no danger when they leap into these relationships. Nothing could be further from the truth! Practice value can be negatively affected by the presence of an associate in an unstructured arrangement.

Dentists approach most associateship arrangements with little in-depth discussion or long-term planning, other than determining hours and compensation. "Let's just start working together and we'll work out the details later," reflects the general attitude among most of us who bring in associates. We think it will all work itself out in the future. Although it's great to be optimistic, optimism can quickly take a negative turn when differing viewpoints about the future of the relationship begin to surface. Nothing is more detrimental to practice value and/or business relationships than putting off the planning process until some nebulous time in the future.

Since few dentists seriously plan for associateships, many fail to see the value of the investment in the services of a transition specialist. I encourage dentists to become aware of the possibilities of problems down the road. Just as we would never start a major reconstruction case without a thorough treatment plan, we should never enter serious business relationships without a business plan.

The plan should be constructed in writing with as many details clearly defined within the plan as possible. The "no-agreement" associateship is a risky, practice-value destroyer. Formal written agreements are a part of any well-laid plan. They do not have to be intimidating legal documents. The purpose of a written agreement is to clarify both parties' goals and desires. These agreements should be written clearly so the intent and language easily can be understood. (See Chapter 8, "Structuring Your Agreements")

Agreements Without Restrictive Covenants. Restrictive covenants (or noncompete agreements) are absolutely necessary to protect practice value.

They are designed for one primary reason: to protect the owner's practice from current and future patient loss by the exit of an associate, co-owner, or selling dentist. When restrictive covenants are constructed with reasonable time and distance requirements, most state laws do enforce them. (Consult your legal advisors for more specific information about restrictive covenants and your state laws.) Without a noncompete agreement in place, practice value can be greatly jeopardized.

The "Here Today, Gone Tomorrow" Associate. There are countless practice situations in which an associate leaves a practice and negatively impacts its value. This often happens when the owner least expects it.

Many selling dentists feel their associate's presence will have little, if any impact on the sale. Occasionally, when we see situations in which the associate is not interested in purchasing the owner's practice, and the owner is looking elsewhere for a buyer, the owner-dentist proclaims that the associate "is no threat to him or her." He or she feels certain that the associate would not move into the area if the practice were sold or represent any real competition to the buyer even if that happened.

Wrong answer! Buyer dentists become quite concerned about the possible impact a non-restricted associate might have on the value of the practice they are considering purchasing. This concern frequently leads to a lower offering price and sometimes discourages the sale. Protect yourself by requiring a commitment from your associate.

Often, seller-dentists are devastated when viable buyer candidates decide not to buy due to the presence of an associate in the seller's practice. But, why should the buyer take the risk that the associate may leave the practice and become a competitor? Why not find another practice to purchase that doesn't have this inherent problem?

Space-Sharing Arrangements. Space-sharing arrangements among dentists became popular years ago, and they enjoy a resurgence in popularity every few years. Dentists enter space-sharing arrangements for a variety of reasons. They are hoping to achieve certain benefits as a result of consolidating their practices into the same facility.

The destructive component of space-sharing usually surfaces when one member of the group decides to sell his or her practice. Although solutions to this problem may seem simple, they can become quite complex. We realize that each dentist in the group views his or her separate practice as just that—separate. However, patients often view the dentists in such a group as co-owners. In the eyes of an outside buyer, the chance of patients transferring to one of the existing members of the group, rather than choosing to see a new member of the group, seems high.

Other questions also arise. How many of the seller's patients have been treated by one of the other dentists? How will other dentists in the group feel about a new buyer and how will he or she feel about them? What interest will the other members of the group have in this new dentist? Will they be just as happy (or even happier) if no one buys the practice, allowing members of the existing group to benefit from the influx of patients who may transfer to them? From the new dentist's perspective, wouldn't it be far less complex to buy a solo practice, without these complications, questions, or concerns?

This scenario will almost always affect the final selling price of the practice and may even prevent a sale.

The "Hurried" Sale. Dentists who need to sell their practices quickly often approach me. Depending on the situation, this frequently forces the seller to accept a lower price—and in some cases, no sale occurs at all.

As previously discussed, unplanned events such as death and disability often necessitate a hurried sale. However, when the sale of a practice must be rushed due to the seller's lack of advance planning, the selling price is reflective of just that.

Dentists should be in the position for the eventual sale of their practices from the first day they open their doors. In-depth planning should begin no later than one to two years prior to retirement. The selling dentist should consider planning sooner if he or she wishes to take advantage of sale options that occur years prior to retirement, if he or she brings in an associate, and no later than five years prior to the desired sale date. (See Chapter 3, "Successful Sales Strategies.")

In smaller towns or rural areas, planning will need to begin much earlier, as a candidate pool is much smaller than in larger cities.

The investment you make in a well-thought-out plan prevents this practice-value destroyer and will repay you many times.

Selling Too Late. This is by far the most common practice value destroyer, particularly for late-career dentists. Whether due to lack of information or procrastination, these dentists often receive less than half of what they could have received for their practices had they planned the sale in advance. As their practice productivity declines, this practice-value loss, when combined with a dramatic reduction in profit percentage (profit squeeze), creates a "double-hit" for many dentists transitioning into retirement.

I cannot emphasize enough the importance of knowing the value of your practice well in advance of retirement. Again, all available options should be considered and game plans should be constructed years prior to the retirement date.

Selling Too Soon. Selling early is a viable option all dentists should at least explore. However, selling early may not be an appropriate choice for everyone. Dentists who plan to sell early, while practice value is at its peak, and continue working for the buyer-dentist, should carefully time the practice sale.

Such timing is crucial. Plans should be constructed in relationship to your target retirement dates. The rule-of-thumb for dentists to follow is to be cautious about selling your practice any sooner than one to three years from your desired retirement.

Be aware that if you plan to work with the buyer after selling, the money and financial security gained by selling early could be in danger. (In fact, these funds could be completely lost if the post-sale working arrangement is shortened due to conflicts that could surface between the buyer and the seller. This is a reality—it *can* and *does* happen.) Be willing to retire within one year of the sale, if necessary. If your financial situation dictates that you must work longer, carefully structure your arrangement and be very sure about whom you sell to. If your relationship severs, you may find yourself having to exit early despite what your agreement may specify.

Co-Ownership Arrangements Without Retirement Buy-Outs. Death and disability buy-outs are customarily addressed in most co-ownership agreements. However, more often than not, retirement buy-outs are not addressed.

Many previous co-ownership or shareholder agreements were structured during a time when practices had little or no value beyond the tangible assets. In these cases, both parties assumed there would be minimal problems other than determining the value of the supplies and used equipment upon the sale of the practice. Likewise, they also believed that there would be no problem selling their individual interest of the practice if an unforeseen situation occurred in the future. This was essentially "sweeping the problem under the rug." Let me assure you that many dentists eventually woke up to worry about this problem down the road.

Disputes often arise when the senior co-owner is ready to retire and there exists no retirement buy-out agreement between the co-owners. If the remaining co-owner already has a busy practice, he or she may not see a reason to buy-out the retiring co-owner. Although there are many benefits for the remaining co-owner to purchase the practice, these often are not perceived. Buying-out an existing co-owner makes way for new associates to enter the practice, enhancing profitability and facilitating future buy-in arrangements.

Buy-Out Options vs. Buy-Out Obligations. Buy-out agreements that allow co-owners the "option" of buying-out a co-worker are common. In most cases, these agreements were initially constructed with good intentions. However, their creators often assumed that co-workers would be easier to buy Out under such circumstances. Unaware of the fact that a buy-out option is a potential practice-value destroyer, many sellers have been left high and dry. In this situation, the seller has no choice but to search for an outside party to purchase the practice. Potential problems like this can be avoided through the construction of buy-out agreements that are *obligatory* (not optional). Thus, each co-owner will have a secure exit plan in place. (Note: Be sure that the buy-out figure is based on the fair market value of the tangible and intangible assets of the practice at the time of the sale, and not just the equipment or some arbitrary value for the seller's stock, which I often see.)

Declining Practice Location. Many late-career dentists find themselves in neighborhoods that have deteriorated over time. These practices often contain a notable patient base and are very profitable, but they are not always desirable in the eyes of a buyer. Unfortunately, the perception of a practice in a declining area decreases practice value and quickly becomes a practice-value destroyer.

Relocation prior to selling often is a consideration for dentists who find themselves in declining areas. The ideal time for relocation is five years (or less) prior to the anticipated sale date. Though this may appear to be costly (and perhaps stressful at this point in the dentist's career), it will definitely enhance the value of the practice. A move of this nature often creates a significant boost in productivity, at times between 25 and 40%.

Why? The newly updated facility presents a better environment for the patients. Change brings renewed growth and energy. The reinvigorated attitude among the staff, the dentists, and the patients aids in the conversion of practice marketability.

Prior to such a move, dentists may find it beneficial to consult with a practice-transition expert to explore possible relocation sites. Studies of theses areas of consideration should be undertaken to determine the possible percentage increase in practice value created by this scenario. Thereafter, dentists should consider employing the support of an experienced management consultant who can help structure and guide the relocation. Having support during this time will reduce stress and protect practice value during this process.

A practice merger is an available option for the dentist who doesn't want the stress and expense of relocation. Prior to retirement, the seller's practice could be sold to another dentist in the same area, eliminating the need for practice relocation.

This can represent a good move on the part of the seller-dentist, particularly if he or she is at a career stage where he or she prefers to simplify his or her life, not complicate it. (See Chapter 5, "Practice Mergers")

Managed Care. A managed-care practice near a famous Florida resort area was netting more than $250,000 in income for the seller-dentist.

This practitioner was working four days per week and took approximately 13 weeks off per year for vacation. (Doesn't sound too bad so far, huh?) Yet, this practice had been on the market for more than two years at this writing and was priced at 20% to 25% less than a similar fee-for-service practice. Not one potential buyer inquired further once the term "managed care" appeared in the conversation.

Only recently have we come to grips with the reality that managed care has had a major impact on the value of dental practices. As of 1996, practices with a large managed-care base were selling for far less than similar-sized fee-for-service practices in most parts of the country. This trend is predicted to continue, due largely to the following:

- Most buyer-dentists prefer traditional fee-for-service practices, not managed-care practices. This fact has great impact on the practice value.

- The perception of value in a managed-care practice is that little, if any, goodwill exists. Many buyer-dentists feel that the patient base in a managed-care situation is less stable than in a traditional fee-for-service practice.

- Managed-care profit margins usually are much less than well-managed, fee-for-service practices. (Why produce $500,000 to make $100,000, when you can produce $500,000 and make $200,000 to $250,000?)

Other considerations for a buyer-dentist to think about include:

- the variances in managed-care pay schedules;

- increased patient flow necessary to generate the same income;

- increased staff support;

- the need for associate dentists to provide services for the managed-care patient base;

- potentially working longer hours for the same or less pay.

The bottom line is that most buyer-dentists feel that managed care practices are unstable and result in "revolving-door" associates and patients.

What can we expect for the future? Good question. Managed care has become well-entrenched in the United States. We have seen little change in this negative value perception from potential buyers. Again, buyer-dentists continue to avoid looking at managed-care practices.

If you currently are considering participation in a managed-care program, weigh the costs of how it will affect your practice value. If your mission is to increase your patient base, consider expanding your practice through an associate who will eventually buy-in or through a practice merger. If you already are participating in a managed-care plan, seek the advice of a trained transition specialist to help you develop a plan to protect the value of your practice, as well as assist you in moving away from managed care. (Figure 7-15, page 184)

Conclusion

Be aware of these practice-value destroyers. Learn from others' mistakes. Seek sound advice from qualified experts who can help you avoid pitfalls and maximize practice value.

Now that you have learned about the tools professionals use to determine practice value—how to break down your Profit and Loss Statement to uncover the real net profit of your practice and how to avoid practice-value destroyers—we need the "reality check" of knowing when to have your practice appraised.

Part Five:
A Reality Check: Knowing When To Have Your Practice Appraised

Regardless of how your practice value is determined, at some point you must test it. Sellers should first look at the transaction as if they were the potential buyers. The best reality check for the seller-dentist is to determine whether or not the practice net income can support the existing overhead, any anticipated additional overhead (such as new equipment), and the debt service of a practice purchase. Before discussing the desired selling price of your practice with any prospective

---

PRACTICE-VALUE DESTROYERS
• **Death and Disability**
• **Casually-Constructed Associateships**
• **Space-Sharing Arrangements**
• **Agreements Without Restrictive Covenants**
• **Selling Too Hurried, Too Soon or Too Late**
• **Co-Ownership Arrangements Without Retirement Buy-Outs**
• **Managed Care**
• **Declining Practice Location**
• **Outdated Equipment and Decor**

Fig. 7.15

buyer, make sure what you're offering makes economic sense if you were the buyer.

I often review practice-purchase opportunities for buyer-dentists. Occasionally, I find that the seller's advisors have not done a reality check before marketing the practice. In those cases in which the buyer's future income has not been analyzed, it often presents a negative picture for the buyer-dentist. A practice sale should be structured to provide the buyer-dentist with a reasonable income—one equal to or better than he or she could make as an employee-only dentist in the same geographic area. Otherwise, it may be very difficult to market and sell the practice.

Flexible financing often is a decision-maker in the process. Whether sellers are willing to finance part of the purchase price or financial lending opportunities exist, this obviously is an area requiring attention. In the past, seller financing was required; now, it is not. New lending institutions have emerged that are happy to loan up to 100% of the selling price of an established practice (based on appraisal).

The Importance of Always Knowing the True Value of Your Practice

Throughout your career, many situations arise which encourage you to know and understand the true value of the practice. Why is it that we always know the true value of our investments, yet we generally tend to put our own price tag on the value of our businesses? In determining the value of our practices, we often use outdated "rule-of-thumb" formulas or set unrealistic value amounts without considering reality. Knowing and understanding the true value of the practice should be a requirement for all practice owners.

Why? As a part of any strategic-transition plan, dentists should always be in position for the possible sale of part or all of the value in the practice. Being in position for transition enables dentists to take advantage of opportunities as they arise. It also allows the owner-dentist to be prepared for unexpected situations such as death, disability, or a need to quickly relocate.

Following are reasons why dentists should invest in comprehensive practice valuations:

Practice Buy-Out Framework. The practice valuation is useful in laying the groundwork for the eventual buy-out of the original owner's remaining interest, as well as the junior co-owner's remaining interest. There are different approaches and methodologies used to determine future value, using the original practice valuation as a benchmark. Since it is probable that the future value of the practice will be much greater than the original value, a practice valuation establishes a baseline, helping to prevent any future surprises.

Prior to Forming a Group Practice. Depending on the group-practice structure, its valuation may be useful in determining the practice profit distribution. This is particularly important when collections of all the practices in the group are deposited into one account, out of which expenses and profits are paid. Most important, the valuation will help determine a buy-out framework upon which each individual can rely on when the time comes. (It's not a case of *if*, but a case of *when*, a buy-out will be desired or necessary.) A clear and easy buy-out can be complicated by the formation of a group, unless all parties involved are willing to buy each other out. All terms and conditions of future buy-outs should be clearly understood and agreed to prior to the co-mingling of their practices.

After the value of each member's practice is established, then appropriate insurance provisions can be instituted to assure that every member of the group will be bought out, particularly in the case of death and disability. Retirement buy-out clauses also can be structured from this practice valuation, as long as there is a clear agreement among the members of the group as to who is bought out when.

Financial-Planning Needs. For many dentists, the sale of the practice is an important part of their retirement plan. In the end, dentists who are dependent on their practice value for retirement often are disappointed with the selling price. As you have seen, most dentists can work in their practice for an additional two years and make a net profit of as much or more than the selling price.

Even though the selling price is important for retirement, don't depend on it too heavily. Most important of all, keep your practice valuation updated so you always know where you stand financially. In order to view the value from a realistic perspective, it is important to have a practice valuation updated on an annual basis.

Prior to Selling. Dentists are easily convinced of the importance of practice valuations prior to selling. Without a comprehensive valuation, the seller is groping in the dark to come up with a credible selling price. A professional practice valuation becomes a benchmark on which to base future negotiations with a buyer and his or her representative. It justifies the practice asking price and helps eliminate some of the doubt buyers and their representatives experience when they anticipate that the price was "pulled out of the air."

A professional practice valuation confirms that the practice valuation is a viable investment for a buyer-dentist. In this instance, the practice valuation becomes part of the overall marketing package, showing the true value of the practice and focusing on more that just the price. At some point, prospective buyers and their business advisors review this package. Lending institutions involved in the sale (for down payment, working capital, or cash price, where applicable) almost always require a professional economic forecast of the practice.

Prior to Practice or Marriage Dissolution. A valuation is essential for establishing an equitable buy-out plan for practice and marriage dissolution. Competent legal counsel should be sought for advice in all areas of dissolution.

In traditionally-operated dental practices, the personal goodwill of the owner-dentist often is the most important value component. In some states, the personal goodwill of the seller is not considered to be a marital asset, as it is not separable from the selling dentist. (If the goodwill value is not considered a marital asset, it will normally not be subjected to distribution to the non-dentist spouse.

Professional or business goodwill is treated entirely differently. The value of this type of goodwill is considered separable from the owner and is, therefore, often treated as a marital asset. For example, a fast food franchise has business goodwill value separable from the owner and has a value separate from the owner. For this and other reasons, it is extremely important to know and understand how the law in your particular state applies in a given situation. A professional practice appraiser, with experience in court testimony, often is employed as an expert witness when the issue of goodwill is questioned.

Prior To an Associate

Invest in a professional practice appraisal prior to any type of associateship. If you are considering a practice-expansion plan to facilitate a potential associateship to buy-in, a comprehensive practice valuation will help you answer the following questions:

- Should I sell part or all of my practice?

- When is the right time to sell part or all of my practice?

- At what point will the associate be able to afford such a purchase, and under what terms and conditions?

- Will the payments on my practice allow me to reduce my schedule should I choose to remain a co-owner? If I decide to retire immediately after the sale, will the amount received from the sale of the practice be enough to support me through my retirement years?

- How much can I afford to reasonably pay an associate prior to the purchase or buy-in?

Virtually all associateship arrangements should be structured to allow the development of co-ownership in the practice. One exception would be the dentist who enters into an associateship arrangement with no plans or expectations for the future. In these situations, neither the associate-dentist nor the owner-dentist intends for the relationship to continue long-term. In my opinion, this should be the only exception to the rule.

By structuring associateships to allow co-ownership (allowing the associate to buy into part of the owner's practice at some point), an equity position can be created. While there are many benefits to this type of relationship, it is extremely important to have all future terms and conditions spelled out, upfront. A comprehensive practice valuation is only the first step in protecting this process.

Obviously, the practice valuation allows the dentist to determine the buy-in price. The actual buy-in price is calculated by multiplying the percent of interest being purchased by the associate or the buyer times the total amount of practice value. Once the price and terms are established, financing can be discussed. As the total amount of the practice loan is amortized, the specific payments can be determined.

From these projections, the buyer's production goals must be considered. The production level the buyer needs to attain to make the buy-in affordable often is a deciding factor in the transition process.

A comprehensive valuation and buy-in format suggests a time frame for the buy-in/buy-out to take place. This format also allows the owner to determine if, and when, part or all of the practice should be sold.

How practice value affects associate compensation

Without first knowing the true net income of the practice, the owner-dentist cannot decide fair compensation for an associate. As part of any properly-constructed practice valuation, the overall "net" income becomes very clear.

Many associateships are casually structured, using an arbitrary percentage paid to the associate (without regard to practice overhead costs or practice collections). This sets up serious problems "down the road."

Start by asking yourself the following questions:

- Should associates make a higher net percentage (including all fringes) of their collections than you, the owner?

- Should there be some increase in this compensation percentage once the associate becomes a co-owner?

- What happens to the associate's net income once he or she begins making payments on the buy-in price?

We often see situations in which the owner's net compensation level is a lower percentage of production than that of the associate. This routinely occurs when arbitrary percentages are applied to associate compensation. When proper evaluation of the overhead percentages and practice trends have not been thoroughly examined, problems are on the way.

Sometimes the starting percentages seem fair. However, many owner-dentists add benefits, such as health and malpractice insurance, continuing education allowance, paid sick days and so forth, causing the true percentage to be much higher. No matter how you look at it, when the owner's net percentage of profit is less than what is paid to the associate, there is little incentive for the associate to buy-in.

The point: A proper practice valuation determines the "true net" of the practice, thus allowing the owner-dentist to determine a sensible compensation level for the associate. The associate-dentist is then provided with comprehensive practice-income projections. By educating the associate-dentist in the area of future owner-level income statistics, the facts most always provide incentive for the associate to buy-in.

"Sweating" Over Sweat-Equity-Associateship Considerations. A few years ago, I was asked to structure a buy-in arrangement between an associate and an owner-dentist. They had been together for five years. The practice numbers looked excellent and everyone was getting along well. Before the transition, I asked the owner some questions:

- When did the associate enter the practice?

- Was there a practice valuation rendered prior to the associate's entry?

- What were the associate's production numbers over the last three to five years, relative to the production numbers of the hygiene department and the owner?

- Was there ever a discussion about how and when the value of the practice would be determined?

- Was there ever a discussion about what value might be added to the practice by the associate's presence?

- Do you think the associate believes that he or she has received fair compensation during his or her employment with you?

It's clear the direction I was heading with these questions, and I can tell you that in nearly 100% of these cases, a problem does surface.

As expected, the associate began to be concerned. Like most associates, he was nervous about how the value of the practice would be determined. He had dozens of questions about how the process would unfold. In addition, the associate was concerned about being able to afford the buy-in price once the value was determined. At last, he inquired as to what consideration of true practice value was reflected prior to him coming on board.

Because the issue had never been discussed, the associate was certain that the value of the practice should be based on what it was worth prior to his entry. He stated that his accountant, lawyer, colleagues, and even his dental school professors seemed to agree. The owner (of course) thought the opposite. It was apparent that some middle ground value had to be agreed upon.

The valuation needed to reflect the entire current value and the negotiated equity credit allowance for the associate. Unfortunately, both parties felt placed in a compromising position before entering into the actual transaction. Because the value was not determined upfront, no agreements had been established to evaluate how practice value would later be determined.

Always determine practice value upfront and avoid "sweating" over "sweat-equity".

Prior to a Practice Co-Ownership Arrangement. Many dentists consider entering a practice co-ownership arrangement in an effort to form a more team-oriented practice environment than is possible through space-sharing arrangements between dentists who own independent practices. Each dentist's practice value should be determined so that each party's interest in the practice (i.e., percentage of ownership) can be calculated.

The most common route to eventual co-ownership is through an initial associate-employer relationship. This arrangement can evolve into co-ownership through the associate buying into a portion of the owner's practice. Associates who plan to buy into a practice at some point will want to know specific future costs they'll be expected to pay.

Financial goals should be set to allow the associate to prepare for the financial responsibility of the buy-in. Associates then can determine if this practice, compared to other practices they may be looking at, better meets their overall needs. Be sure to discuss these issues prior to the beginning of a relationship. Waiting until later is never advantageous.

Co-Ownership Profit Distribution. Since practice valuation helps determine the percentage of co-ownership interest that will be allocated to each of the co-owners, it indirectly tells us how profits should be distributed. This is particularly important if the co-owners are considering creative methods to distribute profits, other than basing them strictly on productivity differences.

As in the associate to buy-in approach, it's important to agree upon how each co-owner would be bought-out in specific situations such as death, disability, or retirement.

A practice valuation becomes an integral part of the practice business plan. As the practice expands, new future co-owners will enter with full knowledge of the value of the existing co-ownership and a basis for future buy-in agreements.

Safely sharing space. The safest space-sharing arrangements are ones that have been entered into as part of a long-term plan for succession and transition. Some of these include associateship to buy-in, practice merger, deferred sale, and pre-retirement sale, all of which are covered in detail throughout this book.

With clear chain-of-succession programmed into these arrangements, dentists in group arrangements always have a built-in buyer for their practice. If you're considering space-sharing arrangements, and you want to prevent problems, consider the following:

Age-staggering enters into this. Dentists at similar career pivot points often share space. This, in turn, creates a problem when one practitioner decides to sell. Because their career positions are similar, they rarely want to buy each other out. To avoid future problems, individuals form ideal groups at staggered ages. This sets up a better situation for natural succession among the individuals involved. This is particularly true when "win-win" succession arrangements can be put in place.

Agree to a buy-in/buy-out plan prior to forming a group. Agreeing to a retirement buy-out plan, prior to forming a group, helps protect existing group members and individuals entering the group in the future. With the proper agreements in place, all members of the group have peace of mind about the eventual sale of their practice.

Large-grossing practices. In outright practice sales, using income multipliers to determine practice value can be disappointing when applied to large-grossing practices. Many dentists with practices grossing more than $600,000 per year may find that their practices do not sell for the same ratio of price-to-gross as lower-grossing practices. This situation differs from area to area, but some sellers may find buyers have upper limits when it comes to paying for practices in an outright sale. Therefore, the market becomes extremely small when looking for buyers in the mega-practice range.

Buyers with concerns about large practices often ask, "Has the practice peaked out and am I buying at the high end? Would I be better off buying a smaller practice with greater upside potential? Will I be able to duplicate what the seller has done to create such a large practice? How much of the practice productivity is due to the special talents of the staff vs. the talents of the dentist? A practice of this size is selling a lot of goodwill—will enough patients transfer for me to be able to make the payments on the practice?"

Dentists with large-grossing practices can receive full value by planning early and selling their practices in increments over a period of time to one or more successors. (See Chapter 4, "Creating 'Win-Win' Associateship to Buy-In Arrangements.")

Enhancing the Value of Your Practice

To effectively counter the practice-value destroyers we have thus far discussed, there are some specific steps you can take to maximize the value of your practice prior to planning any type of transition.

Increase Net Profit

The potential net income of your practice is essentially what a purchaser is buying. The higher the net profits, the greater the practice value. In addition to increasing your *overall* practice net profit, increasing your *percentage* of net profit is equally important. The greater the profit percentage, the greater the value. That is: Two identical practices with the same "true-net" income can sell for different prices if their net profitability percentages differ. ("True-net" income refers to the total compensation, benefits received by the owner-dentist and any associates, and takes into consideration depreciation and any elective expenses deducted by the practice.)

Late-career dentists should be especially careful to maintain gross – and net-income levels in the three to five year period prior to selling. This way, the practice doesn't appear to be on a downslide, which will inevitably impact its value for a potential buyer. Dentists who are considering cutting back on production should first have in place a plan for transferring this production (and its value) to a successor.

Maintain Fee-For-Service Patient Base

All things being equal, the more fee-for-service patients entering your practice (as opposed to managed-care patients), the more desirable your practice becomes. This, in turn, drives up the value. Practices with a large managed-care base almost always sell for far less than similar-sized, fee-for-service practices. This trend is predicted to continue, due largely to the following:

- Most dentists prefer fee-for-service practices,

- The perception of value in a managed-care practice is that little, if any, goodwill exists, and goodwill is a major part of the total value of any practice.

- Managed-care profit margins usually are far less than in well-managed, fee-for-service practices.

If In A Declining Area, Relocate

The more desirable the practice location, the higher the market value. Conversely, deteriorating areas have the opposite impact on the value of a practice. Some mid- and late-career dentists find themselves in areas that have deteriorated over time. Unfortunately, this can become a practice-value destroyer.

Prior to selling part or all of your practice, consider relocating if you are in a declining area. The investment definitely will enhance the value of the practice and may significantly boost practice productivity as well.

Be sure to consult with a practice-transition consultant prior to relocating. This way, you will be ensured of making the right moves. Another option to discuss with the consultant is the sale of the practice to another established dentist in the same area (i.e., a practice merger). This could allow you to sell your practice without having to relocate it first.

Plan Your Sale/Buy-In Early

When the sale of a practice must be rushed due to lack of advance planning, the selling price often will reflect it. In fact, dentists who plan late frequently receive less than half of what they could have received for their practices had they planned in advance.

In-depth practice buy-in or sale-planning should begin no later than one to two years prior to the anticipated sale or buy-in date. Planning should begin even sooner for those dentists wishing to pursue pre-retirement sales options that allow the seller to continue working after the sale. In addition, those dentists practicing in smaller towns, far from metropolitan areas, will need to begin planning even earlier, as the potential candidate pool for those areas is much smaller.

Don't Sell Too Soon

Selling the practice prior to retirement is a viable option that all dentists should at least explore. However, this sale approach is not appropriate for all dentists. Though selling early (while practice value is at its peak) and continuing to work for the buyer has some real advantages, this type of sale should be carefully timed.

What if, after you sell, you find you're not happy with the working arrangement? You need to be prepared for the possibility that you may wish to leave the practice sooner than you might have anticipated. Be sure you have thought through the potential financial impact of such an early exit.

Update Equipment and Décor

Consider replacing any outdated and/or poorly functioning equipment with new and more modern equipment and technology (including computerization where none exists). Previously owned equipment that is 5 or 10 years old often can be utilized, saving thousands of dollars while accomplishing the task. If your office décor is dated, consider giving it a facelift. These improvements go a long way toward enhancing the market value of the practice.

Your Most Important Step: Constructing a Transition Plan

Regardless of the steps you take to enhance the value of the practice, this value remains in a "locked" position for most dentists until retirement. Making advance preparations to successfully transfer this value through co-ownership, pre-retirement sale, and traditional sale arrangements can greatly enhance the final selling price.

This is why your foundation for enhancing practice value lies in a sound plan of transition. Without such a plan, steps taken to enhance practice value are made in vain. What good is this value if there are no plans in place for successfully cashing it in?

Ideally, your successor should be grown from within the practice through some type of relationship leading to an eventual buy-in or sale. To ensure success, all associate, space-sharing, or preplanned sale arrangements should be structured very carefully from the first day. The plan should be constructed in writing with as many details clearly defined as possible. Practice value can be negatively affected by the presence of another dentist in the practice in an unclear and unstructured arrangement. Once your plan is in place, you can feel secure knowing that your practice value is protected in the event of death, disability, or simply your desire to retire.

As dentists become aware of the importance of having a sound transition plan, their view of the transition process often changes drastically. As a result, many dentists seek out different types of associate, co-owner, or purchaser candidates for their practices. Some find it necessary, though painful, to re-examine proposed arrangements they may have with current candidates; for others, it may require restructuring or even dissolving current practice relationships that have been in place for years.

• • •

You've learned how to determine the value of your practice, as well as how to protect and enhance this value. One critical component of planning a successful transition is that of constructing equitable, win-win agreements that both parties can live with. Without this type of agreement in place, your transition (as well as the value of your practice) could be at risk.

In the next chapter, I'll show you specifically how to arrive at an equitable end result once you reach the agreement phase of your transition.

8

STRUCTURING YOUR AGREEMENTS: AN EQUITABLE APPROACH TO MAKING AGREEMENTS WORK FOR ALL PARTIES INVOLVED

Note: The information in this chapter is not intended to replace the advice of competent legal counsel. Please consult an attorney for additional advice or questions you may have.

"This is *not* what I thought I agreed to. You want *me* to sign a non-compete agreement? I am not even sure if things are going to work out between us."

"The contract says that I bought all the furniture and fixtures of the practice. I understand that the antique desk in the consultation room has been in your family for years, but doesn't it now belong to *me*?"

"Wait a minute. I didn't know that the buy-in price was going to include the production I have added to the practice since I've been working here."

"I thought the price of the practice included the accounts receivable. How am I going to pay the bills of the practice without this initial cash flow?"

"My attorney says your attorney's contract is inadequate and he's going to have to redraft it!"

Does any of this sound familiar? If you've ever experienced the process of purchasing, buying-into, or selling part or all of a practice, then you know obstacles and objections come with the territory. In any given practice sale, merger, or associateship to buy-in agreement, we find the opportunity for contention. Commitment is being required from both parties, and each individual in the transaction has a great deal at stake. Money is almost always involved at some point—a normal component when transferring part or all of the ownership of the practice. In my experience, the bottom line to most of the obstacles and objections that come up in a practice-transition agreement is this: Most dentists are comfortable signing agreements when each has good feelings about the other, a positive attitude about the future of the proposed business relationship, and an overall sense of value of the transaction. The key to successfully completing the agreements phase of the transition lies in creating and maintaining all three of these.

Many of the concerns that arise during the agreements phase are due to the lack of knowledge most dentists have about the transition process, as well as the following question: "What issues should be normally covered in such an agreement, and will I be protected?" Seller-dentists want to feel good about what they're transferring, while at the same time they need to feel that their practice assets are being protected. Buyer-dentists need to feel good about what they are buying, and they need to feel assured that the practice opportunity has value and that a reasonable lifestyle can be maintained throughout the buy-in or purchase period.

The agreement phase of a practice transition exemplifies a critical stage of the process. Emotions run high during this time. By creating win-win agreements and removing the basic obstacles in a practice transaction, the negotiation process is much more likely to succeed. The key here lies in understanding what's normal and fair, something that some legal and tax advisors have difficulty in philosophically accepting.

An Important Mission: An Equitable End-Result

This chapter contains valuable information on how to structure equitable agreements for the transition of a dental practice. The information and concepts are based on countless numbers of transitions that I've helped to plan and implement over the past years, as well as the collective experience of many well-respected experts I constantly network with. Hopefully, this information will allow you to better understand the process of constructing comprehensive agreements for the transition of your practice in a nonadversarial environment. You soon may discover that the mystical ingredient is to approach it with fairness and equity.

I discovered a "secret" many years ago: Most dentists want to be fair to each other and they just need guidance on what is standard (and equitable) in the various types of agreements involved in the transition of a dental practice. Unfortunately, in most business transactions involve the transitioning and transfer of the ownership of business, the attitude each side takes is of winning it all (a position frequently recommended by their advisors). This position often is maintained at the expense of the other side. (If the transaction fails to successfully close, then it was at the expense of *both* sides.) Most dentists would like to structure their agreements in a different type of environment—one that would lead to a win-win situation for all in the end.

Complex Agreement Issues

There are many complex issues that need to be addressed in the transition of a dental practice. Most attorneys familiar with transactions of this type tell me that the legal issues involved are straightforward—it's the business issues related to dental practices that make an agreement complex. Use caution with "fill-in-the-blank" agreements or "agreements used by a friend" for his or her particular situation. Comprehensive agreements need to be *individualized*. They require the feedback and expertise of transition specialists who have handled a myriad of different situations.

Dozens of complex issues need to be considered in the construction of a successful agreement for the transition of a dental-practice. Some of the issues are commonly found in other types of business agreements. However, many of the issues are unique to dental-practice transitions. A well-constructed agreement should reflect a blend of both. The following are some key things to consider in the construction of these agreements.

What Encompasses a Good Agreement?

A comprehensive agreement should be thorough and cover the many potential scenarios unique to dental-practices.

The agreement should be empowering, not intimidating, and serve as a reference source for future questions.

An agreement should be understandable by all parties involved; otherwise, its true value often is diminished.

The agreement must become an integral part of your comprehensive transition plan and should be considered a valuable tool prior to, during, and after your practice transition. (Too often, agreements are viewed by the dentists who have signed them as "that contract we read a few years ago that neither of us understood and that is now sitting in a drawer somewhere.")

The Best Way To Start:
Construct a Preliminary Agreement

The final agreement phase should begin with a preliminary agreement. This will be one of the first steps toward solidifying the intentions of the parties in a professional, fair, and equitable manner. Due to the complexity and abundance of issues faced during the agreement phase, it is very beneficial to begin with this preliminary agreement before proceeding to more comprehensive final agreements. Why?

By first agreeing to the basic fundamentals and terms of the transition prior to proceeding to more agreements (that can easily be 40 to 60 pages in length), both parties will find that obstacles and objections tend to "melt away."

A preliminary agreement is an important step in the commitment process. Both parties generally are more committed to the "plan," once they sign a preliminary agreement.

By using a preliminary agreement, the other issues to be discussed and agreed upon are more easily "massaged." This step makes the final agreement more palatable, as the primary issues have been agreed upon first.

Preliminary agreements can cover as many issues as the parties desire, but I suggest that only the primary issues should be focused on at this point. What follows are some of the primary issues that usually are covered in a preliminary agreement. (Figure 8.1, page 201)

Over the course of this chapter, we will cover a checklist of some of the most important items to consider in two of the most common

YOUR PRELIMINARY AGREEMENT
WHAT SHOULD IT INCLUDE?

- **SALE OR BUY-IN PRICE & TERMS**

- **PRICE ALLOCATIONS FOR TAX PURPOSES**

- **ASSETS INCLUDED/EXCLUDED FROM SALE**

- **PROPOSED SALE/ BUY-IN DATE**

- **COMPENSATION PRE- & POST-TRANSITION**

- **NONCOMPETE PROVISIONS**

Fig. 8.1

practice-transition agreements: practice-sale agreements and associate-ship to co-ownership (buy-in) agreements.

Major conflicts can be avoided by clearly defining the structure for these agreements prior to beginning the process. Though it's not possible in this book to cover every facet of these agreements, we will be looking at the basic components.

The Practice-Sale Agreement

This agreement is for the dentist who wishes to sell the entire practice. It can be used as the foundation for any of the practice-sale scenarios (retirement sale, pre-retirement sale, and deferred sale). (See Chapter 3, "Successful Sales Strategies.") A well-constructed practice-sale agreement contains six major parts:

- Part One: Terms of the Sale;

- Part Two: Assets Included/Excluded From the Sale;

- Part Three: Allocations of the Purchase Price;

- Part Four: The Seller's Accounts Receivable;

- Part Five: Seller's Pre-closing Practice Liabilities; and

- Part Six: Seller and Purchaser Warranties and Acknowledgments.

Part One:
Terms of the Sale

1. Purchase Price

2. Terms of Payment

Cash price paid at closing or cash down payment and seller-financed balance

- Interest rate (fixed or variable)

- Will there be an interest-only period?

- Will there be a payment deferral period?

- Will there be a future balloon payment?

- Seller loans or leases being assumed by the buyer

Note: This part of the agreement covers price and terms of the practice-sale. In a cash sale, the agreements are less complex in this area.

Seller-Financing Issues

When seller financing is used, it is not uncommon for an interest-only period (six to 12 months) to be offered to the buyer if the seller is staying on after the sale. This allows the buyer to get on his or her feet before making full payments of both principal and interest. Some situations necessitate a payment-deferral period, where due to cash-flow concerns during the first few months of the transition no payments of any kind are required. Either or both of these commonly are offered in transitions where the seller remains in the practice working for the buyer for a specified period of time after the sale. Once the seller retires from the practice, normal amortized (principal and interest) payments then would begin.

Balloon payments are uncommon in most dental-practice-sale transactions. This is where part or all of the remaining principal becomes due at some point in the future and therefore "balloons." (The "balloon" usually occurs within three to five years of the closing.) This balloon payment approach allows the buyer to begin making payments on a "reduced" basis at the beginning of the payout period and/or allows the seller to convert the balance of the promissory note to cash at some point in the future.

Will there be any loans or leases of the seller that the buyer assumes as part of the sale? If so, will they be in addition to the purchase price, or part of the purchase price?

Ideally, any existing loans or leases of the seller would be paid off at closing. Most lending institutions involved in the transaction would probably require this be done, and as a result, the buyer would be acquiring the assets free and clear of any liens previously placed by the seller's creditors.

Part Two:
Assets Included/Excluded from the Sale

Certain assets are included/excluded from the sale of a dental-practice. A list and description of the assets should be itemized in the agreement, typically as separate exhibits (Figures 8.2, page 204 and 8.3, page 205). Here are some sample clauses for this.

Assets Included in the Sale

Equipment: The clinical, office, and laboratory equipment located in the seller's practice, including, but not limited to those items listed on the attached Exhibit, equipment, furniture, and fixtures: Any telephone systems used in the operation of the practice (whether leased or owned) shall be included in this equipment.

Furniture and fixtures: The furniture and fixtures in the seller's practice as listed on the attached Exhibit, equipment, furniture, and fixtures.

ASSETS TYPICALLY INCLUDED

- **DENTAL OFFICE, LAB EQUIPMENT**

- **FURNITURE AND FIXTURES**

- **OFFICE AND CLINICAL SUPPLIES / SMALL INSTRUMENTS**

- **COMPUTER SOFTWARE LICENSES**

- **GOODWILL**

- **SELLERS NON-COMPETE AGREEMENT**

Fig. 8.2

Office and clinical supplies/small instruments: The office and clinical supplies and small clinical instruments in the seller's practice at the time of closing. The seller is expected to transfer to the buyer at closing a reasonable and customary inventory of these items.

Patient records: Subject to any applicable state or dental-regulatory board requirements, the seller is assigning to the buyer all the financial, clinical, recall, and other treatment records of the patients of the practice.

Goodwill: As part of this practice-sale, the personal and professional goodwill of the seller's practice is being conveyed to the buyer.

Noncompete agreement: In conjunction with the sale of the assets of the seller's practice, and to protect the goodwill being conveyed, the seller is agreeing to all of the terms and conditions of the attached Noncompetition Agreement.

Computer Software: The seller's computer software normally is included with the sale. Typically, the transfer cost of any of the seller's computer software to the buyer is divided equally if valued at $500 or greater. (The seller typically pays all the cost if valued at less than $500.) Make sure this item is negotiated early in the process, as it can be a source of problems.

ASSETS TYPICALLY EXCLUDED

- **SELLER'S PERSONAL ASSETS**
- **SELLER'S CASH ASSETS**
- **ACCOUNTS RECEIVABLE**

Fig. 8.3

Assets Excluded from the Sale

A list of any assets of the practice excluded from the sale should be itemized. Certain assets in the practice that are personal, such as plaques, diplomas, the seller's personal library, antiques, paintings, etc., typically are excluded unless they were included in the original practice valuation. Cash assets of the seller also are typically excluded. This would include cash-on-hand at the time of sale and the seller's accounts receivable and retirement funds.

Part Three:
Allocations of the Purchase Price

This section deals with how the purchase price of the practice is broken down for tax purposes. The Internal Revenue Service currently requires that the purchase price of a dental-practice be broken down (or allocated) into categories similar to the ones listed below. Each category carries with it different tax considerations for both the buyer and seller to consider and to discuss with their tax advisors.

Sample Allocation

Dental office and lab equipment	$50,000
Furniture and fixtures	$10,000
Office and clinical supplies/small instruments	$15,000
Patient records	$100,000
Goodwill/Going concern value	$150,000
Seller's non-compete agreement	$50,000
Total purchase price	$375,000

The Need for a Practice Valuation

I suggest a formal valuation of the practice be provided to determine these different values. This way, should there be a future need to substantiate the allocations, you will have an independent appraiser's opinion on the different values.

Part Four:
The Seller's Accounts Receivable

The accounts receivable generally are considered to be an asset separate from the sale of the practice. It becomes important to determine how these accounts will be collected (as well as who will collect them) following the sale. Several issues surround these accounts receivable.

Accounts Receivable Issues

- Buyers often want to use these accounts receivable for initial working capital.

- Sellers wish to collect as many of these accounts as possible, since they represent services already completed, with the associated overhead already paid for.

- These accounts were most likely not included in the original practice valuation (and were therefore not included in the agreed-upon purchase price).

- If the accounts are to be included in the purchase price, they become additional assets, with price negotiation necessary.

Selling the Practice via Stock

Some incorporated practices are occasionally sold (in total or in part) through the sale of the corporate stock of the practice. Legal and tax advisors often feel that this is the simplest way to convey ownership. It's also desirable from the selling dentist's tax perspective, as the entire price paid for the stock is treated as capital gain. Capital gains are taxed at a rate lower than ordinary income (which is why the seller's advisors often prefer this approach).

Unfortunately, the purchaser is allowed no tax deduction when purchasing this stock. In addition, the purchaser could potentially inherit all the liabilities of the corporation, including claims for mal-practice, taxes, and others. Who would want to purchase a practice under those circumstances? This is why those same advisors that rec-ommended that their seller-client pursue this route would rarely rec-ommend it for their buyer-clients!

In many business transactions, the stock of the company being sold has actual value in and of itself in "the market"—as if you were buying stock in McDonald's or IBM. In these situations, it might make sense to inherit certain potential liabilities in the process and forego any up-front tax deductions. However, it makes no sense to purchase a den-tal-practice this way, especially when there are other legitimate ways to create capital gain treatment for the seller *and* allow a tax deduction for the purchaser—a win-win! (Note: Some of the negative aspects of pur-chasing the stock of an incorporated dental-practice might be mini-mized if the purchaser were able to negotiate a lower purchase price while holding the purchaser harmless from any future liabilities.)

Please consult your legal and tax advisors for assistance in this area.

The collection of the accounts receivable can be handled in one of several ways after the sale. The most common methods include collec-tion by the buyer on behalf of the seller (but not included in the pur-chase price); collection directly by the seller outside of the practice pur-chase, and inclusion as part of the total purchase price of the practice and retained by the buyer once a separate value has been determined for these accounts. (Figure 8.4, page 208)

Since the accounts receivable usually are not included in the pur-chase price in a typical dental-practice sale, the buyer usually collects them on the seller's behalf. The buyer normally receives a fee to cover the costs of collection. The fee usually is a percentage of the collected amount and ranges from 5% to 10%, depending on the period of time required to collect the accounts.

In orthodontic practice, the contracts-receivable and accounts-receivable usually are included in the purchase price and are collected by the buyer. (See Appendix II, "Specialty Practices—Special Considerations.")

The following is an example of a clause to consider for the accounts receivable:

Accounts Receivable—Collection by the Buyer. The buyer shall collect the seller's pre-closing accounts receivable following the closing, as follows:

**ACCOUNTS RECEIVABLE
OPTIONS FOLLOWING THE SALE**

- **COLLECTED BY PURCHASER *FOR* THE SELLER**

- **COLLECTED DIRECTLY BY THE SELLER**

- **COLLECTED & RETAINED BY THE PURCHASER**

Fig. 8.4

For the initial 30-day period following the closing, the buyer shall collect the seller's accounts receivable at no cost to the seller. During this initial 30-day period, the buyer is not required to send out invoices for these accounts receivable.

For the 31- through 90-day period following the closing, the buyer shall receive, as payment, 5% of the seller's accounts receivable collected. This shall be increased to 10% for the period from 91 days following the closing and forward from that date. The buyer's responsibility to collect the seller's accounts receivable shall only include normal in-office collection procedures, including but not limited to, billing and postage, telephone follow-up, and in-office collection letters for all of the seller's accounts receivables.

The following is a sample clause used when the seller collects his or her accounts receivable directly.

Accounts Receivable—Collection by the Seller. The seller shall be responsible for the collection of the seller's accounts receivable. The seller agrees that no such extraordinary measures will be utilized to accelerate the collection of any accounts receivable without first giving advance written notice to buyer. Upon receipt of such notice, the buyer shall have 10 days to attempt to collect the amount due to the seller from the patient or the buyer may elect to pay a like sum to the seller and assume that accounts receivable. If the buyer is unsuccessful in said collection or should elect not to assume that patient's account receivable, then the seller, without further notice to the buyer, shall have the right to use any other legal method of collection available to the seller. In all collection efforts undertaken by the seller, or on the seller's behalf, the seller agrees to clearly notify the patient that the seller is acting for the seller's own account and is not acting for, and such collection efforts are not associated in any way with, the buyer.

Occasionally, the value of the accounts receivable can be added to the purchase price. An example of the formula for the sale of accounts receivable can be found in the diagram, "Accounts Receivable Valuation: Factoring," in Chapter 7, "Determining the Value of Your Practice."

An additional option to consider: loaning the accounts receivable to the buyer with the buyer paying the seller 100% of the collected amount after a specified period of time (usually 90 to 120 days). By doing this, the buyer has obtained working capital for the practice, and the seller and buyer have been spared any "negotiations" over the value of the accounts.

Part Five:
Seller's Pre-Closing Practice Liabilities

- Accrued employee salaries and payroll taxes

- Accrued staff benefits

- Accounts payable

- Prepaid patient fees

Treatment in Progress: Fee-Proration Method

The seller should agree to pay, as of closing (or when due where applicable), all preclosing liabilities of the seller's practice other than those being assumed by the buyer as part of the purchase (see Part 1 of the "Practice-Sale Agreement"). Liabilities being assumed by the buyer would include things such as equipment leases, loans, etc. Liabilities that should be paid by the seller would include all accounts payable, accrued staff salaries and benefits, and any prepaid fees.

The seller should refund to the buyer at closing (or, where applicable to the patient) any fees that might have been prepaid prior to the closing for services not yet begun. If that patient is later treated by the seller (while working for the buyer), the seller would receive his or her agreed-upon compensation for providing these services. (See Post Sale Provider Agreement.) Treatment in progress (i.e., services that were begun *prior* to the closing) scheduled to be completed by the buyer or the seller following the closing should be prorated between the seller and buyer.

The following is a sample clause for such a situation.

Treatment in Progress/Fee-Proration Method: For any services that have been partially completed prior to the closing (referred to as "Treatment in Progress") and which are to be completed by the seller or buyer following the closing, the following distribution of those fees between the buyer and seller shall apply:

Here is an example of fee proration.

Step 1: Determine the total number of appointments required for completion of the service.

Step 2: Prorate the fee collected between the seller and buyer, based on the number of appointments and time spent on the procedures.

Here is a number of appointments example: A crown might normally require two appointments for completion, with two-thirds of the total treatment spent at appointment number one and one-third of the treatment time spent at appointment number two. (Post-seating "checks" and adjustments and/or remake appointments are not counted in this proration method.) (Figure 8.5)

FEE PRORATION EXAMPLE

CROWN FEE $650

- LAB FEE $110 (PRE-CLOSING EXPENSE)

NET ADJUSTED FEE = $540

2/3 OF THE FEE TO THE SELLER = $360

1/3 OF THE FEE TO THE PURCHASER = $180

Fig. 8.5

In calculating the fee proration, any lab expense incurred for the procedure is first deducted from the total gross fee before prorating. The lab fee is to be paid by the seller, since this was an expense incurred prior to the closing.

If the seller completes the case while providing post-sale clinical services for the buyer, then the seller shall receive a percentage of the prorated fee. In the previous example, if the seller were being paid a 30% commission to complete the service, then the seller would have received an additional $54 (30% x $180 = $54).

Sometimes the number of cases in progress is minimal. I generally recommend that the buyer waive this fee-proration option in that situation.

Part Six:
Seller and Buyer Warranties and Acknowledgments

- Seller's and Buyer's Financial Data

- All Assets Owned Free and Clear (subject to any Assumptions by Buyer)

- Warranty (Limited) on Major Equipment

- Pending Litigation, Malpractice Suits or Other Pending Claims

- Buyer's Personal Guarantee on Obligations to the Seller

Buyers of dental-practices generally want the sellers to warrant that all the financial data supplied to them regarding the practice is true and accurate (within reason). The same should apply to any personal financial statements provided the seller by the buyer should the seller be financing any part of the sale. It also is common for the seller to warranty the major equipment for some interim period of time such as 30 or 90 days after the sale. This would apply primarily to items that would be expensive to repair or replace, such as X-ray heads, central vacuum, air compressor, etc.

The assets should be owned free and clear at the time of the sale, or any liabilities associated with the assets could be assumed by the buyer as part of the purchase. The seller and buyer should inform each other of any malpractice suits or other practice-related claims or any investigations by state dental boards. Both buyer and seller should warrant that they are licensed to practice dentistry in the particular state. As part of the purchase, the buyer should personally guarantee any and all obligations to the seller.

Miscellaneous Transfer Provisions

Various transfers should occur at closing.

- Utilities and telephone must be transferred to the buyer. This usually is handled immediately upon or following the closing;

- Manufacturer's Warranties and Maintenance Agreements must be transferred to the buyer; and

- Software Licenses (see "Assets Excluded" section in this chapter) must be transferred to the buyer.

Seller's Transition Services

Letters to patients and referral sources should be sent immediately following closing and following the seller's retirement. A newspaper announcement should be made.

It is customary for sellers to assist in the transition of the practice to the buyer. This would include a letter sent to all patients informing them of the transition. Only one letter is required where the seller is exiting the practice soon after the sale. However, if the seller is staying and working with the buyer for some extended period of time after the sale, two letters may be applicable; one letter sent initially introducing the new buyer (often introduced as "joining the practice") and another sent at the time the seller leaves the practice.

The Seller's Employees

Are there any written and/or oral contracts between the seller and existing employees that can't be terminated upon the sale? Can or will the seller make sure that certain key employees stay? Although sellers cannot guarantee that the employees of the practice will stay with the buyer after the sale, it's been my experience that most employees will. There should not be any agreements with existing employees of the practice that cannot be terminated by the buyer.

Retreatment Needs

Occasionally, patients of the seller may need retreatment after the practice is purchased. How this retreatment is to be handled should be defined, such as who will provide it and how it will be paid for. This can become a complex issue after the closing, so it's imperative that it be resolved upfront.

The Seller's Patient Records

The buyer should agree to maintain the patient records of the practice, as well as notify the seller about any request for such records by third parties. The following is a sample clause:

"Both the buyer and seller shall maintain the confidentiality of the patient records of the seller's practice, and shall abide by any state laws regarding their transfer. The buyer shall become the custodian of all the patient records and shall continue to maintain the records unless transferred to another dentist, in which case the buyer shall obligate that dentist with the same duty.

"The parties shall notify each other immediately in the event that any patient (or representative of any patient) has requested his or her records (or copies) for possible malpractice or disciplinary action. The buyer shall maintain all patient records of the practice for a minimum period of 10 years after the closing.

Third Party Requests for Records: The buyer shall make the patient records available to the seller in the event of any malpractice or other third-party action against the seller. All patient records shall be returned to the buyer upon completion of such action, unless otherwise determined by the courts. Copies of these patient records shall be made available to their respective patients provided such patients have complied with all applicable statutory requirements relating to obtaining such copies.

Buyer's Use of the Premises

• Lease (or Sublease or Lease Assignment)

• Purchase of Premises

- Option to Purchase and Right of First Refusal

Any practice-sale transaction should be contingent upon the buyer acquiring a lease, sublease, or the purchase of the premises. This would not be necessary if the buyer is moving the practice to another location, such as in a practice merger.

Insurance Provisions

- Life

- Overhead Disability

- Malpractice

- Premises Contents

The buyer normally is required to maintain life, overhead disability, premises, and malpractice insurance in the event that the seller is financing any part of the sale.

The seller also is required to carry malpractice insurance should the seller be remaining in the practice after the sale providing services for the buyer.

Various Exhibits Attached to the Agreement

- Equipment, Furniture and Fixtures Included in Sale

- Equipment Leases and Conditions

- Equipment, Furniture and Fixtures Excluded from Sale

- Premises Lease or Lease Assignment (where applicable)

- Bill of Sale

The Promissory Note

This promissory note outlines the seller-financed terms and conditions, as well as the buyer's promise to pay. The following is a sample Promissory Note.

Promissory Note

Date: _____, 19____

FOR VALUE RECEIVED, and subject to the terms of the attached practice-sale Agreement, _____ promises to pay to the order of _____, the principal sum of _____ and 00/100 DOLLARS ($_____), together with interest on the unpaid balance as set forth below. All sums are payable by personal delivery or first class mail, postage prepaid, to an address as designated in writing by _____.

1. Interest and Term. The unpaid balance shall bear simple interest from the date hereof at the rate of _____% (__%) per annum, (computed on a 365-day year), and shall be amortized over a period of _____ ( ) months, resulting in equal monthly payments. Any overdue payment of principal or interest, or both, shall bear interest from the due date thereof until paid at the lesser of eighteen percent (18%) per annum or the maximum legal interest rate allowed by law.

2. Payment of Principal and Interest. The aforementioned principal and interest payments shall be due and payable as follows:

Equal installments of principal and interest of _____ and 00/100 DOLLARS ($_____) shall be paid monthly on the same day for _____ months beginning thirty (30) days from the Closing.

The indebtedness evidenced by this Note may be prepaid in whole or in part at any time without penalty. Any payment made under this Note shall be applied first to accrued interest and then to principal. Prepayments shall not postpone the due date or change the amount of any of the monthly installments until the obligation has been paid in full.

3. Collateral. To secure payment of the obligation evidenced by this Note, and of any other liabilities of _____, _____ has granted _____ a security interest in certain collateral as per the attached SECURITY AGREEMENT, between the _____. Concurrently with the execution of this Promissory Note, _____ shall have purchased and shall maintain for so long as any amount remains outstanding under this Note one or more life insurance policies insuring the life of _____ for the declining face amount of this PROMISSORY NOTE, and will assign such policies to the Payee. Both _____ and its insurance company shall provide not less than 30 days' prior written notice to _____ of any and all cancellation, termination, or other modification of the policy and this provision must be inserted into the declaration page or other applicable page

of the insurance policy to assure the insurance company's compliance with notification.

Concurrently with the execution and delivery of this Promissory Note, _____ will purchase and maintain for so long as any amount remains outstanding under this Note an overhead disability insurance policy that will pay for all normal and necessary practice overhead, as well as any outstanding payments due the Payee on this PROMISSO-RY NOTE for a period of twelve (12) months from the date of the first disability payment made to _____.

4. Default. The Payee may accelerate the due date of the entire principal evidenced by this Note upon the earliest to occur of any of the following events:

(A)   The default in making of any payments due under this Note within thirty (30) days of receiving written notice thereof; or

(B)   An Event of Default under the attached SECURITY AGREE-MENT, or in the event of any breach of the Practice-Sale Agreement; or

Upon _____ death, if this Note is not paid in Full within thirty (30) days after the date of death from the proceeds of the life insurance policy required to be maintained by _____ under paragraph 3 above or otherwise;

(C)   Upon _____ disability, unless prior to the end of the Disability Period (hereinafter defined), a replacement dentist or dentists reasonably satisfactory to _____ shall have been designated to operate the Practice on a full-time basis and the Practice shall continue to be so operated until Maker resumes the full-time practice of dentistry. For purposes of this Promissory Note, "disability" shall mean _____ inability for any reason whatsoever to engage in the full time practice of dentistry for 90 consecutive days (the "disability period").

If the due date is accelerated, the remaining unpaid balance, and interest accrued to that date, shall become immediately due and payable.

5. Late Penalty. In the event that any payment due hereunder is received more than ten (10) days after the due date, _____ shall pay a late penalty equal to five percent (5%) of the payment due. However, should _____ be given written notice of a late payment more than five (5) times during the term of this Practice-Assets Sale Agreement, the late penalty shall then apply to all payments received more than three (3) days after the due date.

6. Waiver. _____ and any guarantors and endorsers of this Note severally waive any and all exemption rights they may have

under any Constitution or laws, and all requirements necessary to hold each of them liable as makers, guarantors, or endorsers, and agree to all renewals, extensions, and partial payments before or after maturity.

7. Attorneys' Fees. If this Note is placed in the hands of an attorney for collection, or if it is collected through a bankruptcy court, a probate court, or any other court after an event of default, then _____ shall be entitled to payment from _____ of reasonable attorneys' and paralegals' fees and expenses.

8. Compliance with Usury Laws. All agreements between the _____ and _____ are hereby expressly limited so that in no event shall the amount paid or agreed to be paid to _____ under this Note exceed the maximum amount permissible by law.

9. Choice of Law. This Note shall be governed by, and construed, and enforced in accordance with the laws of the state of _____.

10. Binding Effect. This Note shall be binding upon the _____ and _____ personal representatives and heirs and shall inure to the benefit of the _____, and the representatives, heirs, and assigns of _____.

IN WITNESS WHEREOF, _____ has executed this Promissory Note on _____

The Security Agreement

This part of the agreement deals with various issues that secure the seller's interest in the collateral of the practice in the event that the seller is financing any part of the sale. Some of the issues dealt with in this part of the agreement are the collateral, late payment and default provisions, and lease or premises rights upon default.

Seller's Collateral (Equipment and Other Assets)

When seller-financing is involved, the seller will want to maintain a lien on the assets of the practice until paid off. If there also is a bank involved in any part of the financing, who will be first in line for the lien? The seller should, when possible, maintain a first-priority lien (like a first mortgage) on the assets that were sold and which are now being used as collateral. This often will depend on how much the seller is financing vs. how much any lending institution involved has loaned for the transaction.

Remedies Upon Buyer's Default of Payment

In addition to other remedies the seller should have upon the buyer's default of payment, the seller should first be able to repossess the practice.

Purchaser's Noncompete Agreement

It has become quite common in dental-practice transactions for the buyer to have a similar noncompete agreement with the seller (as does the seller with the buyer) in the event the buyer defaults on payment to the seller. With such a provision in place, the seller has a better chance of reselling the practice in the event the buyer defaults. Without this provision in place, the seller may not be able to resell the practice to another dentist.

Seller's Noncompete Agreement

As part of the practice-sale agreement, the seller is agreeing not to compete with the buyer after the sale. The enforceable time and distance restrictions will differ from area to area. In general, smaller distances are common in dense metropolitan areas, with larger distances the norm in small towns. In rural areas, the distances can be quite large (as much as 50 miles). The time restriction should be based on how long the seller promises not to compete with the buyer after leaving the practice. This is of particular importance in situations where the seller continues to practice with the buyer for years after the sale. I often see time restrictions of three to five years following a sale. (Be sure to consult with your legal advisors.)

Post-Sale Provider Agreement

This is the seller's agreement with the buyer to provide ongoing clinical services after the sale. It is not unusual for the seller to stay with the practice for six months to a year after the sale. Although not necessary, it does make the transaction smooth and helps the buyer with initial production needs. In some sale scenarios, this is essential. In others, it is less critical that the seller stay with the practice after the sale. The post-sale provider agreement should contain some of the following:

- terms of seller's employment;

- seller's compensation;

- scheduling;

- expenses paid by seller;

- malpractice insurance requirement; and

- termination provisions.

Seller's Compensation

The seller usually is compensated based on a percentage of the seller's collections, excluding fees for services generated by the seller's hygienist (exceptions would be doctor's examination fees and supervision fees for root-planing and scaling).

HIV Status

This has become an increasingly important issue in practice transitions. It obviously could be important for a buyer to know the HIV status of the seller and the seller's staff. It also would be important for the seller to know the HIV status of the buyer. Disclosure in this area still looks like treacherous territory, so please contact your attorney for advice.

Associateship to Co-Ownership (Buy-In) Agreements

An associateship to co-ownership (or associateship to buy-in) agreement carries all parties from the initial association to co-ownership and eventually through the retirement of the "senior" co-owner. In the next few pages, you will find some of the most important technicalities frequently considered in final agreements.

There are five basic sections in the associateship to co-ownership agreement. As we end part five, we'll explain the requirements of a preliminary agreement and list necessary items to be included in the initial-agreement stages.

The five parts of the associateship to co-ownership agreement are:

Part One: The Associate Employment Agreement. The initial part of the agreement takes the owner and the associate through the initial employment phase up until the time the associate buys in.

Part Two: Pre-Buy-In Terms and Conditions. This part of the agreement addresses "housekeeping" issues (such as prorated expenses, how to handle accounts receivable, allocating funds between "old" and "new" in the checking accounts, etc.) that must be considered prior to the actual buy-in.

Part Three: The Buy-In Agreement. This checklist covers the specific terms and conditions of the buy-in, which occur at the end of the associate employment phase.

Part Four: The Co-Ownership Agreement (often referred to as the Partnership or Shareholder Agreement). This is the "partnership" agreement between the parties, addressing the day-to-day management considerations, as well as long-term issues surrounding the practice.

Part Five: The Buy-Out Agreement. This section deals with how each co-owner's interest in the practice is sold upon retirement, relocation, death, disability, etc. It also should address how new associates enter the practice and become co-owners in the future.

Part One: The Associate Employment Agreement

Employee or Independent Contractor Status: What is the status of the associate? Employee or Independent Contractor? (We recommend employee status; however, always check with your tax advisors regarding this issue.)

Term of Employment: What is the initial starting date of the associate and projected ending date of the contract? The end date of this agreement should coincide with the date of the anticipated buy-in. The employment agreement automatically extends until the actual date of buy-in.

Associate's Duties and Responsibilities: An official job description listing the associate's required duties is needed. Will the associate's role be to provide strictly clinical services or will there be any management roles or other responsibilities? Documentation should state that the associate must abide by normal ethical standards and is subject to the rules and regulations of local dental regulatory boards.

Services to be Provided: A description of services to be provided by the associate is needed. Will there be any limitations to what services the associate can provide? Review specialty services currently being referred to specialists. Can any of these procedures be delegated to the associate? Will there be a requirement or structure to refer specific cases or treatment to the owner-dentist?

Scheduling: What days and hours will the associate dentist be available to provide patient care? Does the associate have full- or part-time status? Will the associate be allowed to work anywhere other than the dentist-employer's office?

After-Hours Emergency Coverage: Guidelines are needed for associate emergency-call duty. How are after-hours practice emergencies to be covered? Will there be alternating coverage of emergencies between the owner-dentist and the associate dentist? Will the associate dentist handle all emergencies?

Patient Retreatment Provisions: Occasionally, there may be a need to "retreat" a patient. Normally, the associate would handle his or her own retreatment cases. However, should the associate leave the practice, there should be an agreed-upon method for handling such cases. Will there be any reimbursement to the owner-dentist for the cost of retreating any of the associate's patients should the associate leave the practice? (The cost of remakes could be deducted from any accounts receivables remaining or retained earnings of the associate.)

In some situations, any "good faith deposit" being retained by the owner (to be applied toward the buy-in of the owner's practice) could be used to pay the owner for future retreatment needs of the associate's patients in the event of the associate's exit.

Patient Records: Typically, patient records always are the property of the owner. However, the associate may take copies of these records when mutually agreed-upon by both parties. In some instances, an agreement allowing the buy-out of an associate's noncompete agreement will allow for the reproduction of patient records by the associate.

Associate Compensation: The terms and conditions of the associate's compensation need to be addressed. Percentage of collections? Salary, draw or combination? Most associates receive compensation based on a percentage of their collected production, with 30% as an average rate of compensation seen across the country. Occasionally, a salary is established as a "draw" against the associate's collected percentage. Lab and credit card fees occasionally are deducted "off the top" of the associate's collected production before multiplying by the established percentage. When lab fees are first deducted, the percentage used often is 5% higher. (See Chapter 4, "Creating 'Win-Win' Associateship to Co-Ownership Arrangements.")

Associate Benefits: Typically, any benefits received by associates who are paid a percentage of their collections become part of the overall percentage of compensation (other than the employer's portion of the associate's FICA). For example, the owner may choose to pay associate benefits such as malpractice insurance, society dues, publications, continuing education, and so forth, deducting these expenses from pre-tax earnings of the associate.

Associate's Fees: Fees charged by the associate for services are established by the owner-dentist. All collected funds for the associate's productivity are deposited into the practice bank account in the owner's name. We discourage arrangements where associates directly collect their own fees received for services and pay the owner a percentage. This can create a "separate-practice" mentality in the mind of the associate and the patients, potentially hurting the chances of a future buy-in.

Vacation, Continuing Education, Holidays, and Sickness: A maximum number of days off per year (collectively) should be agreed upon for all of the above.

Working Facilities and Expenses: The owner-dentist normally assumes all facility, lab, supply, and staff costs, with the exception of any laboratory expenses that may have been factored into associate compensation.

Licensure: Proof of licensure must be presented to the owner-dentist and a copy given at each renewal. The associate is required to notify the owner-dentist immediately of any loss-of-license notification and/or any disciplinary actions.

Insurance Provisions: Liability (or malpractice) insurance should be a requirement in all associate agreements. The associate must provide proof of such insurance to the owner on a periodic basis. Associates customarily pay for their own liability insurance unless it's made part of the compensation "package" (commonly seen in specialty practices). Other insurance, such as health, life, and disability insurance, ordinarily are paid by the associate or can be paid by the owner and deducted pretax.

Termination of Agreement: Thirty to 90 days' written notice is required for terminating the agreement by either party. Exceptions are death, prolonged disability, loss of license, grossly improper conduct, or criminal acts.

Noncompete Agreements (Restrictive Covenants): These outlines the terms and conditions under which the associate dentist agrees not to compete with the owner in the practice of dentistry. The restricted covenant is constructed to prevent the associate from practicing within a certain number of miles from the owner's practice (or other geographic area) for a certain number of years after leaving the practice. The distance varies, based on the geographic area you're dealing with (i.e., a metropolitan area vs. a small or rural town). In the event that both parties decide to change this agreement, noncompete buy-out provisions can be considered. Buy-out provisions allow the associate to pay a specific sum of money to "buy-out" the non-compete agreement. Laws regarding non-compete agreements differ from state to state, so always consult a competent legal advisor for assistance in this area.

Non-Solicitation Agreement: This is a common requirement, in which the associate agrees not to solicit patients or staff upon leaving the practice. The non-solicitation clause prevents the associate from enticing patients and staff to an office just outside the non-compete area. Staff- and patient-loss prevention is very disruptive and expensive for the owner-dentist.

Dispute Resolution—Mediation, Arbitration, and Litigation: Consider mediation or arbitration clauses for resolving major disputes. The American Arbitration Association publishes guidelines and contract language for this clause. An example of this commonly used clause is this:

"Disputes, Mediation and Arbitration: It is the intention of both parties that no dispute under this Agreement shall be the subject of any court action or litigation in the court system. The parties recognize that the processes of mediation and arbitration are proper to resolve issues between the parties.

"If any party wishes to resolve an issue under or relating to this Practice-Assets Sale Agreement, then such party must give notice of a request for mediation to the other party, which notice shall set forth the names of not less than four court-approved mediators from the lists available from the local circuit court. The party receiving such notice shall agree upon one or more of such mediators within seven days of receipt of such notice and a mediation will be scheduled as soon as feasible between the parties and their respective advisors. The parties and their advisors will cooperate fully with respect to sharing of information and attendance at meetings in order to seek resolution. The parties will share mediation expenses, with the party requesting mediation to pay one-half of such expenses of the mediator fees and the other party to pay the other one-half of such expenses. However, if the mediator should find the charge of the complaining party to be groundless, the mediator may direct that the complaining party shall pay all expenses.

"If resolution of the matters between the parties cannot be resolved in mediation within 20 days of the selection of a mediator by the party receiving such notice, then the matter shall be presented to formal arbitration pursuant to the rules of the American Arbitration Association with a single arbitrator to be retained on behalf of the parties by the mediator that has been working with the parties. Arbitration shall take place as soon as possible and the decision of the arbitrator shall be binding upon the parties for all purposes. Any party in violation of this Agreement shall pay all reasonable fees and costs, including attorneys' fees, incurred by the other party relating to such violation, and all other fees and costs shall be paid as agreed in mediation or as determined appropriate in the arbitration proceeding.

"It is the intention of the parties that this Agreement shall be construed and interpreted in a fair and equitable manner based upon the facts and circumstances of the parties, taking into account the present intention of the parties to have a fair and equitable agreement under the terms and conditions set forth herein.

Part Two: Prebuy-In Terms and Conditions Agreement Checklist

Certain housekeeping and bookkeeping issues arise just prior to the buy-in. Here are some of the most important terms and conditions to consider:

Assets Included/Excluded from the Buy-In: A list of these assets should be attached to the agreement. They usually consist of the cash assets of the practice, including the owner's accounts receivable (unless they were included in the purchase price), as well as any personal assets in the practice belonging to the owner which should be excluded.

Were there any assets added to the practice after the associate started, and will the value of the practice be increased accordingly?

Pro-Ration of Pre- and Postbuy-In Expenses: Practice expenses should be prorated between the old and the new. In essence, a new practice entity is formed upon the buy-in. Rent, utilities, telephone, and insurance represent some examples of these expenses.

Accounts Receivable: Again, old and new accounts receivable should be identified. Accounts receivable obtained prior to the buy-in belong to the owner, subject to any amounts owed the associate for prebuy-in services provided. Options for handling these accounts are covered in the Practice-Sale Agreement section of this chapter.

New Bank Account Provisions: Set up a new bank account upon the buy-in. The previous account can be used as a "clearing account" for paying prior accounts payable and depositing prebuy-in receivables (provided the accounts receivable was not part of the sale).

Part Three: The Buy-In Agreement

Buy In Date or Production Target: A specific date (or at least a production target) should be set upon which the buy-in should occur.

Buy-In Price and Terms: This section of the agreement would include the total buy-in price, the down payment, and the number of months the balance is paid over. Typically, a buy-in is seller-financed over a five- to seven-year period, unless the owner is paid cash.

Will Stock or Assets Be Purchased? If stock is being purchased, how much of the total price will be allocated for this stock? (Stock is not normally a deductible expense for the buyer.)

If assets are to be purchased, how will the total price be allocated (broken down)? This is covered in the Practice-Sale Agreement section of this chapter.

Buy-in Payments: Amortized Payment Method or Salary Reduction Method? As discussed in Chapter 4, "Creating 'Win-Win' Associateship to Co-Ownership Arrangements," there are two commonly used ways that buy-in payments are usually made to the owner (when financed by the owner): (1) through a salary-reduction method, in which the associate's pre-tax salary is reduced by the amount of the buy-in payment; or (2) by the associate paying the owner in normal amortized payments of principal and interest, after which the associate depreciates the assets being purchased over a prescribed schedule, as dictated by the Internal Revenue Service.

Part Four: Co-Ownership Agreement Checklist
This often is referred to as the Partnership or Shareholder Agreement Checklist.

Name of Practice Entity: Example: Smith and Jones, DDS, P.A.

Admission of New Associates and Co-Owners: How are new partners admitted and how often?

Ownership Interest and Partnership Compensation: Will there be equal ownership among the partners? Will compensation be based on: ownership, production, or both? I suggest that co-owners be compensated based on a combination of productivity and ownership. (See Chapter 4, "Creating 'Win-Win' Associateship to Co-Ownership Arrangements.") In this way, both are recognized and rewarded, with the "lion's share" of the net income always going to the highest producer.

Patients and Scheduling: How and on what days are the co-owners scheduled to see patients?

Required Production Levels: Minimal production levels can be required to maintain co-ownership status if the co-owners are receiving some income based on ownership. Co-owners consistently producing below this required amount may be forced to sell their interest in the practice (at the option of the remaining co-owners).

Insurance Provisions: Liability, health, disability, and life.

Buy-Out Policies (Key Man Insurance): The co-owners should agree to acquire and maintain various insurance policies during (and sometimes after) the term of their relationship. Health insurance is commonly provided to the co-owners, though it's not normally a requirement of the practice to do so. Liability insurance is an obvious policy that should be carried by both co-owners. (Believe it or not, I've seen situations in which one co-owner was not carrying a malpractice policy and the other co-owner was unaware of this! This is why it needs to be a part of your agreement.)

Disability and life policies are important not only for the welfare of the individuals involved (and the families), but are instrumental in buying out the interest of any deceased or disabled co-owner.

Sale by a Partner Due to Death, Disability, or Retirement/Relocation: This section of the agreement deals with how a co-owner's interest is purchased upon his/her death or disability. Death and disability buy-outs customarily are found in co-ownership agreements, but more often than not, voluntary retirement buy-out provisions are not. There should be clear language regarding retirement buy-outs (as described in the next section). It's obviously not a case of *if* this event will occur but *when*. Disputes often arise in these areas, as described in the section on practice-value destroyers in Chapter 7.

Part Five: The Buy-Out Agreement

Buy-Out Provisions—Option vs. Obligation: It's wise to obligate all "junior" co-owners to buy out all "senior" co-owners. Otherwise, it may be difficult to sell a co-owner's share to an outside party, making the exiting "co-owner's" practice potentially unmarketable. Equitable approaches to these situations can be established, including an agreement by all co-owners to bring in new partners at various intervals to help buy out any exiting co-owners.

Buy-Out Price Determination: Pre-agreed-upon price tied into a percentage increase each year? Appraised at the time of the buy-out? An agreed-upon price is determined once each year to be used during that year?

Future Practice-Appraisal Guidelines: Who is to appraise the practice? Will there be a predesignated appraiser chosen? Will one be chosen at the time of the appraisal? Can just anyone appraise the practice, or should it be someone who is considered an authority and who actively appraises and sells dental-practices?

One to three appraisals by dental-practice appraisers can be used, with the two closest ones averaged when multiple appraisals are used. This is the best way to determine true market value at the time. The following is some sample language commonly used in agreements:

"The value of the practice will be determined in the following manner: The parties will each hire and pay for a dental-practice appraiser to determine the value. If this value is not accepted by either party, then the rejecting party shall then hire and pay for a second dental-practice appraiser to determine the value and the two appraisals shall be averaged. If this value is not accepted by either party, then the rejecting party shall then hire and pay for a third dental-practice appraiser to determine the value, averaging the two closest appraisals. If no two appraisals can be deemed the closest, then the three appraisals shall be averaged and that figure shall be used."

Earned Equity Provisions: How will the increase in practice value (that often occurs after associates join practices) be treated? Who will this equity belong to? The associate? The owner? A combination of the two?

How this earned equity is treated should be agreed upon in advance of any associate relationship. (See Chapter 4, "Creating 'Win-Win' Associateship to Co-Ownership Arrangements.")

Buy-Out Terms: Once the buy-out price has been determined, will the price be paid in cash or will terms be offered to the remaining co-owners?

Dissolution Provisions: Equitable methods of dissolving the co-ownership arrangement should be established. This avoids litigation and helps the parties to separate in an equitable, professional manner.

Leasehold Interest Upon Dissolution: Who gets to stay in the practice facility (vs. who has to leave) if the partnership splits up? Who gets to keep the equipment?

Generally, the first option to stay would be with the original founder of the practice (if still a practicing co-owner). Otherwise, this interest would pass in succession.

Noncompete Provisions Upon Dissolution: Noncompete provisions may be needed upon dissolution if one co-owner's interest was sold to another.

Premises Purchase Provisions: First Right of Refusal and Option to Purchase: Should any co-owner(s) own the premises, real estate, fair-market lease guidelines should be established so that the rent will represent the "norm" for a given area. It is normal to offer First Right of Refusal and Option to Purchase for the purchase of the real estate to junior co-owners at some point.

In addition, any equipment being leased to the practice by any co-owner also should be subject to fair-market value. I recommend that any equipment be sold to the practice upon the buy-in to minimize any problems surrounding this area.

Conclusion

Comprehensive agreements for sale or buy-in transitions easily can be 40-60 pages in length. Make sure the advisor you use for this project has had experience in this area, specifically in *dental*-practice transitions.

The best framework to construct agreements for the transition of a dental-practice is one of a "win-win" strategy. This should be a worthy goal for all dentists and easily achievable when working with experienced and fair-minded advisors. Be sure not to enter into the agreement process without this type of support.

It is completely counter-productive to enter the agreement arena from an adversarial posture. Do not allow your advisors to position themselves for any type of "arm-wrestling match." Haggling over practice transition issues that probably have been incorporated already into an equitable format somewhere can be a waste of time and money. Why reinvent the wheel?

Employ advisors and select them carefully. (See Chapter 9, "How To Best Utilize Your Financial, Legal, and Business Advisors.") Avoid advisors who see themselves as advocates or agents for "one party vs. the other." Agreements that take advantage of the other party can start a chain reaction that can cost you thousands of dollars, as well as the loss of a potentially good transition relationship in the process.

The use of an experienced and knowledgeable third party, acting as an intermediary between the parties, is always a better approach—at least in the beginning, planning stages. With this approach, the needs of both parties can be balanced, leading to an equitable end result. As always, prior to finalizing your agreements, seek the sound legal advice and guidance of a professional attorney who is well versed in the area of practice transition.

As you begin the process of seeking advisors to guide you, it will be extremely important to do your homework. Ask your colleagues for recommendations of professionals you can trust. Check the references of the advisors you choose. As we move to the next chapter, you'll learn how to establish an open relationship with the people who guide you and know how to get the most for the advice you pay for.

9

Get What You Pay For: How to Best Utilize Your Financial, Legal and Business Advisors

Steve was a general dentist practicing in a small town community of about 500,000 people. Having suffered a brain injury during the early years of practice, he had lost the ability to understand and calculate numbers. Mary, a loyal and devoted employee, assumed the role of Steve's business manager after the accident. For years, Steve relied on Mary to manage the business, make all the financial decisions, and take care of his investments.

Over the course of his dental career, Steve built a strong foundation for a very successful practice. With Mary by his side, the practice prospered financially. However, after 18 years of private practice, the overall financial picture of the business began to change. At first, this was difficult for Steve to understand, especially since he seemed to be working harder than ever before. Mary monitored the numbers very closely. She showed him how the numbers were dropping and explained that there just wasn't a lot of extra cash flow in the business. For this reason, she cautioned him about any unnecessary spending and watched the budgeted expenses very closely.

During this time, Steve maintained a very close working relationship with his accountant, Bill. Bill worked for a small accounting firm in town and was well-liked by most people. His laid-back style and low-key personality made it easy for most clients to work with him. Steve liked the idea that his accountant was a "down-to-earth" kind of guy. Steve always understood when his monthly reports ran two to three months behind. After all, Bill's fees were very reasonable and who could beat the price he was paying for accounting and tax preparation?

On occasion, Steve voiced his concerns to Bill about his steadily increasing practice-overhead percentage. Over the last four years, overhead went from 62% to more than 75% and none of this overhead included any creative and elective expenses, such as those described in Chapter 7, "Determining the Value of Your Practice." Although Bill was mildly perplexed with the drop in productivity and increased overhead, he was not overly concerned. Whenever Steve had questions about his numbers, Bill simply referred him to Mary, who seemed to be doing a good job.

While attending a national dental meeting, Steve had dinner with a former classmate. Steve's friend encouraged him to join him in taking a course on managing profitability being offered by a practice-management firm. One criteria of the course outline was for each owner to bring a copy of his or her most recent Year-End Profit and Loss Statement to the meeting for evaluation.

Upon attending the course, Steve was assigned a consultant support assistant. With the help of his support assistant, Steve discovered that more than $300,000 was somehow "missing." Realizing that Steve's monthly production was only running about $35,000 per month, the consultant became extremely concerned. As he questioned Steve about the overall picture of the practice, it became very clear that Steve needed help quickly.

Steve decided to employ the consultant to perform an initial evaluation of the practice. A few weeks later, the consultant arrived at the airport and was greeted by a grim-faced Steve. He informed him that Mary had resigned the day before. After more than 20 years of service, she had left with little warning or explanation. He was concerned that perhaps Mary had become intimidated with the idea of a "consultant" coming in to the office and hoped that the consultant might be able to talk Mary into coming back.

As you may have guessed, the consultant discovered that Mary, in fact, had embezzled in excess of $850,000 from the practice over the past four years. This is, unfortunately, not uncommon to hear about, particularly since dentists are "slow" about hiring outside advisors to look over their practices. How and why does this happen?

Perhaps part of the answer lies with the fact that, as dentists, our life theme has been to take care of others. Traditionally, our focus has been to always put the patient first. As a result, we dentists often have been labeled as "poor businessmen." Even today, the stigma associated with the "Dr." title carries with it the same flavor. It is no secret that business courses were not a high priority for most dentists, and certainly were not taught much in the area of practice establishment, practice management, or practice transition. For this reason, we have frequently relied on the support of other business professionals to guide us through the trenches.

The advisors we have chosen over the years were often chosen the same way patients choose their dentist—often based solely on whether or not they liked them as opposed to their skill level and experience. (How many of you know a very nice dentist in your community who is not very competent clinically?) The same applies to all professionals, and there are many out there acting as practice-transition advisors who know less about the process than the dentists themselves do. (I not only see this every day, but I experienced it in the transitioning of my own practice.)

Many dentists are not sure whether or not they need experienced advisors for their practice. This is especially true in the area of practice transition. In fact, many transition advisors I network with tell me they spend much of their time undoing the mistakes of well-meaning dentists who botched the transition of their practice. Dentists also are very independent by nature, which is good in many situations. However, an independent attitude can sometimes evolve into an "I-can-do-it-all-myself" mentality in areas where dentists have had little or no experience. This can lead to poor or disastrous results.

At least once a month, I speak with a dentist who has been attempting for some time to sell his own practice. After having little success on his own, he turns the job over to his CPA or better yet, office manager. (After all, who knows more about the practice than they do?) Ads were placed in various journals and the responses were handled accordingly. Initially, there seemed to be a fair number of interested parties calling, but with little or no results. Office managers, CPAs, and financial planners are excellent individuals for purchasers to talk to at some point regarding the "inner workings" of the practice, but they generally know nothing about the art and science of selling a dental practice. It's a unique entity—and I have a great deal of respect for them—that helps dentists with this project!

An interesting article appeared in the April 1997 issue of *Dental Economics* magazine. It was written by Dr. Robert E. Hamric, a well-known dentist and practice management consultant located in Birmingham, Alabama. In his article, "Funding Your Future," Hamric discussed how a dentist could fund his pension plan with the dollars received from the early sale of his or her dental practice. Hamric also stressed the importance of utilizing transition specialists in the planning and implementation of any type of practice transition. Hamric cautioned dentists against relying solely on an attorney or accountant, pointing out that many of these advisors can actually "mess up a viable deal." He blames this on their lack of experience or a tendency to battle over every single issue that must be dealt with in the transition (and there are dozens of them).

I see this situation every day. Advisors get "hung up" on worthless minutia (at $200 per hour), while totally losing sight of the fact that their clients came to them in the first place to focus on the "big picture" and to put together a fair deal with which everyone can be happy.

Here are some questions you should ask yourself when considering the use of advisors in planning the transition of your practice:

Questions To Ask Yourself

"What different types of advisors will I need in planning and implementing the transition of my practice?"

"How will I know if my existing advisors (or the advisors I hire in the future) are experienced enough in the area of dental-practice transition?"

"How many dentists have these advisors actually worked for?" (Note: All transitions are not equal, and medical-practice transitions are quite different than dental).

"How many successful transitions have the advisors actually implemented (from start to finish)?" An even more direct question to ask would be, "How many dental practices have they personally appraised and sold in the last two years, and would they be willing to provide you with a list of their clients to contact?"

After asking your advisors these questions, another more general question surfaces that you should ask yourself.

"What information is available to read to verify if the advice I'm receiving is current, equitable, and in the best overall interest of my practice transition?"

In my experience, I have found it important to utilize three different types of advisors in the transition process—first, a transition specialist; second, an accountant; and third, an attorney. This is also the order in which I recommend you use these consultants. (Figure 9.1)

Beginning the Process: The Transition Specialist

Transition specialists are a new breed of consultant. They have emerged over the last 20 years, and their backgrounds are interestingly varied. Some have practice-management backgrounds, while some come from the legal and accounting fields. There are even those who were practicing dentists at one time and experienced the intricacies and challenges of practice ownership and transition first-hand.

By beginning with the consulting services a transition specialist can provide, all available transition options can be explored before proceeding in any particular direction. (Until you are absolutely certain of your direction and timing, all possible options should be explored first.) This would include options such as selling part or all of your practice, merging, bringing in an associate, as well as putting any transition plans "on hold" for a specified period of time. Not all dentists have the same implementation time frame. For example, I have roughly an equal number of dentist-clients on the back, middle, and front burners as it

THE TRANSITION PROCESS ADVISORS TO USE
• **TRANSITION SPECIALIST**
• **ACCOUNTANT**
• **ATTORNEY**

Fig. 9.1

relates to the timing of their particular transition options. These various transition options are initially described in Chapter 2, "Options for Practice Transition," and are further expanded in other chapters throughout this book.

There are several nationally recognized transition specialists that can help dentists with their transitions, and they are as close as your telephone and fax. (This arrangement works well in our "practice" also, as most of our advisors are long-distance, as well.) Those requiring a transition consultant in their area should check with local dentists to find out who they trust for advice and help in the area of practice transition. It's wise to talk to dentists who were on both sides of the transition fence (i.e., associates as well as owners, buyers as well as sellers) to see how they felt about the individual you are considering as an advisor. (Example: As an owner-dentist, it will do you little good to choose a consultant who, for whatever reason, buyers or associates don't trust.)

Those transition specialists whose primary income is derived from practice brokering—putting together buyers and sellers and "closing the deal"—might appear to be biased in what they recommend a dentist should do at a given point in time. This is often the way stockbrokers and financial planners are viewed—they only make money when they get their client to buy or sell something *now*.

Commissioned practice brokers are sometimes faced with this credibility problem. If they're compensated based on a percentage of the selling price of the practice they sell, can they actually provide an unbiased opinion as to when the seller should sell, as well as an unbiased valuation of the practice? Can they really look out for the best interests of the buyer, too? And what about companies that charge both the buyer and seller? Where do they stand?

Some practice brokers represent the seller only, unless the buyer (i.e., a buyer's broker) hired them. In some states (such as Florida), practice brokers must be licensed. Other states require no such licensing. I don't necessarily feel that licensure is necessary. What is important is the experience, honesty, competency, and integrity of the transition specialist you've chosen, regardless of how or who pays the consultant.

(Florida has recently created a third type of relationship among the buyer, seller, and broker—*a transaction broker*. Here, the broker doesn't solely represent buyer or seller, but works for the overall good of the transaction, promising fairness, competency, and honesty to both parties involved in the transaction.)

Regardless of licensure and/or specific representation, I prefer the transition specialist play the role of an intermediary, with the goal of constructing a fair and equitable end result for all dentists involved in the transition. I find this environment greatly enhances not only the success of the transition, but increases the likelihood that both parties feel good about the end result.

Accountants

The next advisor to involve in your transition is your accountant. One of his or her primary interests in a practice transition is to minimize the overall financial risk, as well as the tax impact of any transition-transaction that his or her client might undertake. (Note: Though risks involved certainly can be minimized, they rarely can be eliminated totally, as there are few worthwhile projects in life that come without risk.)

When dealing with your accountant, do not let them destroy a perfectly good transition opportunity for you while trying to eliminate all risk. (Note: Most of the risk involved surrounds seller financing, which can be eliminated by receiving cash for the sale of the practice.)

If your accountant also is your financial planner, then his or her role also will be important as it relates to the timing of your practice transition. As an example, timing the outright sale of your practice would have a greater financial impact than, say, an associateship leading to co-ownership transition.

I have seen situations in which a dentist desiring to sell his practice outright was advised by his financial advisor not to do so. The seller-dentist was financially "set" and had more than adequate funds on which to retire. In addition, health concerns were forcing him or her to begin focusing on quality-of-life issues as opposed to just continuing to "do dentistry." In discussions with the advisors, it became apparent that an advisor's "wounded ego" was the real culprit, because the advisor had not been in total control of the transition process from the very beginning. Don't let this happen to you!

In a practice transition involving the sale of part or all of the practice, each side's accountant takes a different position regarding tax issues. It's common for these positions to be extreme. Why not start from the beginning with an equitable middle-ground format both parties can live with and feel is fair? It's certainly achievable and can prevent a lot of stress and anxiety. It can take months of agonizing negotiations and thousands of dollars in an accountant's fees if you approach these transition issues from an adversarial posture.

Lawyers

The next advisor in line should be your lawyer. I don't find them very useful in the early planning stages and they often put a damper on the relationship we're trying to build between the parties as the process unfolds (no offense intended to any lawyers reading this book!). One lawyer confided to me that he "didn't really understand how to marry individuals— only divorce them!"

Nonetheless, when you and the buyer are presented with final agreements to review, you will both sleep better knowing that each of your lawyers has reviewed them. My suggestion is that you locate a lawyer who has no objection to a "fair deal" as an end result.

Here's an important question to ask: Is your lawyer knowledgeable in the area of practice transition, and will he or she be able to stay focused on the "big picture?" In my 16 years' experience, I have found only four to five lawyers nationally that truly understand the transition process and what it really takes to make it work. Most legal advisors feel their job is to protect their client at all costs. Seek out those who feel it's all right for the other side to also be protected (i.e., those who believe protection and security actually can be balanced between the two parties).

The Team Approach

Most reputable transition specialists are happy to work with your accountant and attorney, and hopefully vice versa. When presenting the idea of a "team approach" to your accountant and attorney, see how each reacts. See if they are interested and open to such an approach or if they seem aggravated or deflated at the mere suggestion. I see more of the latter than the former, and I have found a direct proportion between the experience level of the advisor and his or her willingness to work with others (i.e., the greater the experience, the greater their comfort level in working with others).

Willing advisors do exist out there—you just need to look for them. (Figure 9-2, page 239)

Additional Advisors To Consider

Financial Planners. Financial planners and other similar advisors also like to give input on their client's practice transition. They often render opinions as to what they think the value of their client's practice is, as well as the terms and conditions under which the practice should be sold. The key here is the same—seek out advisors who have real knowledge of the marketplace and real experience in dealing with practice

YOUR ADVISORS
QUALITIES TO LOOK FOR

- *ACTUAL* EXPERIENCE IN DENTAL-PRACTICE TRANSITIONS

- UNDERSTANDS THE NEEDS OF BOTH PARTIES

- A WIN-WIN "BIG PICTURE" OUTLOOK

- OPEN TO A TEAM APPROACH

Fig. 9.2

transitions. Otherwise, you could lose out on potentially good transition candidates because your practice wasn't realistically priced or negotiated by someone with real experience.

Specialized Lending Institutions. Here's a source of advice that many dentists don't think about: Getting advice from individuals at lending institutions that deal with financing dental-practice transactions on a daily basis. Since these institutions are interested in financing only those practice transactions that make economic sense, they often have real market knowledge about how to judge whether a particular practice opportunity is viable or not.

Some of the newly-emerged lending institutions (like the Matsco Companies) will loan up to 100% of the value of the practice in cash (including the goodwill). They also can provide the funds within days of your providing them with requested information. This is of great benefit to both parties, but is especially helpful to the buyer. Nothing can be more frustrating to a buyer than losing thousands of dollars in "lost practice income" while waiting for the loan to be approved, the funds to be distributed to the escrow accounts of the bank lawyers, and the closing date to be agreed upon and set. Also, many of these new lenders charge no points, closing costs, or loan origination fees (most banks do). I recently had a client charged more than $14,000 in loan-origination fees, closing costs, and bank's attorney's fees on a $500,000 loan. Let me assure you that the great interest rate he thought he got didn't look so great after he got hit with all the hidden charges.

I highly recommend checking out these new lending institutions as sources for practice-purchase financing. They know the process, they service their loans quickly, and they understand the needs of dentists.

What about traditional bankers? As discussed earlier, there were few (if any) lending institutions in the past that would loan any substantial amount of money for the purchase or buy-in of a dental practice.

Even those that did would loan little over the salvage value of the used equipment, which often represents 20% (or less) of the total purchase price. In addition, they *often* require the seller (who's financing 80% of the sale) to subordinate his or her interest in the collateral (the hard assets being sold) by taking a security position second to the bank. In this case, the bank is loaning the smallest portion of the purchase price, but it still wants to be first in line in the event of a problem. On top of that, the spouse and other family members' co-signatures often are required. Banks frequently have even "funnier" requests.

I had a banker tell me he would be happy to loan my dentist-client $150,000 (at 10% interest) to purchase a practice if he or his parents would "just put a $150,000 CD in his or her bank as collateral." (The bank would, of course, pay a top rate of 5.5% interest on the CD. "Gee, thanks Mr. Banker," I thought.) I later replied, "If my client had access to $150,000 through himself or his parents, why would we be talking to you?" I remain constantly amazed at the intellect of some bankers.

In summary, in the comprehensive planning of your practice transition, the best results occur when all advisors involved welcome the use of a knowledgeable transition specialist acting as a third-party intermediary. (Be wary of advisors who show an unwelcome attitude toward this. They are often protecting their "turf," rather than truly taking care of their clients' best interest) These specialists can greatly enhance the overall success of the transition at all stages, from initial planning to practice valuation, to the negotiation phase, to implementation of final agreements. Take advantage of this new breed of available consultants!

10

PURCHASING OR BUYING-IN TO A PRACTICE: ADVICE FOR EARLY-CAREER DENTISTS

Remember your first experience riding a bike, learning to swim or snow skiing? How about that first injection you gave in dental school (or the one you *received* from your classmate knowing it was the first one he or she ever gave?) For most of us, we conquered these events with caution. In most cases, after careful instruction, we were ready to dive in. Taking the "plunge" is what early-career practice is all about. From day one in dental school to the long-anticipated graduation date, there are many first-time experiences to help prepare us for the initial plunge into practicing dentistry. Collectively, those experiences may still not provide all the necessary tools required to walk into private practice.

For the early-career dentist facing the challenges of a first-time practice, there are many options to consider. From the rapidly growing dental clinic to the well-established fee-for-service practice, from the military-perspective option to considering starting from "scratch," opportunities continue to exist for the early-career dentist. The process by which decisions are made in early career may be the most important step to beginning the practice life cycle.

The Decision-Making Process

The decisions made in early career may very well control your destiny for the future. How you feel, what you decide to do, and ultimately what you will contribute all help create what you will become.

For the early-career dentist, it's not about what's happening right now or what happened in dental school that determines success—it's about the choices you make now and how you make them. Your decision about which practice options to consider, what things are important to you, and what you're going to do about them will best determine your ultimate destiny.

Too often, we see dentists in early career make unconscious decisions about the initial approach to practicing dentistry. Many early-career dentists facing the challenges of significant student loans, family obligations, and survival jump into early career without ever deciding where they want to end up. In a short period of time, they get caught up in current events. Current events, current fears and current challenges all contribute to unconscious decisions about the future. For many, these events overshadow the ability to stop and decide which direction is actually right for the future. Easily caught up in the environment instead of making choices directed by personal values, the early-career dentist often finds it difficult to make conscious decisions.

How can you turn things around on the front end? Either make a decision to take the plunge head-first and see what happens—or decide to plan ahead. Set a course for where you really want to go and have a plan for making quality decisions along the way. Base your decisions on core beliefs. By making decisions based on core beliefs, you'll be able to adapt better to the ever-changing dental marketplace.

Early-career dentists should pay close attention to one very important element in the process—the ability to overcome the fear of making the *wrong* decision. There is no doubt that during the course of your practice life cycle, you certainly will make wrong decisions. Let's face it, we *all* screw up. But many transition options that exist today for early-career dentists are almost a "guarantee" of success! And let's face it—no matter what decisions you make, your economic situation will inevitably improve when compared with the way it was in dental school! Whatever decisions you make, always allow yourself to be flexible. Look at the consequences of your choices and learn from them. Use your lessons as tools to make better decisions in the future.

Dentists at all career levels need the support and advice of strong leaders. Especially in early career, it is invaluable to find a role model in the process—someone that's taken the journey before you and has a good map for you to follow. Talk to others who have recently purchased or bought into a practice—they will have a wealth of information to pass on to you. Seek the advice of those who have been the most successful, those with the most financial insight and strong people skills. These mentors can save you years of pain and help lighten the load along the way.

My map for early-career dentists includes many of the same overall guidelines as those found in Chapter 6, "New Practice Establishment," Chapter 4, "Creating 'Win-Win" Associateship to Co-Ownership Arrangements," and Chapter 3, "Successful Sales Strategies." The buy-in or purchase of an established practice can be one of the most important decisions you will make in your entire career. You will be glad to know that the track record for either of these options is excellent, since the majority of dentists who purchase or buy into established practices are economically far ahead of those who go into associateships or set up practices from scratch.

With that in mind, the following checklist of things to consider should help you with the decision-making process leading to the successful purchase or buy-in process.

Practice Location

Where do you want to live? Do you enjoy city life or rural, big city or small town, suburban or downtown? What's the education system like for your children, are major airports nearby, and are there sports teams? It's also very important to consider your *personal* long-term wants and desires at this time. I deal with many dentists each year who, after many years in practice, have decided to sell their practices and move to the area that they *always* wanted to be, but for some reason were not. Because they failed to address their personal needs when they first started practice, they are now faced with the task of uprooting. Location, then, is definitely an important consideration when examining your *personal* needs.

Location also is considered when determining what type of dentistry you'd like to do. If one prefers an L.D. Pankey or Pete Dawson style of comprehensive dentistry, then a rural practice may not be in your best interest. On the other hand, some very large and profitable practices are found in rural settings just because there isn't a dentist on every corner. Do you want a cash, insurance, PPO, HMO, or clinic-type practice? Where are these different types of practices to be found? (Note: Although nothing prevents you from providing comprehensive dentistry to patients in rural and small towns or blue-collar locations, it definitely will be more challenging to *sell* this type of dentistry in most areas like this as opposed to others). Location, then, is definitely an important consideration when examining your *business* needs.

Practice Size: Physical Size and Productivity

In looking at practice size, there are two factors to keep in mind—the physical size of the office *and* the production history.

The physical size of the office is certainly one of the first things to consider in the purchase or buy-in of a practice. Determine whether the current, as well as potential, production can be adequately handled in the current space, and if the space will accommodate you as an associate in a buy-in arrangement. If not, could the office space be laid out differently or possibly expanded? If there are potential opportunities to *grow* the practice by merging with other dentists in the area who may be selling in the future, think about whether the facility could accommodate such a merger.

The production history (*and* potential) of the practice also is important to consider. Ultimately, the size practice you purchase or buy into will probably be dictated by your prior practice experience and your overall comfort level with the current practice-production numbers. It also may depend upon whether the selling dentist (if you're purchasing) will be providing dental services for the practice during the transition and for how long a period of time following the purchase date. If the seller *is* staying and providing services for a year or more *following* the sale, the size practice that you purchase could be *larger* than you would have normally considered purchasing. If the transition of the seller has been properly planned and mutually agreed upon, you can gradually phase *in* to increased production (as your clinical speed improves) as the seller phases out of the practice.

As a potential purchaser, here are some general questions you might ask yourself:

- Do you prefer to purchase a large practice grossing $500,000 or more *or* would you prefer a smaller practice, say in the $200,000 to $400,000 range?

- Are you experienced enough or will the seller be able to properly assist you if you were to purchase a large practice?

- Do you prefer a practice with limited staff or a larger practice with more than one hygienist, two or more assistants, and multiple front office staff?

- How many treatment rooms does the practice have?

- Can you expand if you needed? (Buyers occasionally think three treatment rooms will be enough, not realizing they may quickly be using those rooms themselves and, thus, not having space for a hygiene room.)

- Do you want to own your own building or do you prefer to rent? What advantages or disadvantages is there to each approach?

- Will you be personally happier and/or better off financially purchasing a practice vs. buying in to a co-ownership arrangement?

Again, these are just a few of the many decisions that must be made before purchasing or buying into a practice.

Price, Terms, and Financial Overview of the Practice

Make sure that the purchase price of the practice reflects *fair-market value*. In fact, a formal valuation of the practice is a good investment for a buyer to consider prior to purchasing or buying in, and can be provided through using services of an experienced transition consultant. This tool enables the buyer to determine whether or not he or she is making a sound investment in the practice. It may also be used to compare against any valuation that may have been provided by an advisor of the seller. A practice valuation also can give you an idea as to how the practice compares to similar practices in similar areas.

(Note: A "typical" practice in a reasonably nice area to live will sell for one and one-half to two times its "true net" income, with some selling for more and others for less. This can vary widely from one area of a given state to another, as well as from one area of a city to another.) ("True net" is determined by taking the owner's salary and adding to this amount various expenses of the practice. See Chapter 7, "Determining the Value of Your Practice.") For those buying in at some point in the future, make sure the practice is valued prior to the time you begin working in the practice. Otherwise, disputes can result over the value at a later date (See the "Associateship to Co-Owner" chapter.)

The *terms* of the purchase also are important and often will make the difference between a successful end result and a poor one. Terms would include some of the following:

- The Interest Rate: How does it compare to prime?

- Will There Be Any Interest-Only Period? This could afford you some breathing room in the beginning.

- How Long A Payout Period? Over how many years can the purchase or buy-in payments be stretched?

- Will There Be Any Payment-Deferral Period? Can the payments be delayed initially?

- Will There Be Any Prepayment Penalty? If I can pay off the debt early, will I be penalized?

If fairly structured, the terms of the purchase or buy-in will allow you to pay the existing overhead of the practice (or *share* in the paying in a co-ownership situation), the payments on the buy-in or purchase price, and still make a reasonably good living in the process. If this doesn't appear very clear to you, then proceed with great caution.

Here are some general questions you might ask yourself: What type of a practice can you afford? At what point is a practice too *large* to buy into or purchase? At what point is one too *small*? What are your current debts and how will the debt of purchasing or buying into a practice affect your family's lifestyle? How much money *do* you need to live?

As a buyer of a practice, you should be provided with a projection of what your income will look like during the time you're making payments on the practice. This projection is based on the present overhead and collections of the practice, less the practice payments. (Figures 10-1, page 248, and 10-2, page 249) In order to project an accurate picture, it is necessary to determine what the "true net" income of the practice is. It should also reflect what expenses the owner currently has that the buyer *won't,* as well as expenses the buyer *will* incur that the owner *doesn't* have. Some of these expenses include excess supply costs, depreciation, continuing education and travel costs, and the amount of facility rent the owner is paying in situations where he actually owns the facility. Some *additional* expenses a purchaser (as opposed to some one buying in) might incur would include initial working capital and marketing costs, as well as the cost of any reequipping or the improvement of existing decor.

Someone buying into a practice would need a more complex projection than someone involved in an outright purchase. This projection should be part of a practice buy-in format as described in the chapter, "Associateship to Co-Ownership."

Structure and Management of the Transition

An Outright Purchase Scenario

One of the first concerns a buyer has is how to maintain cash flow during the initial three-to-six month critical period following the purchase date. In some situations, you may want to protect the cash flow of the practice by having the seller stay with the practice, and providing dental services during a transition period. This can be particularly important during the first few months following the purchase. Each situation should be handled on an individual basis—in some situations it is most advantageous for the seller to stay; in others, it's best for the seller to leave as soon as possible after the sale.

If you are ready (clinically and managerially) to take on the practice by yourself, by all means do so, and limit the amount of time the seller stays with you in the transition. However, if you are *not* ready for the entire responsibility yourself and the seller is willing, keep the seller working in the practice for six months to a year following the purchase date.

Here are some general questions you might ask yourself:

ASSOCIATE COMPENSATION Adjusted Percentage	
ASSOCIATE'S COMPENSATION PERCENTAGE	
ASSOCIATE'S GROSS COLLECTIONS	$10,000
ASSOCIATE'S LAB BILL	$ 1,000
ADJUSTED GROSS COLLECTION	$ 9,000
ASSOCIATE'S COMPENSATION (35%)	$ 3,150
ASSOCIATE COMPENSATION Flat Percentage	
ASSOCIATE'S COMPENSATION PERCENTAGE	
ASSOCIATE'S GROSS COLLECTIONS	$10,000
ASSOCIATE'S COMPENSATION (30%)	$ 3,000

Fig. 10.1

- Do you want to buy a practice and have the owner leave right away (the retirement sale) or would you prefer he stay for a limited number of days per week for a period of time following the purchase date (the pre-retirement sale)?

- Would you prefer to purchase a practice in a deferred-sale scenario in order to have time to improve your clinical skills and learn the business aspects of the practice before assuming ownership? (See Chapter 3, "Successful Sales Strategies.")

- Or, would you prefer a *buy-in to co-ownership* scenario, with the benefits of having a partner to share expenses, management, and office coverage?

- Are you willing to share in the management and decision process with someone else, or will you be happier "in total control"? (See Chapter 4, "Creating 'Win-Win' Associateship to Co-Ownership Arrangements.")

PROFORMA

	YEAR 1	YEAR 2	YEAR 3	YEAR 4	YEAR 5
COLLECTIONS	$460,291	$483,306	$507,471	$532,844	$559,487
REFUNDS	$0	$0	$0	$0	$0
NET COLLECTONS	$460,291	$483,306	$507,471	$532,844	$559,487
OWNERS	$347,962	$365,360	$383,628	$402,810	$422,950
HYGIENE 24%	$112,329	$117,945	$123,843	$130,035	$136,537
PURCHASER ADD'L PROD	$0	$25,000	$0	$0	$0
ASSOCIATE ADD'L PROD	$0	$0	$0	$0	$0
TOTAL COLLECTIONS	$460,291	$508,306	$507,471	$532,844	$559,487
EXPENSES					
ADVERTISING	$2,000	$2,100	$2,205	$2,315	$2,431
ACCTG/LEGAL	$3,500	$3,675	$3,859	$4,052	$4,254
BANK CHARGES	$500	$525	$551	$579	$608
CONT'D EDUCATION	$1,200	$1,260	$1,323	$1,389	$1,459
DUES/SUBSCRIPTS	$1,411	$1,482	$1,556	$1,633	$1,715
INSURANCE-MALPR	$3,000	$3,150	$3,308	$3,473	$3,647
INSURANCE HEALTH	$3,500	$3,675	$3,859	$4,052	$4,254
INSUR.-PREMISES	$2,232	$2,344	$2,461	$2,584	$2,713
LAB FEES	$45,854	$48,147	$50,554	$53,082	$55,736
LAUNDRY/UNIFORMS	$500	$525	$551	$579	$608
MISCELLANEOUS	$4,000	$4,200	$4,410	$4,631	$4,862
MOVING COSTS	$500	$0	$0	$0	$0
PAYROLL TAXES	$17,666	$18,549	$19,477	$20,451	$21,473
RENT	$24,953	$26,201	$27,511	$28,886	$30,331
REPAIRS/MAINT	$1,000	$1,050	$1,103	$1,158	$1,216
STAFF SALARIES	$106,900	$112,245	$117,857	$123,750	$129,938
STAFF BENEFITS	$1,500	$1,575	$1,654	$1,736	$1,823
SUPPLIES-DENTAL	$18,536	$19,463	$20,436	$21,458	$22,531
SUPPLIES-OFFICE	$3,822	$4,013	$4,214	$4,424	$4,646
TAXES/LICENSES	$1,000	$1,050	$1,103	$1,158	$1,216
TELEPHONE	$2,232	$2,344	$2,461	$2,584	$2,713
UTILITIES	$2,500	$2,625	$2,756	$2,894	$3,039
TOTAL	$248,306	$260,196	$273,206	$286,866	$301,210
NET INCOME	$211,985	$248,109	$234,265	$245,978	$258,277
PRACTICE PMTS	$61,783	$61,783	$61,783	$61,783	$61,783
NET AFTER DEBT	**$150,202**	**$186,326**	**$172,482**	**$184,195**	**$196,494**

Fig. 10.2

Here are some questions you should ask (or have your transition consultant ask) the owner prior to purchasing or buying into a practice:

- What were your yearly gross collections for the last three years?

- Of that, what part was hygiene and what percentage of fees were received from private patients, insurance/direct reimbursement, prepaid/capitation/HMO, and Medicaid/Medicare?

- Is the practice computerized? What type of software does it have?

- Does the practice have an intraoral camera?

- Is the practice location in a high-growth, moderate-growth, or stable area?

- How many treatment rooms does the practice have? Can more be added? What is the total square footage of the office?

- How many active patients are there? How many new patients per month? What is the average number of patients seen daily?

- What is the collection percentage of the practice and what is the total accounts receivable?

- How many staff members are employed and what are their salaries and benefits?

- How many total hygiene days per week are there, and is there a non-surgical perio program in place? What's the percentage of endodontics, periodontics, pedodontics, oral surgery, and implant placement that's referred out?

- Is the seller willing to finance part or all of the sale or buy-in? If not, is outside financing available? (Figure 10-3, page251)

PURCHASING OR BUYING-IN MAJOR THINGS TO CONSIDER

- **LOCATION**

- **PHYSICAL SIZE**

- **PRODUCTION HISTORY**

- **PRICE AND TERMS**

- **MANAGING THE TRANSITION**

Fig. 10.3

Look at Several Practices Before Making a Decision

Looking at a practice to purchase or buy into can be somewhat like looking for a house. Don't judge from just the outside appearance. Walk through and get "a feel" for the place. Speak to the owner about philosophy of care. Most of all, know the numbers of the practice you're considering, because this is far more important than the brown shag carpeting and paneling. Does potential exist for higher production because of the large patient base? Is hygiene underproducing as compared to the total office production? With, say, 40 new patients per month, are comprehensive exams being done and treatment plans provided for greater production? Do you prefer to buy an *underpotentialized* practice (and at a lower price), knowing it can be greatly expanded with good management? Or, would you prefer to pay a higher price for a practice that already has successful systems in place?

You definitely should look at more than one practice before making a final decision. You then will be able to narrow down your options before proceeding. If you are purchasing and the staff is aware of the owner's transition, you will most definitely want to visit the practice while it's in operation. Once you know it's "the right" practice for you, it's time to proceed to a preliminary agreement. (See Chapter 8, "Structuring Your Agreements.")

Most early-career dentists are anxious to establish a practice. Purchasing the practice of a soon-to-be-retiring dentist is an extremely low-risk path for accomplishing this. The more experienced the buyer-dentist is, the less transition time required. Those buyer-dentists desiring a more extended transition time should pursue seller-dentists interested in the pre-retirement or even deferred-sale scenario. Those desiring minimal transition time between the seller and buyer (and less "adjustment" time for patients) will fare better under the retirement sale scenario (all of these scenarios are described in detail in Chapter 3, "Successful Sales Strategies.")

How To Locate a Practice To Purchase

It's extremely easy to locate practices for purchase today as opposed to years past. Local and national dental journals are one of the first places to look. Word of mouth also is a good source of prospects, particularly if you're looking for a practice in a specific area or location. Practice opportunities can even be found on the Internet.

Practice brokers (or consulting companies offering brokerage services) are an excellent source of practice opportunities. Some brokers are part of nationally networked groups (as are we), allowing a buyer to quickly locate multiple-practice opportunities throughout the country. This way, a buyer in one area of the country can easily locate and explore opportunities not only in his or her own area, but in other parts of the country as well.

As discussed in the previous chapter, some buyers feel that a broker may appear to be biased in their opinions of what a practice is worth, since their compensation usually is directly based on it. Many buyers I work with wonder if the broker through whom they're purchasing a practice really is looking out for their best interests, based on the financial relationship that exists between the broker and the selling dentist. Some brokers charge the buyer a fee in addition to the commission charged the seller. Buyers' legal and financial advisors become concerned about what they refer to as "dual agency." Some states require that brokers be licensed and some have created what's called a *transaction broker* who represents neither buyer nor seller, but who works for the overall good of the transaction. The broker promises fairness, competency, and honesty to both parties involved in the transaction.

The key is this: If you work with an experienced transition specialist who's honest and competent, then it really doesn't matter what type of broker he or she is, or how the broker is being paid.

The Patient-Transition Process

A great deal of misinformation surrounds the patient transition and retention process for dentists who are considering purchasing part or all of a practice. After all, what did they buy if the transfer of patients isn't successful? When the patients are informed properly about the transition, the seller's exit (or the gentle shifting of some of the patients to the future co-owner) should not cause a mass exodus of patients. Even though most people avoid change, patients are accustomed to this type of transition and have experienced this with their physicians and other professionals who provide them with services. This is why we have seen such a long history of successful patient transfers to new dentist entering established practices.

When the seller transitions out of the practice quickly, this actually *shortens* the patient-transfer time to the new dentist. Contrary to what many dentists think, the success of a transition mostly depends on the maturity level, communication skills, and clinical experience of the new dentist, as well as the performance of the remaining staff, and not on the seller's *presence* after the sale. In preparation for the new dentist, the staff should be well-prepared with "scripts" for introducing the new doctor in person as well as over the telephone. A personal letter of introduction from the seller also is important to consider. A successful transition means that the majority of patients transfer, thereby establishing reasonably good cash flow for the buyer three to six months into the transition.

Accomplishing a successful transition from the owner to the new dentist is both an art *and* a science. Overall, most practice transitions are successful, which makes purchasing or buying into a practice a logical move in today's marketplace. No one can promise, however, that the practice will stay the *same*. Production and collections can change; however, buyers often are ahead, anyway, when compared to other routes to practice establishment.

Most outright purchasers of practices with whom I have worked over the years have shown *higher* gross-collections figures than the previous owner was experiencing, even in highly compromised, less-than-ideal situations. Most of the dentists with whom I have worked, who bought into practices, have greater incomes than those in associate-only positions.

A Successful Transition Story

I recall a story about a well-known dentist, in a small town in central Georgia, who passed away suddenly. The estate was unable to find a dentist to work in the practice, so the office was idle for a full two months. This is not a good situation and can definitely destroy the value of a practice. However, the staff continued taking phone calls from patients, most of who were willing to wait for a replacement. The staff was naturally skeptical. Although patients tend to say nice things, would they really come back?

After about 60 days, a young dentist and his wife came to look at the practice. This couple was interested in small-town life. This practice presented an opportunity that might not come along too often. However, they had some concerns. They assumed that the patients had probably already left and felt hesitant to "buy" the practice. However, the estate didn't want someone to just "work" in the practice. It was important to the widow that the practice be sold.

Even though there was no way to know what was going to happen until a new dentist began working in the practice, the estate had made the practice price low enough to be attractive in these circumstances. In addition, the staff and the widow offered personal encouragement, which helped the dentist decide to take a risk and buy.

What happened then was nothing short of amazing. The majority of patients did indeed wait for a successor and before long the appointment book was filled. Apparently, a new, young dentist arriving in town created some excitement and many new patients soon entered the practice.

Eighteen months after the purchase date, the buyer's production was far greater than the seller's had been at the time of his death. This productivity was accomplished without those things we usually think of as being required for a successful transfer. There was no letter of recommendation to patients from their previous dentist, which is always part of a well-planned transition. There was no personal introduction by their previous dentist in the office or at an open house. There was also no way to put an announcement in the local paper to introduce the association of this newcomer to the established dentist's practice.

Even in the absence of these important steps, the transaction worked well. Why? Because, realistically, there was no real reason for the patients to instantly switch dentists when their dentist died. Most patients hoped for a replacement dentist in order to continue their care at the same practice. The few who did leave did so because they had friends who were dentists, or the practice location had become geographically undesirable. Many patients continued with the practice even after moving away and despite the inconvenience of the location.

Often, from a patient's point of view, a new dentist has a certain appeal—up-to-date techniques and recent education, for example. The new dentist's young face, as well as the "facelift" often given to the facility, also are refreshing differences noticed by long-time patients.

This story often allays the fears many early-career dentists have about patient transfer. Even in the worst possible situations, patient transfer can be successful.

Summary

Be sure to look at more than one practice opportunity before making a final decision. You will then be able to compare the pros and cons of each so that you can begin to narrow down your options before proceeding. Think about whether you prefer to purchase or buy into an *underpotentialized* practice at a lower price, knowing that it can be greatly expanded with good management, or pay a higher price for part or all of a practice with successful systems already in place.

Once you are sure that the *location* of the practice you've chosen to purchase is in a geographic area that you and your family will be happy with long term, make sure the *specific location within that area* will continue to be a good one for the practice.

Be sure to have the practice appraised, so that you have a starting point from which to begin initial discussions. It also may serve as a back-up for any valuations that may *already have been provided* by the seller.

Make sure the terms of the purchase price will allow you to make a reasonable living while paying off the buy-in or purchase price of the practice. Remember to check with some of the new lending institutions that loan money to dentists strictly for this purpose. They are often quick to respond and willing to offer a number of *flexible payment plans*.

Be sure to choose the practice-establishment scenario that best fits your desired direction. A buy-in to co-ownership arrangement is a much more gradual transition of the practice and develops into a much longer working relationship between the dentists than does the outright purchase of a practice. The former situation creates a group practice; the latter most often becomes a solo-practice situation.

In most outright purchases, the patients will transfer to the new owner without any extended working relationship between the buyer and seller after the sale. If you are able to maintain the normal and necessary production of the practice without the help of the seller, then keep the transition time to a minimum if you wish. However, if the sell-

**PURCHASING OR BUYING INTO A PRACTICE
A CHECKLIST**

First Step

Determine:
    Where You Want To Live
    The Size Practice You Are Comfortable With

Second Step

Practice Valuation
Income Projections and Proforma For An Outright Purchase
Income Projections and Associateship-Buy-In Format For A Buy-In
Preliminary Agreements For Purchase or Buy-In
Secure Financing For:
    Down Payment (With Seller Financing), or
    Cash Paid at Closing
Final Agreements
Closing

Fig. 10.4

er's production *is* necessary for some period of time from a cash-flow perspective, then consider setting up such an extended working arrangement with the seller following the purchase.

And, finally, choose an experienced transition specialist to help you with the purchase of the practice. This individual can advise you on the price and terms of the practice, provide practice-valuation services, negotiate the terms and conditions of the sale, and provide extensive practice sale agreements that have been specifically designed for dental practices—all while providing comfortable *insulation* between you and the seller. Most importantly, hire a consultant who has a win-win attitude—all is lost if you enter this arena from an adversarial position. (Figure 10.4)

11

CASHING-IN THE EQUITY IN YOUR EXISTING PRACTICE: ADVICE FOR THE EARLY-, MID-, AND LATE-CAREER DENTIST

Today's dentists are interested in learning ways to maximize, ensure, and successfully cash in the value within their practices—value that did not exist years ago but which now represents a substantial part of their net worth.

For many of you, the cashing-in process will be represented by a single event at or near retirement. This will be the best approach by far to transfer your practice to a successor, and it will be an event that you may long remember as being both exhilarating and terrifying at the same time. (See Chapter 3, "Successful Sales Strategies.")

Some of you may find this cashing-in process to be a "multiple-event," represented by selling portions of your practice equity at various stages throughout your career. Dentists who choose this path will not only enjoy cashing in their equity years in advance of retirement, but will be establishing, in the process, symbiotic relationships with other professionals that will inevitably lead to further practice value expansion that can continuously be built upon and sold. (See Chapter 4, "Creating 'Win-Win' Associateship to Co-Ownership Arrangements.") (Figure 11-1)

For this cashing-in event to be successful, there are a few critical requirements:

- The first and foremost is to be willing to invest the time and the resources to develop your plan, with an end design specifically tailored to your situation, and not someone else's. Chapter 13, "Developing A Strategic-Transition Plan," will help you develop an individualized approach to the transition of your practice.

- Second, be *absolutely* certain that your transition plan allows for a clear as well as equitable means of transferring the value of your practice to your successor or successors.

- Third, be certain that you (and the advisors you have chosen to help you) understand the needs of both parties and are willing to work toward a win-win end result.

What follows is a story written by a dentist who cashed in the equity in his practice prior to his actual retirement. It illustrates the points we have covered.

• • •

In January 1991 at the age of 58 years, I moved into a new dental suite in a small office park next to a large shopping mall. I had a rather large practice—3,500-4,000 families, six office-staff members (two front offices, two hygienists, and two dental assistants) along with a stable mid-six-figure gross practice income. My practice progressed with more new patients each month and practically no patients lost as a result of my move to a new location.

I had open-heart surgery (mitral valve replacement) in 1989 and, as a result of this, in 1992 I began to have an uneasy feeling about my

CASHING IN PRACTICE EQUITY

- ### PRACTICE BUY-IN

  - #### Leads To Co-Ownership

  - #### Can Occur Multiple Times

- ### PRACTICE BUY-OUT

  - #### Single Event

  - #### Multiple Options

    - ##### Retirement Sale

    - ##### Pre-Retirement Sale

    - ##### Deferred Sale

    - ##### Goodwill-Only Sale

Fig. 11.1

ability to keep up my active pace. Realizing that my future might not be as wide open as it once had been, I discussed the problem with my wife, Ann. Together, we made the decision to try to sell my practice in order to relieve my stress in managing and running a full-time dental practice.

I began to pursue that objective, knowing that I was under no immediate pressure to sell due to health or other factors. I love hands-on dentistry and wanted to be able to continue practicing on a reduced scale. I didn't want to completely give up the patient relationships I had established over the past 35 years or so. Selling and walking out the next day just didn't appeal to me.

A well-known practice management consultant recommended I contact a transition specialist to discuss my overall objective. Many contacts with perspective buyers were made and numerous interviews were conducted over the next 10 to 12 months. I now understand that, for me, one of the most difficult parts of the entire procedure was to open up all my personal practice records to any number of potential buyers. I finally realized it was a very necessary step towards a fair and equitable arrangement for both the buyer and seller. Two young dentists who were in practice together in a smaller facility, approximately eight miles from my office, seemed to be the best candidates for my practice. Dr. Griggs had previously appraised my practice in three different ways and so a price was established. I was willing to finance the sale so as long as I was allowed to remain in it on a part-time basis (as was my goal).

This accomplished two points: First, I was able to continue the practice of dentistry in the same office setting and on the same patients; and secondly, it enabled me to play a vital part in helping transfer, as much as possible, patient loyalty to the new dentists. This transfer is a vital part of any practice sale, as far as I can determine.

The official practice transfer took place in December 1993. Today, I am still working two days each week, albeit not as hard as in the past years. I truly believe that all parties in this agreement have benefited from this arrangement and have been pleased with the results.

Some important points I would like to reiterate relating to a practice sale are:

- If the practice transfer is to be successful, the seller must diligently urge patients to accept treatment from the new dentist(s).

- Plenty of time must be invested to allow both parties to obtain a rewarding arrangement.

- All practice details must be given to buyers.

- Financing arrangements must be fair to both parties so that excess strain is not placed upon the buyer, and the seller maintains a good income.

- Finally, give advice only when it is requested, because when you sell your practice, you have to realize and accept the fact that it is no longer yours (admittedly, hard to do).

I really believe, as the old saying goes, that "I can have my cake and eat it, too." This is because I sought and found competent advisors, was not in a rush to sell, had no immediate problems (health or otherwise), and, lastly (but very importantly), finalized in my own mind and with my immediate family the idea of selling before I started negotiations.

My wish to those of you reading this book with the idea of a purchase or sale in mind is that you will have the same success I had."
—Bobby C. Brooks, DDS, Atlanta, Georgia

• • •

You have spent tremendous energy, time, sweat, and tears in building a practice. Only another entrepreneur could begin to know the cost. You have served patients to the best of your ability and spent long hours solving personnel problems and managing your practice. You have established relationships with many patients over the years. But it is now time to have your practice serve your personal needs and goals. You have made deposits into your practice bank account over the years—now you would like to make a few withdrawals. You may not want to withdraw *all* the equity at one time, but do so over the next 10 years. It's time to plan for you and your family's next transition.

Making the decision to cash in your practice equity through one of the many options described in this book is an exciting fantasy to some dentists. Five patients cancel and two are no-shows; the dental assistant walks out and the hygienist wants a higher percentage; the equipment breaks down once again, and you get scheduled for a 5:00 p.m. new patient (who's been in pain for two weeks. Could this be the day to cash in and get out? Probably not, but it sounds great, doesn't it?

Cashing in the equity in your practice can be emotionally and financially rewarding in mid-career. In fact, mid-career dentists frequently are reaching productivity highs and are ready to enjoy quality of life. Then why think about cashing in the practice equity? Because well-established, productive practices reach peak values during this time, and so it makes good sense from a business point of view. However, as you read in the beginning of this chapter, there are important points to remember related to this process. The cashing-in process works best with a sound transition plan in place first.

Here are a few questions you should ask yourself:

- What are your current and future financial obligations to your family?

- How much money will you need beyond the sale proceeds to meet these obligations?

- What other sources of income do you have?

- What is your retirement target date?

- Do you have another profession or business you'd like to pursue and will selling part or all of the equity in your practice allow you to do this?

- Will you feel happy and content practicing dentistry part time or not at all?

- How long can you be happy working in an office where you are no longer in control?

- Will you be able to gradually phase into retirement (and do you want to)?

- Are you willing to cheerfully and confidently hand your patients over to the buyer to enable a smooth transition?

- Will you cooperate in working with the staff, letting them know that you're no longer "in charge?"

- Will you encourage the staff and help them successfully introduce the buyer to the patients?

- If you remain in the practice, are you truly able to give advice only when it is requested, and can you accept that another dentist may do dentistry differently than you do?

I urge you to sit and ask yourself these questions and honestly answer them. Go through them with your wife/husband, or with close friends who know you well. Again, if you plan ahead and read your map, your path may lead to cashing in the equity. Sometimes, one's path takes a turn that results in disability or health problems.

Here is a story about cashing in the equity due to a disability.

• • •

After practicing successfully for 23 years in a metropolitan area of Atlanta, I was compelled to sell my practice due to a disability. I transitioned my practice to an associate who had practiced with me for two years. We were contemplating merging an adjacent practice and expanding our patient base. After consulting a transition-management consultant, I realized I did not have the energy or health to actively continue as an owner in private practice. This emotional up-and-down feeling intensified during the negotiations over the transfer. Although I completely trusted the buyer and knew he would be successful, I sometimes felt as if he didn't realize how hard everyone had worked over the years to build the patient base. I wasn't sure he would ever truly appreciate the "true" value of my practice.

Selling my practice and working in the office for one year, helping with the transition, was definitely the right decision for me. Saying good-bye to lots of nice patients who had supported me was sad. Finding a new identity and giving up oversight of a seven-member team was emotionally challenging. I missed the support of my staff tremendously. Some days, I just couldn't stay away from the office. There were times when I thought I would just be unable to make it without the emotional support of the team who had become a part of my family. I missed the praise and admiration of my patients. It seems when you stop practicing, you only remember the good patients and the good times with staff. But, somewhere in my memory, I can recall times when things were pretty stressful. I guess I felt like I had undergone surgery and lost a part of my anatomy. My question was, which part? Was it my right hand or was it a giant hemorrhoid?

After a well-deserved month's vacation, I realized I was emotionally ready to begin another practice, but physically, I just couldn't do it.

The two years following the sale of my practice were stressful at times due to what I label now as "entrepreneurial terror." What could I do to capitalize on the time spent in dentistry and the skills I had learned?

The consultant who helped me was as much a broker as a consultant, and that aspect was very important to me. Selling or buying a practice is a serious business and must be thought out well. The true "win-win" approach he was committed to helped me see that maybe I could put my talents to use in that area. With all the experience I had as a practicing dentist working through the transition, I felt I could work with dentists at various career levels. I began my career as an associate, purchased the practice, sold an existing practice to a partner, and eventually bought out the partner and practiced solo. I practiced later with three associates and, finally, sold to my associate and became his associate. I realized I had a lot to give to the profession of practice transitions.

I now am helping young dentists find their niche and aiding others in the transition of their practices, which has been an answer to my prayers. What for five years was very scary and doubtful has truly turned out to be very positive.

—William W. Adams, DDS
Marietta, Georgia

• • •

Cashing in equity due to a disability is not generally a scheduled part of the transition plan. Although none of us likes to think that a disability will be a part of our plan, it is, in fact, a consideration that should be given attention. Too often, dentists rely solely on the crutch of insurance in the event of a disability.

Always planning for the unexpected will allow you freedom of choice when it comes time to cash in the equity that lies dormant in your practice. As you can see, there is life after disability.

What follows is a story about an early-career dentist who sold his practice.

• • •

After 10 years in solo private practice, I sold my dental practice at age 36 years. During that 10-year period, I purchased my first practice from a retiring dentist, later purchased and merged another small practice, designed and renovated another existing facility, moved my practice, and seriously considered buying another, larger practice in my area. With each carefully-planned step, positive results were realized and during this time, I learned how to welcome change.

The idea of selling my practice developed over my last three years of practicing dentistry solo. Many factors affected my decision to sell my practice; however, the main reason involved creating more time to pursue other interests. The fact that I was single and had learned to live well within my means made my decision to sell much easier. With both my parents young and in good health, having no college education funds to save for, and no extravagant expenses consuming my monthly earnings, it was a relief to know that no one else was depending on my income. I realized that all these factors made my personal situation unique and I decided to take advantage of the opportunity.

I truly enjoyed the hands-on practice of dentistry and the many wonderful relationships I had developed with patients, staff, and colleagues. Even though the economic and managerial sides of the profession were undergoing many changes, I had developed a successful fee-for-service practice with a great staff and excellent business systems. My final year in practice was the most profitable and enjoyable one of my career.

The desirable style, size, and location of my practice created an immediate response when I finally reached the decision to sell. Within one month, I had received offers from three qualified buyers. Without a doubt, the most difficult part of the entire process was deciding which perspective buyer to sell to. I made an excellent choice and all phases of the sale of my practice, from contracts through the transition period, went smoothly.

Emotionally, there were some difficult adjustments to make, such as learning to give up control and saying farewell to patients and staff when the time came for me to leave. But I knew I was leaving after giving my best and with a feeling of true satisfaction. My worst fear during the process was that I might regret the decision I had made. Two years have now passed since the contracts were signed, without a moment of second-guessing. I still am practicing dentistry on a part-time basis and enjoying my work more than ever. I have traveled extensively since selling my practice. I have had the wonderful opportunity to participate in dental-volunteer projects in Peru and Nepal and recently completed a four-month trip around the world. Recently, I was accepted into a graduate program in public health, which I plan to pursue part-time as an adjunct to dentistry.

In the midst of all of my career change and activity, the untimely heart attack and instant death of my brother-in-law at age 34 occurred. This loss was a jolting reminder to me that we must pursue our goals now—and with great vigor—rather than waiting for an indeterminate "someday" in the future.

—Sid Williams, DMD
Atlanta, Georgia.

• • •

Selling portions of practice equity has a different impact on the selling dentist than does selling the entire practice. A buy-in leading to co-ownership leaves the selling dentist still "in control" and doesn't signal all of the life changes that selling out does. Selling the entire practice also is irreversible (usually), as few sales transactions are reversed once set into motion.

Since most late-career selling dentists are not re-entering practice or entering other businesses, different considerations are in order. The next chapter, "When You Finally Decide to Sell Your Practice," covers some of the most important personal issues to consider.

12

WHEN YOU FINALLY DECIDE TO SELL YOUR PRACTICE: ADVICE FOR THE LATE-CAREER PERSPECTIVE

Before You Finally Decide to Sell Your Practice

Deciding to sell your practice can be difficult. Guess what? "Life after dentistry" can be challenging.

For most dentists, there is a tremendous amount of self-worth tied into practice ownership. The relationships with colleagues, staff, and patients are also an important part of the process. Selling the practice often represents the end to long-term relationships that the dentist has spent years building. Being productive and having the capability to control financial destiny is another consideration. The list goes on and many factors continue to unfold in the process. However, selling your practice can often give you the opportunity to experience the most rewarding phase of your career, or it can lead to many surprises.

From our experience, dentists who truly enjoy retirement are those who plan in advance for the future sale of their practice. Spending the time to plan allows the late-career dentist to leave the practice with a true sense of peace regarding the decision to sell. There are three areas to explore in this phase of the transition cycle.

What follows is a typical reaction to this process.

• • •

I am thankful for this opportunity to share my experience relating to the transition and sale of a general dental practice.

After graduation from the Ohio State University College of Dentistry in 1954, I came to Florida to take the state board examinations. In September of that same year, I started practicing in central Florida. I enjoyed many years of a rewarding solo practice. In the mid-1980s, I began thinking seriously about the future of my practice, in relation to my age, my ability to keep building the practice, and my wife's failing health.

There also were some other thoughts going through my head at the time. I was a feeling stress-related "burn-out." The everyday dealings with the office staff, patients, labs, overhead, the feeling of being tied-down over a period of many years to that "x" number of square feet, all of that was getting to me emotionally. The thought of being able to make a change was something pleasant.

I finally realized that the best time to arrange for the sale of a practice was now, rather than waiting until my income was declining.

In 1986, at the age of 63, I had my practice valued and established a selling price. The valuation gave me some solid facts concerning my practice. I then went through the formality of signing a contract with a transition consultant, which gave me the "go ahead" to find a buyer suitable for my practice. After an interested buyer was found, we were introduced, became acquainted, and agreed upon a selling price. A detailed agreement was drawn up for each of us to examine. This included many, many details, which were meant to protect both the seller and the buyer. After a reasonable length of time (one to two weeks) we signed the agreement.

In my particular situation, I elected to stay with the practice (on a part-time basis) for two years. This allowed me a smoother transition, including introducing my patients to the younger dentist who was taking over the practice.

In all fairness, I must say that there were a few points of contention that came up during the ensuing years. When something of this nature would arise, having a transition consultant to help figure out a resolution to the problem was invaluable. (By the way, I would recommend without reservation this type of support to any of my colleagues.)

As it turned out, things ironed out quite nicely. My retirement years have been spent continuing to practice dentistry on a part-time basis. After leaving Orlando, Florida and following the death of my wife, I made a decision to re-enter the dental arena.

At late career, I began a new life. Having remarried to a wonderful woman (who has also completed a rewarding career in the health care industry), I am enjoying my retirement years on the beach. I continue to practice dentistry in the large group practice I joined a few years ago. I now practice in a rural area of Florida and have enjoyed the challenges of being an employee-dentist.

Without the daily pressures of ownership, I have been able to experience renewed energy in my profession. Staff members often come to me with their problems and ask for my advice. (Interesting how that doesn't bother me much anymore; in fact, I always take the time to listen. Perhaps I enjoy it?) Being a mentor for the three associate-dentists in the practice has been very rewarding and has given me the opportunity to give back to my colleagues. The owner-dentist respects my opinion and he knows he can count on me for support. My production per hour continues to grow and case acceptance is almost never a problem. I look forward to seeing my patients on a regular basis and leave each day with a feeling of accomplishment. Surprisingly enough, every once in a while a former patient wanders in the door to say hello.

Who am I without my practice? Good question! I guess the answer to that question is I am the same person, only a little more blessed from the experience. Perhaps someday I'll consider cutting back, but for right now I have been afforded the opportunity to give back to my profession. Continuing to practice dentistry still brings me much happiness.

–Dr. C. W.,
Central Florida

• • •

The "Before:" Prior to Deciding To Sell

What does true retirement mean? Is it something you really want? Or is retirement something you need? Are you not quite ready to golf, fish, or play shuffleboard every day? Do you have plans to travel? (Do you still *like* to travel?) What hobbies do you have? Many dentists haven't taken the time to really develop hobbies and interests outside the practice.

Before you decide to sell your practice, explore your outside interests. Look at your financial goals. Will you need to change your standard of living after retirement? What was considered to be a healthy retirement fund 20 years ago will possibly not support a year's salary in the future. Dreams and aspirations of world travel are many times saved until long after the transition cycle is complete. Often, the treadmill dentist's entire career comes to a screeching halt with the sudden impact of retirement. We are professionals who allow ourselves to function at a highly stressful level. This stress often becomes an addiction and ending this cycle may be quite an adjustment during the slow-down period. All the more reason to know the answers to the above questions prior to selling your practice.

The "During:"
Facing the Challenges of Selling Your Practice

Once you have decided to sell your practice (and you begin to see light at the end of the tunnel), it is common to feel a sense of relief coupled with anxiety. As much as you would like for things to run smoothly, chances are there will be some obstacles and challenges along the way. It is important that you stay focused on the outcome during this time.

The "letting-go" process begins now. This stage of the transition is very important. Why? Not only because of the ultimate outcome, but getting "off-track" might sabotage the entire transition. Many dentists arrive at this phase only to find they are not emotionally prepared to "let go." This is the time to refer back to all the goals and plans that were put in place prior to the sale. Making a checklist will insure your initial transition goals are being met. Because this is a very emotionally driven phase, it is extremely important that you progress through it by always putting the business first. After all, what you are really selling is a *business*. Emotions and business are a dangerous combination.

The "After:"
Opportunities Exist for Late-Career Dentists

Once you get to this phase, the picture should be clear. You will be financially sound. You should feel comfortable with the new dentist in your "former" practice. ("Former" is the key word here.) By this time, the letting-go process should be well on its way to completion. The years of retirement are something to look forward to as a step to a new life. Often, this can be one of the most rewarding phases of the transition cycle. Looking at life and the fruits of all of your efforts should be a time of celebration.

In reality, there is only one facet of dentistry that ever ends for the dental practitioner…and that is the physical act of performing clinical dentistry. All other facets of being a dentist remain. Most dentists stay involved in the profession by volunteering their services and helping others. In making a decision to sell, your identity should not be lost.

However, face one important aspect before, during, and after the sale of your practice: You will need to put down your handpiece for the last time. You will need to dismiss your last patient. You will need to thank the last staff member. You will need to pass the torch to the person who continues your life's work. You will need to lock the door for the last time. You will need to know how to say good-bye.

Saying good-bye to your practice is an important step in the process. Practice ownership has offered many rewards. It's hard to say good-bye to the daily appreciation and respect gained from patients, staff, and associates. It's difficult to say good-bye to the "four walls" which became your home-away-from-home. And it's almost impossible to let go and allow someone else to take control. Planning ahead allows you to say good-bye. Saying good-bye will give you the freedom to get what you deserve by planning for what you get. In the next chapter, we'll discuss how you can successfully plan your practice transition and reap the rewards of the process.

13

DEVELOPING A STRATEGIC-TRANSITION PLAN: STRUCTURING YOUR COMPREHENSIVE TRANSITION PLAN

At 62 years of age, Dr. M sat wearily staring at the production and collection numbers of his practice for the previous month. He knew his practice had been on a "downslide" for quite some time, and he wasn't quite sure what to do about it.

Looking back at his overall career, he felt that dentistry had been good to him. However, some years ago, he had begun to lose interest in the practice, allowing it to gradually decline. Now his practice was only marginally profitable, and the minimal cash flow that it generated was not enough to invest in upgrading equipment and decor.

Suddenly, an even bigger fear hit him: the day was soon approaching when he would have to put his practice up for sale, and he feared that it would not be marketable. Would a comprehensive transition plan have helped Dr. M maintain a profitable practice even as he slowly decreased his clinical schedule? Would such a plan have allowed him to maximize and preserve the value of his practice, and even have a ready and willing built-in buyer?

It seemed like only yesterday that he had opened his doors, literally from "scratch." In those days, there was little need for a practice establishment plan, much less a transition plan. He had always assumed that he would be able to sell the practice and add a significant amount of money to his retirement plan, particularly with practices in his area recently selling for what he felt were record prices. Perhaps he should have thought about selling sooner. Why did he wait until the almost the end of his career to think about a plan of transition?

Planning the Transition

Most of us would like to just put our lives on automatic pilot and somehow get the quality-of-life results that come from strategic, comprehensive planning. But life doesn't afford us that luxury. We can't just stay in idle gear and expect a successful end result. We have to envision, create, and cultivate a strategic plan if we are going to enjoy the consequence.

Of course, we have a choice to not plan. In many cases, the transition of your practice might still turn out okay. However, the difference between our own active involvement in the process and neglect can often represent the difference between peace of mind and constant stress and worry.

Lack of planning provides us with a limited view, causing daily problems to steal our focus. Urgency and inefficiency often take the place of effective planning. A comprehensive approach to the planning of your transition creates a bigger picture and lets you see the mountains for what they really are. The various transition pivot-points that you will inevitably reach during the life cycle of your practice will take on more appropriate dimensions when viewed in the context of a comprehensive, well-structured plan.

This chapter will help you to achieve peace of mind surrounding a very important part of your life—the eventual transition of your practice to a successor. It will help you to identify what's important in the process and what to focus on for the best overall end results.

As I present the steps in the process, I suggest you consider them carefully. Make notes and keep a checklist. I want to emphasize the fact that the transition plan I will help you to design is no magic solution to success. Only you can make the difference, and your plan should ultimately be designed with your life goals in mind.

Realistically, a well-planned transition should have as part of its central core a clear and equitable means of transferring the value of the patient base to one or more successors. In fact, it's this sought-after value that drives much of the transition process as we know it today. However, a great deal of missing data as well as misinformation exists regarding the transition process. This is why many dentists are still unable to maximize the economic value locked inside their practices until at or very near retirement—and even then, few reap more than half of the potential value they could have received had they vigorously set a plan in motion.

It's been shown that with proper planning, practice value can be converted into a passive income stream to be enjoyed at anytime in early, mid-, or late career. What's more, in the spirit of a "win-win" fair exchange–

- the individual purchasing or buying into this value will benefit from the immediate income and career stability created in the process,

- and steadily accumulate practice value that he or she also can transfer to a successor at some point in his or her future.

If the original plan is constructed on an equitable basis, the same framework can be used over and over again as new future successors enter the practice. Successful professional firms have captured the essence of this process.

There are five basic steps in the process of developing your comprehensive transition plan. (Figure 13.1, page 276)

```
┌─────────────────────────────────────────────────────────┐
│        YOUR COMPREHENSIVE TRANSITION PLAN                 │
│                    THE FIVE STEPS                         │
│                                                           │
│  • DETERMINE WHERE YOU ARE                                │
│  • CHOOSE THE RIGHT TRANSITION OPTION                     │
│  • BEGIN PRACTICE FINANCIAL ANALYSIS                      │
│  • DESIGN & IMPLEMENT YOUR PLAN                           │
│  • PROTECT YOUR INVESTMENT                                │
└─────────────────────────────────────────────────────────┘
```

Fig. 13.1

Step 1:
Determine Where You Are.

The first important step in the planning process is determining where you are in the transition cycle. This includes both where you are chronologically as well the direction in which you intend to take your practice. You will find this step to be absolutely essential when making decisions between one transition option and another.

Chronology. Where are you at present? Early, mid-, or late career? For the purposes of planning, we'll assume a particular dentist's career span will be 36 years (age 28 to 64), with the three phases divided as follows: early career: the first 15 years; mid-career: years 16 through five years from retirement; and late career: five years or less from retirement.

These time frames will differ from one dentist to another, depending on how soon (or late) in life he or she began his or her career as a dentist, and what each of his or her target retirement dates are. For example, a successful dentist who plans to retire by age 52 will find that he or she is entering late career at age 47. For most dentists, however, this would still be considered mid-career, as most dentists at this age have more than five years of clinical practice left before retirement.

The direction that you wish to take your practice will also influence your plan. In what direction do want your practice heading over the next five, 10, 15, or more years?

We've entered an era where all dentists need to quickly determine whether they want to be in a building, leveling-off, downsizing, or phasing-out mode. (They also need to be clear on "where they stand" regarding managed care.) The boutique or niche practice; the fee-for-service only practice; the managed care practice, the hybrid practice (incorporating both fee-for-service and managed care components), the practice that's purchased and managed by new corporations—these are all directions being considered by dentists. You can't possibly choose the correct transition option for yourself until you are clear on your direction. Otherwise, your future will be directed by default, as opposed to by design.

Do you want to expand or phase-out? I work with many dentists who want to downsize their existing practices. I have others who want to expand their practices through associateship to co-ownership arrangements and/or practice mergers. Still others want to sell their large practices and relocate to other geographic locations to start smaller versions of their existing practices. (This has become an extremely popular option among mid- to late-career dentists who would prefer to live and practice elsewhere and/or whose patients have slowly moved away from the area, yet still come to the practice.) There also are many dentists who have decided to sell early and assume a nonmanagement role while providing dental services for the buyer.

Timing: What is the status of your personal and financial health? Health and financial status may influence "where you are" as it relates to planning. They also have an impact on timing, since each of these factors (personal and financial health) will have great influence over which options you pursue as well as how soon you pursue them. For example, a solid financial status might allow a dentist to decrease his or her current clinical schedule, creating a slot for an associate. For others, financial success could possibly mean an early retirement (like the dentist who will be retiring at age 52).

Does your health (or that of a loved one) alter your retirement date or enhance your need to have an associate or partner in your practice? I frequently work with dentists who are medical "walking time bombs." This alters the type of associate or buyer candidate that I look for as a transition candidate. The candidate's experience and his or her overall readiness level must be considered because at anytime he or she may be thrust quickly into the "owner's seat."

Choosing an inexperienced individual and/or someone who isn't ready for ownership may lead to a disastrous situation in the future. In a crisis, the dentist (or the estate) may be left without a buyer, and outside buyers may become nervous about the associate's presence in the practice.

Step 2: Choose the Right Transition Option

Based on where you are, which transition option best fits your plan?

- Practice Sale?

- Associateship to Co-Ownership?

- Practice Merger?

Early-Career Considerations. If you are an early career dentist and desire practice ownership in one form or another, you have a few directions to consider. For those independent enough to "do their own thing" and brave enough to be pioneers, Chapter 6, "New Practice Establishment," will help them make the right decisions necessary for this particular journey. I personally recommend that early-career dentists consider only two ownership options: the outright purchase of an established practice or becoming a co-owner of a practice through buying-in. (See Chapter 4, "Creating 'Win-Win' Associateship to Co-Ownership Arrangements," and Chapter 10, "Purchasing or Buying Into a Practice.") (Figure 13-2)

In today's marketplace, entering an already established practice as a buyer or future co-owner makes the most economic sense of all options, and it certainly accelerates the process of building practice equity. Why not position yourself in a guaranteed cash-flow stream as early as possible in your career, with the same opportunity to sell part or all of the practice when it's your turn?

Mid-Career Considerations. If you're a mid-career dentist, make it a part of your transition plan to seek out opportunities to expand the profitability and value of your practice. Consider bringing in an associ-

EARLY CAREER OPTIONS
• **PRACTICE PURCHASE**
• **ASSOCIATESHIP TO CO-OWNERSHIP**

Fig. 13.2

MID-CAREER OPTIONS
• **Associateship To Co-Ownership**
• **Merger-Acquisiton(s)**

Fig. 13.3

ate and/or consider a merger-acquisition of other established practices in your area. This injection of patients into your practice will immediately enhance your profitability and increase the value of your practice. (See Chapter 5, "Practice Mergers.") (Figure 13. 3)

Late Career Options. This group should be very cautious as they plan their transitions. This is the group most likely to get hurt in this entire process, primarily due to poor timing and/or by choosing the wrong transition option for their particular situation. This group also has the least amount of time to waste at this point in its career, and statistically has the poorest record for being able to recover from mistakes made in this area.

Most transition consultants will agree that three out of five late-career dentists unknowingly lose a substantial part of their practice value as they phase into retirement. This is why early planning is crucial. For those late-career dentists who are ready to sell immediately and retire, early planning becomes less of an issue. If you fit this situation and you feel that your practice value has declined, consider hiring a transition management consultant to get your practice back on track before selling. Your investment can easily be recouped by the higher selling price you receive, not to mention the enhanced profitability you will enjoy up until the time of sale.

All transition options are not created equal. The transition that is best for you will depend on where you are in your career at the time you implement it. The right transition option for a dentist to consider at one career pivot point may be a totally inappropriate option to consider at another. This is where many of the biggest mistakes are made in transitioning. A common example of this occurs with asssociateships. Bringing in an associate to buy into your practice may be an excellent transition option to consider in mid-career, but it may be a very poor option to consider in late career (five years or less from retirement). Dentists who are this close to retirement may want to consider more timely transition options than traditional associateships or buy-in arrangements. (See Chapter 3, "Successful Sales Strategies.")

Selling your practice too early is another big mistake. Many mid-career dentists (and early late-career dentists) sell too soon. Many are just "road weary" and are looking for some relief. The thought of selling and then working for the buyer initially sounds great—it's a chance to be freed from the management and overhead responsibilities of practice. Unfortunately, many of these individuals find, years later, that they are unhappy because they are no longer in control of the practice. They also often find that their income drops dramatically following the sale—after all, they are no longer in control of how patients are scheduled, and their compensation is almost always less than what they made as an owner. Many of these early sellers later seek out practices to buy (i.e., starting all over again) to regain control. These events can totally negate the profit "windfall" received from the sale of the practice.

Note: Despite my words of caution, selling before retirement (See Chapter 3, "Successful Sales Strategies") has been a superb way for many dentists to sell. However, a "look before you leap" strategy should most definitely be utilized. (Figure 13-4)

When **do you want to get to** *wherever* **it is you're going?** For the early-career dentist, this can mean when to take that big step into practice ownership. For the mid-career dentist this can mean when to bring in an associate to expand the practice and cash in practice equity. It can

LATE CAREER OPTIONS

- **Associateship To Co-Ownership**

- **Practice Sale Strategies**

  - **Retirement Sale**

  - **Deferred Sale**

  - **Pre-Retirement Sale**

  - **Goodwill Only Sale**

Fig. 13.4

also mean when to consider expanding the practice through merging with a nearby retiring dentist. For the late-career dentist, this can mean when to sell and how to go about the sale based on the available options. (See Chapter 3, "Successful Sales Strategies.")

Step 3:
Practice Financial Analysis

Once you've determined where you are and you're comfortable with a transition option, you should proceed to a Practice Financial Analysis. This analysis would normally include a practice valuation and a strategic transition plan (or format) to serve as a guide through the various steps of whatever transition option has been chosen (i.e., much like a comprehensive treatment plan for a patient). I recommend having such an analysis prepared and reviewed prior to proceeding with any type of practice transition. Financial projections should be included, showing the future economic picture for the dentists involved in the transition. (Figure 13.5, page 282)

Step 4:
Implement Your Plan

Once you have all the necessary practice information in place, you're ready to proceed to the implementation of your plan. Depending on your timing, you can then proceed to the following steps. (Figure 13. 6, page 283)

Construct Practice Prospectus. Normally, some type of practice prospectus is constructed to give the candidate (as well as his or her advisors) general information as well as area demographics. Proformas (income projections) showing current and anticipated expenses of the practice, along with the debt service associated with the purchase, are also provided. The debt service is determined by calculating the total payments due the lending institution and/or seller for the financing of the purchase price. (See Chapter 7, "Determining the Value of Your Practice," and Chapter 10, "Purchasing or Buying Into a Practice.") This

---

PRACTICE FINANCIAL ANALYSIS

- **Practice Valuation**

- **Strategic Plan (Format)**

  - **Associateship To Co-Ownership Format**

  - **Practice Sale Format**

  - **Practice Merger Format**

Fig. 13.5

proforma conveys to the buyer the true value of your practice. Rather than focusing on just the space, profit and value can be emphasized. This is an important selling tool, and will often make the difference between whether or not a practice sells.

Locate a Transition Candidate. With a plan firmly in place, it's time to begin thinking about the right candidate for your transition plan. Ask yourself this question: "Do you want to find your own candidate or would you prefer that a third party consultant or broker do this for you?"

I hear mixed comments from dentists as to how they feel about locating their own candidates for a transition. But whether you locate one yourself or have a third party do this for you, know that finding candidates to interview for your practice may be the easiest part of the process. The real challenge comes in educating and converting that individual into a financially and emotionally committed "transition partner." In some situations, dentists who locate their own candidates will find that some consulting companies and brokers will charge a lesser fee (and in some cases a flat fee).

Bringing Your Records Up to Date. The quality of the practice records is very important. The list of records would include patient, financials, income, insurance, and so forth. Transitioning dentists need to be able to substantiate the number of new patients per month, the number of recare visits per month, the number of managed care and fee-for-service patients entering the practice, and so forth. Additional records to consider are your list of referral sources, if applicable.

IMPLEMENTING YOUR PLAN STEPS

- **Construct Practice Prospectus**

- **Locate A Transition Candidate**

- **Review Practice Financial Data**

- **Negotiate Terms and Conditions**

- **Construct Agreements**

- **Protect Your Investment**

Fig. 13.6

Marketing Your Practice as a Purchase or Buy-In Opportunity

To effectively market your practice for any type of transition, it's necessary that you obtain information on the current market in your area. Having the ideal practice isn't enough. You must know what the current demand is for opportunities in your area, or much of your work will be in vain. You could waste years of your life in the process.

What Kind of Market Are You In? Are you in a buyer or seller's market? How many other practices in your area are offering opportunities to purchase or buy-in? How is the average practice sale or buy-in structured so that behind the surface appeal, your practice will be financially viable for someone to consider?

In most areas of the country, there has been a gradual shift from a seller's to a buyer's market. Increasing numbers of dentists reaching retirement age (as well as those selling early), coupled with the fact that there are fewer graduates, probably causes this. Some locations will require different marketing efforts. Some need to emphasize the benefits and culture of the community and not just the practice, for instance. From my perspective, the Sunbelt states (Texas, California, Florida) are enjoying the greatest amount of interest. Licensing requirements enable other states to enjoy similar opportunities, particularly the coastal and/or metropolitan areas within those states.

Typical Purchaser Profile. Most buyers have been out of dental school five years or less. Let me repeat that. *Most buyers have been out of school five years or less.* Often, the image a selling dentist has of the purchaser of his practice is quite different from the reality of the marketplace.

Unknowingly, many selling dentists shy away from younger candidates and search for more mature and experienced buyers. Few such candidates exist; for many sellers, it will be like finding a needle in a haystack. In other words, most of the more mature and experienced dentists are already settled, as are their families. Few dentists relocate after they have established successful practices. This limits the buyer pool to those who have not yet landed on an opportunity.

Because most buyers are inexperienced and hold massive school debt, financing has only recently become easier to obtain. As mentioned throughout this book, entities such as the Matsco Companies have filled this market void with a win-win result for everyone involved.

'To Do's' Before Marketing Your Practice

- Attend seminars and workshops to discover advice on locating candidates and working with candidates you've already found or with whom you are already practicing.

- Have your practice valued.

- Determine whom you're going to use for assistance.

- Gather all manufacturers' warranties and inspection reports for X-ray and sterilization equipment, and so forth.

- Provide any needed maintenance or repair.

- Keep production and collection numbers stable or on an upswing.

- Construct a preliminary agreement (as described in Chapter 8).

- Determine your methods of advertising as well as how the inquiries will be handled (by your CPA? A post office box? A transition consultant?).

There are several ways to market your practice opportunity. Below are just a few of the most common venues to consider.

- **Dental Journal Ads:** Most national, state, and regional dental associations accept this type of classified advertising in their publications.

- **Direct Mail:** You can obtain a list of recent successful board candidates from most state agencies, as well as lists of all licensed dentists in your state or region. Many state and national journals publish lists of dentists with their age and graduation date from dental school.

- **Dental Schools:** Dental schools will sometimes send you lists of their graduating class members for direct mail. Others will post letters about your practice in certain designated areas of the school.

Regardless of which route you go, I recommend that you prequalify your prospects before proceeding too far in the process. It is perfectly appropriate to ask for credit reports and financial statements, particularly if you hope to sell part or all of your practice to this individual in the near future.

Ask for a Confidentiality Agreement (Nondisclosure). If you are interviewing candidates on your own, it's wise to have them sign a confidentiality agreement (nondisclosure agreement) before giving them any confidential financial information on you or your practice. Although you may feel uncomfortable asking for this, it's certainly important to request it.

Review Your Practice Opportunity. I don't normally recommend that you review and negotiate the price and terms of the transaction directly with your candidate. Consider the use of a third party to help with this. The third party can act as insulation between the two of you, hopefully preventing the situation from becoming adversarial in nature.

Note: Most buyer or associate candidates will view your lawyer or accountant as an adversary, so try not to use either of these individuals as your intermediary.

Step 5:
Protect Your Investment

Protecting your investment begins with comprehensive agreements. First of all, what is your investment in this process? It may consist of the money owed you in a seller-financed sale or buy-in. It may also represent the ongoing income you wish to generate from clinical dentistry during the transition, requiring the relationship you have with the buyer be clearly defined.

As suggested in Chapter 8, "Structuring Your Agreements," begin with a preliminary agreement before proceeding to more an extensive final agreement. This important step will help ensure that both parties are agreeing to the major terms and conditions before proceeding. (Why waste all that time, energy, and money on final agreements until you are sure you are both agreeing to the basics?)

For some dentists, protecting their investments might mean securing cash for the sale of the practice, so there will never be any worry about getting paid. As discussed throughout this book, cash is now available for up to 100% of the selling price of the practice. Some candidates are unable to get cash. Others prefer, for tax purposes, not to take the entire sale proceeds in one lump sum. In these cases, a properly constructed Security Agreement (which should be part of a Practice Buy-In or Practice Sale Agreement—see Chapter 8, "Structuring Your Agreements") will go a long way toward protecting your interests. Dentists who are selling outright and soon retiring have greater risk than those who are only selling part of the practice and intend to continue practicing for years to come.

Transition Management

Incorporating a transition management program into the practice following the sale makes a lot of sense—particularly in those instances of seller financing. The buyer-dentists also enjoy the services of the transition management consultant—in fact, they do at least 20% better than those in non-managed transitions.

It's been my experience that most dentists who think deeply about personal needs and desires also have the ability to plan for what they want. They have an awareness of the true principles that govern their quality of life. In some respects, this book is a reminder of things that, deep inside, most of us already know.

The fact that we know—but do not always transfer into practice transition planning—is often the gap between knowing what we want to have happen in our practice transition cycle and asking for what we need.

It's also my experience that most dentists want to lead meaningful lives and make a contribution to the dental health of the individuals they treat. They want to learn, give, and leave a legacy imbued with fulfillment, balance, and joy. Practice transition is about all of these things.

However, more often than not, the traditional practice life cycle gets in the way. Comprehensive transition planning keeps us focused on what's urgent and important. Certainly, we all want the tremendous benefits of the accomplishment of our goals—but we need more. Making transition decisions at the last minute is no substitute for making the right decisions now. We need a well-constructed plan along with the necessary tools to empower us to fulfill our basic needs and capacities in a balanced, principle-centered environment.

Bottom-line, the power to create quality of life is not in any comprehensive transition plan. It is not in any specific technique or tool. The secret does not lie with one advisor who has all the magic answers. It is not limited to our ability to create and construct a plan for the life cycle and transition of our practice. None of us knows what opportunities, challenges, surprises, or unexpected turns the next road will bring.

The power to create quality of life is within each of us. It's in our ability to develop and listen to our inner voices and so act with integrity in the moment of choice. Whether that "moment" involves planning a new practice, cashing in the equity of an existing practice, or selling a practice built on the foundation of our life's work, to be effective our plans must be aligned with reality, structured for enhanced development, and guided by our inner compass.

Planning for what you want in your practice transition is sometimes tough. We often allow fear to hold us back. We make mistakes. We fall back into old habits of urgency rather than moving ahead with comprehensive planning.

The more we exercise personal leadership and move into comprehensive transition planning of our practice transition, the more we can feel growth. We can then begin to really enjoy life—an upward spiral, each part adding to what's gone before. The end result? Quality of life.

Conclusion

What is this stuff about "quality of life?" The quality of life I'm talking about comes from the function of our deepest inner hopes, goals, and desires. It's joyful living. It's found in the midst of planning, not running from it.

The best way to create quality of life may well be to learn to listen to and live by conscience. The most critical turning point in your practice transition life cycle is *now*. Now is the time to make decisions about the eventual transition of your practice. In taking the first step to develop a comprehensive transition plan for your future, you will begin to enjoy the consequences and reap the rewards rather than allowing fear to rule your future.

We have been given the great gifts of time and the freedom to choose. We often forget that we also have the responsibility to direct our efforts in the use of time we are given.

As dentists, for the most part, we've spent our time taking care of business. As the new era in the practice transition cycle appears, it will be important that we make changes for our future. Rather than *spending* our time, perhaps we should look closer at *investing* our time.

As in any other investment model, time spent is gone. Time invested increases rewards and enhances quality of life. The quality of our lives is dependent on many factors. In the ever-changing world of practice transitions, let us never fail to remember how fortunate our profession has been to those of us who have devoted our lives to dentistry. How many people in the world have the opportunity to be as blessed as we are in the dental field?

Ask yourself one question: "Is there something I can do to make a difference in the end result of the transition of my practice?"

Think about it. It most often will require hiring an advisor and "learning to let go." It may be that you begin to plan now for the eventual transition of your practice. Your contribution to your practice transition life cycle will impact your family, your team, your patients, your practice and your community. There are many things you can do. There are many decisions you can make. Let us be the first to encourage you to act on making changes in your practice life cycle.

Wherever you are in the transition process, I urge you to act on what your heart tells you. Make this promise to yourself and keep it. Set your goal and achieve it. In the end, our hope for you is that you will be able to look back and know that dentistry was in fact, worth it all.

I

APPENDIX:
PITFALLS, MYTHS,
AND MISCONCEPTIONS

One of the original "missions" behind writing this book was to reveal some of the many pitfalls, myths, and misconceptions encountered by dentists when planning their transitions. Many dentists tend to delay the planning of their transitions. This in turn *greatly* increases their chances of failure. It's a viscous cycle. Learn to identify and then avoid pitfalls. Gain a better understanding of the circumstances surrounding the myths and misconceptions. You will save a great deal of time and money, not to mention a lot of heart muscle and stomach lining. (Figure A-1.1, page 290)

Most of the pitfalls dentists encounter can be attributed to poor (or the complete lack of) pre-transition planning. As the overall interest level in transitions has increased over the last two decades, so too have the number of mistakes dentists have made. Transition mistakes in the past cost dentists little if any money—perhaps a few thousand dollars. Those mistakes cost the dentist emotional wear and tear but since overall expectations were minimal, less stress and anxiety resulted. Today, the stakes are much higher. Tens and even hundreds of thousands of dollars are at risk, along with serious emotional trauma resulting from a failed or flawed transition.

COMMONLY ENCOUNTERED PITFALLS
• The Associate "Revolving Door" Syndrome
• The Associate With No Contract
• The Overkill Restrictive Covenant
• The Over-Compensated Associate
• Hiring An Associate In A "Slow" Practice
• Buy Out *Options* Versus Buy Out *Obligations*
• The Overpriced Practice
• An Acountant's Practice Valuation
• The Over-Lawyered Transaction

Fig. A-1.1

What follows is a few of the most notable of these—and what you can do to avoid them.

The Associate "Revolving Door" Syndrome

We have certainly seen this situation on countless occasions. We watch a colleague bring in a new associate on what appears to be a revolving-door basis. First, it was Dr. Smith, *then* it was Dr. Jones, and so forth. Each time this seemed like a good decision, yet for some reason, these relationships just never seemed to last. (For some of you, this may sound familiar.) For most dentists, the continuous cycle of associates is extremely frustrating—and for the patients as well. How embarrassing it is to have to constantly explain to patients why Dr. Smith is "no longer here." (I went through this in my own practice, and there was always this *dead silence* afterwards.) It's even more embarrassing a second and a third time, especially when the *same* patient keeps asking about the "previous associates." Many dentists tell me they will bring no more associates into their practices because "they always seem to leave before the end of the first year."

As they share their "associateship problems," I inevitably find that they *all* approached the associate arrangement on a very casual basis. This attitude toward the planning of associateships can literally make for a "revolving door" of young associates. Prevent this problem by constructing a clear plan up front. Openly discuss *all* the details. I have found that associate-dentists who are serious about making a long-term commitment are happy to go through this process. Associates who aren't interested in making a long-term commitment (and perhaps have other agendas in mind) usually appear disinterested and impatient with the process. Often anxious, they "just want to start working." Detecting this attitude early can help both parties find practice situations that will better meet the needs of all concerned. If the associate really wants to own a practice and just needs a job in the interim, then let's match that individual with an owner-dentist who doesn't want a long-term association. It's just that simple. Due to the fact that many dentists don't really talk to each other about "details," the dentists often get wrongly matched together. This repeatedly happens.

The Associate with No Contract

This is another form of a casually constructed associateship. Many dentists prefer to start their business relationships with associates on a trial basis. They often have no contract or prefer to use "simple" contracts, often incomplete and without any non-compete provisions. (These provisions protect the practice against competition by the associate should the associate exit from the practice.) Without this protection in place, it is no surprise that many owner-associate relationships fail. As an owner-dentist, do not use incomplete documents, particularly ones without non-compete agreements. Be sure to integrate this into your plan; this is a *very* important part of your business agreement.

The "Overkill" Restrictive Covenant

Often, restrictive covenants (also referred to non-competition agreements) are constructed from an "overkill" perspective. Examples:

- An owner's advisor trying to protect the client from competition from a young associate-dentist.

- A buyer's advisor trying to protect the client from the seller's potential competition.

Much like the tendency we have to over-insure some assets, there's a tendency to be over-insured in this situation by the use of an excessively restrictive covenant. Example:

- Some legal advisors recommend non-compete agreements covering an entire county, but there are few practice situations where an *entire* county would be an appropriate. Most restrictive covenants cover *much* smaller areas (exceptions could be rural areas of the country). A non-compete of this size is probably "overkill."

Any advisor who's familiar with dental practice transitions would know that this area is excessive. Quite often, this creates animosity in the mind of the associate who suddenly begins to think that there must be other areas of unfair overkill in the contract. The non-compete area should cover a distance that will *adequately* protect the owner from competition and cover the area where the *majority* of the patient base is located.

Literally hundreds of issues are at stake in practice transition agreements. When either side starts with an overkill mentality, there will be a tendency for every single issue to be addressed in the same way. If one issue seems unfair, suddenly every issue will appear that way. Avoid this common problem. (See Chapter 8, "Structuring Your Agreements.")

The Over-Compensated Associate

As discussed in Chapter 4, "Creating 'Win-Win' Associateship to Co-Ownership Arrangements," one serious problem to avoid is that of over-compensating the associate.

This problem is often very obvious at the outset: An associate is paid a higher percentage than is the owner. It can start benignly, with the associate being paid a "customary" percentage of his or her collections. Next, the owner decides (or is asked) to pay the associate's malpractice and health insurance. Later, a continuing education allowance is requested so the associate can provide better clinical services to the patients.

Eventually, through salary and other fringes, the associate ends up with a higher percentage from his or her production than the owner is making from his. Not only is this an inequitable situation for the owner, but we have now created a tremendous problem for the associate—tremendous disincentive to buy in. Here's why, upon buying in, the associate may end up making a lower net percentage as a co-owner than as an associate.

Who would want to buy in under these circumstances?

Hiring an Associate in a "Slow" Practice

Although more and more dentists are becoming wise to this particular pitfall, I still meet with dentists who think that hiring an associate will automatically expand their patient base. In most geographic areas, there aren't patients out there "looking for dentists." It's often just the reverse. If the associate is expected to market and do all those other things necessary to build the practice, there needs to be a healthy nucleus of patients in place for him or her to build *from*. Otherwise, the arrangement will fail economically. Avoid this mistake, and consider marketing or merger options to create a nucleus of patients for an associate.

Buy-Out Options Vs. Buy-Out Obligations

This is a big mistake dentists make—putting an option in an agreement by which the practice will be purchased by an associate. Many dentists believe that if an associate were presented with the opportunity, there would be no way he or she would turn it down. Well, an option to say *yes* is also an option to say *no* and, unfortunately, the *no* option is the one most often pursued. This is particularly true in the situation where the associate is comfortable with the size of the practice he or she has built within the owner's.

The Over-Priced Practice

I often encounter a situation in which a dentist's CPA (or other financial advisor) recommends not purchasing a practice because it "costs too much"—even though it would generate good cash flow for the buyer. Often, these advisors have never actually handled the sale of a dental practice, yet they give this advice. (Some of these advisors brag about their work with "hundreds of doctors and dentists" over the years that supposedly makes them experts. But performing quarterly and annual tax returns for health care professionals each year doesn't qualify them to be dental practice appraisers or practice transition experts.) Before you take advice from anyone regarding the purchase or sale of a dental practice, ask him or her one question: "How many dental practices (not medical) has he or she sold in the last three to four years?" Can they supply you with the names of these dentists? If you discover he or she has had little or no real experience in this area, quickly find someone who has.

An Accountant's Practice Valuation

This is a classic situation: The accountant-valued practice. No offense intended, but few accountants have had much (if any) true experience in the real market of selling dental practices. (Those that have had experience are fairly well known nationally and are therefore easy to locate for assistance.) As a result, few accountants know what practices are actually selling for, which is crucial information to know if you are going to hold yourself out as an appraiser of dental practices. A well-known restorative dentist told me one time that, "It probably makes as much sense to hire an accountant to appraise your house as it would a dental practice, since he or she has probably never marketed and sold either."

The "Over-Lawyered" Transaction

It's very easy for your practice transition to end up being "over-lawyered" and often by two lawyers with totally opposite opinions on nearly every issue concerning the proposed transaction. I understand the reasoning of most lawyers. In the process of "taking care of their clients" the opposing lawyers make dozens of "overkill" demands from the other side, with each lawyer striving for a one-sided end result (win-lose). I certainly believe in defending my position but approaching transitions from an adversarial position is not a positive direction for you or your candidate. Thousands of dollars can be spent with opposing lawyers going back and forth with endless changes and demands, with each lawyer trying to out-do the other (and often over issues that they know little about). This explains why many practice transition deals are killed in the process. Exert some control over the process before you begin working with your lawyer. Don't give him or her *carte blanche* and be sure he or she understands you are interested in a fair deal for both sides.

Now let's examine some common myths and misconseptions (Figure A-1.2, page 295).

"Associateships Don't Work"

As long as I can remember, I've heard dentists comment that associateships don't work. This attitude was literally "branded" into us in dental school, which may have had a lot to do with why my first associateship was short-lived. (Since I was convinced it wasn't going to work, it didn't.)

Six months into an associateship with a great dentist in Stone Mountain, Georgia, I departed to strike out on my own. There was a new, rapidly growing area northeast of Atlanta and I was certain it was the right place for me to go. In retrospect, had we had some help constructing a long-term plan leading to some type of co-ownership of the practice, we might still be together today.

I have been consulting with dentists long enough to understand the reasons why many of our associations don't work. A lot of it is due

---

MYTHS AND MISCONCEPTIONS

- **"Associateships Don't Work"**
- **"Let's Work Together First and Talk About the Details"**
- **"Wait Until the Buy-In to Value The Practice"**
- **"Sell the First Half to One Dentist, the Second Half to Another"**
- **"Most Patients Leave the Practice When it's Sold"**
- **"I Can't Afford To Buy A Practice"**
- **"Don't Buy Goodwill"**
- **"Mergers and Group Practice Are the Same"**
- **"My Practice Is Worth One Times My Year's Gross"**

Fig. A-1.2 *Myths and Misconceptions*

to our independence, but there are also other reasons. First, few dentists enter these relationships with much forethought or planning. We focus more on the clinical and not the business aspects of practice, taking a casual attitude toward our associations. Rather than taking the relationship seriously, we instead want to become "friends" with our associates, feeling that dealing with the business details might take away the friendliness. This lack of attention to the business details leads to a higher degree of associateship failures.

"Let's Work Together First and Talk About the Details Later"

Dentists frequently begin working together in various practice associations before discussing (and putting in writing) all of the proposed details of the relationship. Without a clear understanding of the mission between well-matched individuals, our associations have little chance of lasting. I know few dentists who started their relationships from such a casual perspective (other than the "lucky" ones) who are still together today. That is why we are still very much in a solo profession. All you have to do is look around to find that what I am saying is true.

It's interesting when you think about it. As dentists, we've taken most other phases of our education and career very seriously, methodically planning ahead for each step we've taken. First there was college, then dental school, then the state board exams, and finally, private practice. Suddenly, we find ourselves in an arena where we've had very little education—the transition phase of a dental practice. All of the planning mentality we used so successfully in the past suddenly disappears. Later, when our professional relationships fail, we scratch our heads and wonder why.

A well thought-out, well-planned associateship can work. With the trend going toward "groups" (at least from my perspective), it certainly makes sense to explore ways to improve the way we plan for and eventually structure them.

Wait Until the Buy-In to Value the Practice"

This is another common mistake—waiting until the proposed buy-in date nears (i.e., after the associate has been working in the practice) to have the practice valued. If the associate is unaware of the proposed buy-in price, the situation can become disappointing and even explosive. The owner and associate often have totally different opinions as to how practices should be valued, and the time to discuss this is at the beginning of the relationship, not the end. Without doing this, you are jeopardizing the relationship and placing your proposed buy-in at risk. Why spend two to three years together only to find out that you and your associate are miles apart on this very important issue? Many associateships never reach the buy-in stage because of this.

One common problem area is that of earned equity—that is, what the associate feels he or she has added to the practice. Most associates don't want to pay for what they think "I have built." Therefore, they don't want the value of the practice (and therefore the buy-in price) to be determined after they have helped build it to the level where it's being valued. (I have found this to be a tremendous disincentive for the associate. The harder he or she works, the more he or she will have to pay later). Each practice situation must be looked at individually, and it's important to address this issue up front.

"Sell the First Half (of Your Practice) to One Dentist, the Second Half to Another"

Although this may seem like a logical approach, it's best to sell the second half to your "partner," allowing him or her to repeat the buy-in process simultaneously with a third dentist. Bypassing an existing co-owner in the practice may not help position the appropriate chain of succession you're striving to maintain. If there's an obligation in place for each junior co-owner in line to buy out the senior co-owners, this transfer of practice equity downstream facilitates the entry of new associates who will buy into part of the practice previously purchased by the junior co-owner.

It's like a relay race. One passes the baton to the other. This allows the same type of relationship to be established with each dentist who buys in. Each dentist has his or her own junior partner to buy in and eventually to buy him or her out.

Most Patients Leave the Practice When it's Sold"

I have never seen a specific survey about patient attrition after the sale of a practice. I've certainly asked buyers how the transition was going, but I have never talked about numbers. One of the reasons is that good statistics aren't available and there are no "norms" to compare. You see, few dentists track the number of patients leaving their practice on a "normal" basis (i.e., in the absence of any transition). Without a baseline for comparison, the number of patients that happen to leave the practice during a transition becomes meaningless.

In the majority of situations that I have seen, the purchasing dentist's gross income following the sale is usually greater than the income of the seller-dentist prior to the sale. Whatever patient attrition occurred seemed to be less significant to the buyer than the fact that he or she is doing as well or better than the seller was. In a well-managed transition, the transfer of the patient base should be very successful.

"I Can't Afford to Buy a Practice"

Many young dentists who are clinically and emotionally ready to own a practice are convinced they cannot afford to buy a practice. They feel they don't have the money or the financial backing to fund the purchase.

Many lending institutions today (such as the Matsco Companies) will loan young dentists enough money for a reasonable down payment for a practice. I suggest buying a practice as early as possible in your career. When comparing the income you can make as an owner versus the employee, a young dentist can't afford *not* to purchase a practice, in most cases.

"Don't Buy Goodwill"

Buyers of dental practices are often concerned about purchasing goodwill. This goodwill is very intangible in the eyes of a buyer, as it's not an asset that he or she can actually put his or her hands on. One thing is true: There's no guarantee that the seller's goodwill will transfer to the buyer. But there's a greater likelihood that it will than that it won't, if the transition is handled properly. Patients should be properly informed about the transition (through letters and a properly "scripted" staff), and if handled correctly, most patients will transfer over time. When looking at the monthly cost of purchasing the seller's goodwill compared to the thousands of dollars spent by dentists on Yellow Page advertisements to try to bring in new patients, purchasing goodwill is a bargain. I feel the quality of the patients is much greater when referred from a selling dentist than from a Yellow Page ad.

"Mergers and Group Practice are the Same"

Practice mergers differ from traditional group practices. In a true practice merger (usually involving two dentists), one of the dentist's practices is purchased by the other, forming a single-practice entity. One of the goals of the selling dentist is to phase into retirement, relocate, or pursue another career. In a group practice, you have multiple dentists with individual practices sharing the space. When available, I believe practice mergers to be superior arrangements when compared to group practices. Here we have blended individuals together with opposite but complimentary goals—one dentist wants to build and the other wants to phase into retirement. In group practices, you often have individuals together with the same goals, all trying to get to the same place at the same time.

"My Practice is Worth One Times My Year's Gross"

Many dentists believe that their practice is worth one times their most recent gross collections. At one time this might have been true—especially orthodontic practices. Often, this one year's gross value included the accounts receivable and/or other cash assets of the practice. It also often reflected creative financing by the seller (such as interest-free financing).

If you weigh these additional factors in the equation, you'll see how this value was attained.

Some of the new dental management companies are offering high prices for practices in some areas and under certain circumstances. However, if one reads between the lines of their offers, it's not always clear as to what the seller is actually receiving. Be sure to have a competent advisor review any dental management contract you're considering.

II

APPENDIX: SPECIALTY PRACTICES, SPECIAL CONSIDERATIONS

Most of the information found in *Planning Successful Practice Transitions* is applicable to specialty as well as general practices. However, some specific differences do exist between the two in some of the following areas: practice valuation considerations, associate compensation methods, and the different transition requirements that exist for the successful transfer of a *doctor*-referral base as well as a patient-referral base. It is important for today's dental specialist to be aware of these differences and not mistakenly apply concepts used in general practice.

Though an entire text would be necessary to cover all of the differences to consider between general and specialty practices, the following checklist covers the primary ones. (Figure A-2.1)

Practice Valuation Considerations

There are different factors to consider in the valuation of specialty vs. general dental practices. Much of this difference lies in the good-

---

TRANSITION VARIABLES
SPECIALTY GENERAL PRACTICE

- PRACTICE VALUATION CONSIDERATIONS
- THE VALUE OF REFERRALS
- ASSOCIATE COMPENSATION
- ORTHODONTIC PRACTICE
- TRANSITION REQUIREMENTS
- PRACTICE BUY-INS vs. OUTRIGHT SALES

Fig. A-2.1

will value of the practice and the ability and mechanism for properly transferring this value. In Chapter 7, "Determining the Value of Your Practice," we saw that goodwill *value* is often based on a multiplier of the gross or net income of the practice. In the general practice marketplace, this value is supported in the mind of the buyer by ongoing regular visits by patients through the recare program and new patient referrals into the practice by others. Many buyers of general practices find that the re-care/hygiene program alone can support the monthly payments on the purchase of the practice.

Goodwill in a specialty practice is more difficult to measure, maintain, and transfer than in a general practice. (In some cases, the goodwill value may be minimal or even non-existent.) From the perspective of most buyers, the goodwill in oral surgery and endodontic practices is the most difficult to transfer. This is why it's essential for dentists in these specialty areas to plan early, selling their practices in increments (See Chapter 4, "Creating 'Win-Win' Associateship to Co-Ownership Arrangements.")

The goodwill in pedodontic, periodontic orthodontic, and prosthodontic practices is more readily transferred, largely due to the patient referral base that exists. In orthodontics, we have the additional benefit of having contracts-receivable in place, contributing to add-on value.

There are more buyers seeking general practices than specialty practices, making it a more active market. Goodwill value is easier to build and calculate because referrals depend on patients, and, as we all know, referrals are the life-blood of a general dental practitioner. When dentists buy a general practice, they are buying the re-care patient base and, we hope, a group of people who like nothing more than referring their dentist to others.

Specialty practices depend on professional referrals, so we must look at different components to establish the true value of the practice, as well as different mechanisms of "untapping" the goodwill that *is* present. Many newly graduated specialists I speak with still believe they can set up a practice on their own, and this attitude does affect market value. (I do sense that this attitude among specialists is slowly changing.)

In general, specialists will often enjoy higher market values for their practices when they plan ahead and sell *portions* of the practice through buy-in arrangements.

For many years, orthodontic practices were valued higher than other practices, largely because of the tangible value of the contracts receivable. Most types of dental practices don't have this kind of contracted care. Patients agree to monthly payments, which transfer to the buyer if the practice is sold mid-contract. This arrangement guarantees income for a buyer, which drives up the value of the practice. Some orthodontic practices have traditionally sold for a price equal to 100% of the annual gross, but now 70% to 80% has become more common. (See Chapter 7, "Determining the Value of Your Practice," with particular emphasis on the importance of net income vs. gross income.)

Orthodontic practices also have the advantage of patient referrals, much like the pediatric dentist. The combination of contracts receivable and referrals is a powerful one. In addition, patient referrals are by definition more valuable than professional referrals. A patient-referral base is secure and stable and doesn't depend on a large number of referrals coming from a small number of people. In orthodontic practice, the contracts receivable as well as the accounts receivable are usually included in the purchase price. The contracts-receivable are in essence what the buyer is buying—the accounts receivable are usually thrown in to offset any "retreats," treatment overruns, or prepaids the buyer may find.

The Value of Referrals

Referral bases are not created equal, particularly in specialty practices. The younger and more diverse a referral base is, the more valuable it is. For example, if your referral base consists of older dentists who are about to retire, how will a potential buyer view the value of the practice? This one issue makes it even more important to plan for a transition in which the specialist sells part or all of the practice.

Look at it this way: As dentists mature and settle into practice, they often stop doing the promotional activities they engaged in when they first started out. But if a mid-career specialist brings in an associate, the referral base continues to expand. The younger specialists end up with more referrals because other general dentists, particularly those who are new to the area, better know them. If specialists bring in new associates, the newcomers can continue the hard work of building a professional referral base. These young dentists are usually happy to "court" new and relocating dentists, which expands professional alliances.

Diversity is also an important issue. The greater number of referral sources, the less important the loss of one is. Buyers are understandably nervous when they hear that 70% of referrals come from one source. What if that dentist doesn't like the buyer? It's much more valuable to have a few leading referral sources that comprise a large percentage of the base.

These realities drive home the value of having a specialist associate who can keep the referral base young and viable. When a referral system is smooth, selling part or all of the practice can be easily accomplished.

Associate Compensation

To some degree, associate compensation packages also differ in specialty practices during the pre-buy-in phase. In general, associates in specialty practices are paid a higher margin of profit (typically 5% to 10% higher) than in general practices. (Example: a typical general dentist associate paid 30% might find that in the same area, an associate specialist might be paid 35% to 40%.)

In addition to this percentage compensation, it's not unusual for owner-specialists to provide their associates with certain benefits as part of their compensation. Some of these benefits include malpractice insurance, a continuing education allowance, various dues and membership fees, and an allowance for entertaining referral sources. Often, a *guaranteed* annual salary is given to specialty associates, at least for the first year. These salaries vary from area to area and practice to practice, but at some point they must be based on reality, meaning how much net profit the practice is producing. Often, bonuses are paid based on the associate's collections exceeding certain pre-set goals.

Orthodontic Practice

In an orthodontic practice with two or more practitioners, patients may not always be treated and/or checked by the same individual, as is usually the case in general practices. Therefore, compensating an associate based on personal collections would be difficult to calculate. Paying an associate based on some prorated percentage of overall office collections usually works better.

An orthodontic associate in the pre-buy-in phase usually receives a salary based on the present and projected growth and profitability of the practice. Once the buy-in occurs, compensation may be based on an ownership-productivity arrangement (See Chapter 4, "Creating 'Win-Win' Associateship to Co-Ownership Arrangements.") The productivity compensation component is usually based on a combination of years of experience and the number of days each dentist worked.

In a situation where a more senior, more productive orthodontist is working with a younger, less productive orthodontist, it would probably be unfair to allocate the production income based strictly on days worked. I typically incorporate a sliding scale that allows equal division of this profit, once the two orthodontists have worked together for a certain number of years. This scale may require a 5- to 10-year period before the younger partner's equal productivity is rewarded. For example, in a situation where orthodontists have worked together long enough to have approximately equal productivity, production income is divided equally, based on each specialist working the same number of days. This amount is prorated, based on any differential in days worked. If one doctor works four days and the other works five, a ratio is developed and multiplied by the remaining net.

Compensation Example:
Dr. A works 5 days per week
Dr. B works 4 days per week
Total doctor days = 9 days per week
Dr. A. receives 5/9 of the profit; Dr. B receives 4/9 of the profit.

Transition Requirements

In general practices it is often preferable to have the seller-dentist stay with the practice through some minimal transition. Some situations requite it—others don't. But this is almost a *requirement* in specialty practices, because you are transferring an entirely different type of goodwill, namely relationships with referring dentists and other professionals. A longer transition period helps minimize (if not eliminate) any loss of referral sources. When I practiced dentistry I was more comfortable referring to new specialist-associates once there had been some extended relationship between the associate and the owner with whom

I had the original relationship. The presence of the experienced partner was reassuring.

This is a logical situation, since general dentists may be concerned about the competency of the new specialist. A general dentist feels responsible for the patient's well-being as a result of the referral, so if the experienced practitioner remains with the practice, there is time for confidence to develop. As it becomes clear that the associate, who is also going to be the new owner, is highly skilled, then the referral source remains intact. This issue is much less important in general dentistry referrals, which are usually made by patients.

Practice Buy-Ins Versus Outright Sale

Fewer specialty practices are able to accomplish profitable outright sales than general dentist practices. This is why you see a higher percentage of specialty practices structure buy-in arrangements that will lead to an eventual sale. Specialists also go beyond solo more often than general dentists due to the greater need for practice coverage.

III

Appendix: Frequently Asked Questions

Practice Sale Strategies

What practice sale options can a dentist consider today?

There are basically three practice sale options to consider: the retirement sale (also referred to as the walk-away sale), the deferred sale, and the pre-retirement sale. Each sale option has its distinct advantages and disadvantages, depending upon the personal and career situation of each individual dentist.

In the retirement sale, the seller-dentist plans to retire from practice immediately upon, or within a short period of time following, the sale. (When the dentist is not retiring, but perhaps is only relocating, this option is also referred to as a walk-away sale.) The selling dentist generally stays just long enough to complete any treatment in progress and to make any necessary introductions. The retirement sale option works best for the dentist who isn't interested in or is unable to sell the practice any earlier.

In the pre-retirement sale option, the sale of the practice occurs in advance of seller's retirement date. In most pre-retirement sale scenarios, the sale is consummated 1 to 3 years or more from the dentist's target retirement date. Following the sale, the seller continues to practice for the buyer, but in an overhead and management-free environment. Since the needs of both the selling and buying dentists will vary from one situation to the next, each pre-retirement sale must be structured on an individual basis to insure a successful end result.

In the deferred sale option, the actual sale of the practice occurs at some predetermined date in the future. During the time leading up to the sale, the future buyer works in the owner's practice as an associate. Both associate and owner have signed an agreement spelling out all terms and conditions of the sale in advance of their association. Upon the agreed-upon sale date (which may not occur for years), the transfer of practice ownership occurs automatically.

The deferred-sale approach allows the buyer and seller adequate time to prepare for the transfer of ownership and the gradual transition of the patients. This approach is most often needed in situations where the associate is not yet experienced enough to assume ownership in the beginning, and/or where the owner is not yet ready or able, to sell the practice. By specifying all terms and conditions up-front, both parties are making a commitment to the future direction of the relationship. This also avoids future misunderstandings and better insures that the sale will actually take place.

How early should a dentist begin planning for the sale of his or her practice?

Most dentists should begin thoroughly planning for the sale of their practices five years from their desired target retirement date. By planning ahead, not only can the right practice sale option be determined, steps can be taken to enhance and preserve the value of the practice prior to the proposed sale date. Often, those same steps will increase the ongoing efficiency and profitability of the practice, providing the owner-dentist a double-windfall—an increase in profits prior to the sale and a higher selling price for the practice.

Those dentists who have existing buy-out agreements with current associates or partners have less preplanning to be concerned with than those without transition candidates. With built-in buyers for their practices, these dentists have eliminated the often stressful and time-consuming process of looking for a candidate and negotiating the terms and conditions of the sale when the time comes. They just need to make certain the agreements cover important issues such as how the value of the practice is to be determined at the time of sale. Make sure that all possible buy-out scenarios are addressed such as death, disability, breakup of the association, relocation, or voluntary retirement.

Is selling a dental practice before retirement a good option to consider?

Whether or not a dentist should sell his or her practice prior to retirement will depend upon several variables at the time—some personal, some economic. Many late-career dentists that I've spoke to over the years tell me that they'd like to find a way to gently glide into retirement as opposed to abruptly selling and retiring at the same time. But slowly phasing-out of practice is difficult for most dentists because much of the overhead is fixed and not related directly to practice production levels. Selling before retirement eliminates this dilemma, allowing the late-career dentist to transition-out of practice at his or her desired pace without overhead as a constraint. The pre-retirement sale also protects the value of the practice by locking it in before any production decline pulls the value down—another common scenario among late-career dentists. By having the option to continue practice in an overhead and management-free environment, the selling dentist is able to pursue other personal or business interests without the worry of running an office. If ensuring maximum practice value while gradually cutting back as you glide into retirement sounds appealing, then the pre-retirement sale option should be closely examined.

What happens to the value of a dental practice when the owner dies suddenly?

Unfortunately, the value of a dental practice immediately plummets the day the dentist dies,—often as much as 50%. Without some type of transition, or at the very least, a letter of introduction from the selling dentist, the value of the practice becomes questionable in the minds of prospective buyers—and every day that follows the dentist's death the value continues to plunge.

With a built-in-buyer in the form of an associate or partner, the deceased dentist's estate would not be saddled with this problem and could receive full market value for the practice upon the dentist's death.

Without one, the estate would be lucky to receive 30% to 40% of what the practice was worth prior to the dentist's death.

In the absence of a built-in buyer, what are some specific steps that a spouse should take in the event of the dentist's death?

Step One: The dentist's spouse should immediately contact a professional who is in the business of selling dental practices. Hopefully, the dentist will have included a provision regarding who will specifically handle the sale of the practice.

Step Two: Locate a dentist who would be willing to cover the practice until a buyer can be found. Be sure to locate a dentist who is practicing outside the general area, so that patients would be less tempted to later follow that dentist to his or her office.

Step Three: The dentist's spouse should to be emotionally prepared to accept much less for the practice than what it was worth prior to the death, which is why it's important for the practice to be valued on an annual basis. Knowing the real market value of the practice under ideal circumstances will enable the spouse to determine what selling price might be appropriate under the circumstances. Too often, I see grieving widows and widowers holding out for unrealistic offers, often leading to tragic consequences as the practice value continues to drops.

It seems common for late-career dentists to cut back on their production as they approach retirement. How much will this affect the value of their practices when it's time to sell?

Much of the value of a dental practice is directly related to its production history. Therefore, a drop in gross income will in most cases cause a direct reduction in the value of the practice. In addition, in most practices a gross income drop results in a lower profit percentage as well. The resulting blending of these two forces results in something I refer to as profit squeeze. I saw one practice in which a production decrease of 10% resulted in a profit decrease of 23%.

Net profit percentages drop because many practice expenses are fixed, despite decreases in production. Some dentists mistakenly believe that the only downside they face when cutting back production is a proportional reduction in profit. Little do they know that the percentage of profit they are netting on every dollar they continue to produce also drops. This can be a double-whammy and catches many dentists by surprise. Dentists should examine all available transition options prior to cutting back on production. Consider bringing someone into the practice as an associate, partner, or future buyer to transfer this production to. Otherwise, the value of this production will be forever lost, as few, if any, buyers will pay for what no longer seems to be there. And the percentage of profitability you make on the dollars you continue to produce will be dramatically decreased.

Profit Squeeze
Example: Production $1,000
Profit (35%) = $350
10% Production Decrease = $100
Remaining Profit $350-$100) = $250
Plus Expenses Eliminated* = $20
Adjusted Profit = $270
Profit Loss = $80
The decreased production of 10%, resulted in a profit loss of 23% ($80 = 23% of $350).

*Expenses Eliminated
Lab (10%) = $10;
Supplies (All) (9%) = $9;
Misc. (1%) = $1;
Expenses Eliminated = $20

What steps are involved for the dentist who wants to sell and retire?

Step One: Get your practice valued. It's an essential step, and without it, you are taking a risk by subjecting your selling price to arbitrary negotiations between you and the buyer.

Step Two. Search for viable buyer candidates. If you wish to look for buyers yourself, you might first consider dentists who are already practicing in your area. Ideally, their practice should be close enough to yours to merge, resulting in an ideal end result. Experienced dentists in the same area make great buyers—they are often more mentally and financially prepared for the purchase than typical buyer candidates, and you obviously don't have to "sell them" on the area as a great place to practice as compared to other areas.

Buyers outside your area can be found through placing ads in various state and national dental journals, as well as checking with local supply dealers. Dental schools are also a consideration, but the new-graduate pool isn't usually the best place to look for a buyer.

If you're considering using a transition specialist to help you locate a buyer and structure and negotiate the sale, you are probably making a wise choice. Locating, screening, and negotiating with buyer candidates (and their CPAs and attorneys) can be stressful and exhausting. Looking for candidates is one thing—it's actually the easy part of the job. Negotiating and structuring the deal—and most importantly, convincing the buyer to follow through with the sale and write the seller a check at closing—are the most difficult parts of the process. Those dentists who locate buyer candidates on their own should also use the services of a transition consultant to put the transaction together. It's been my experience that dentists who try to market, negotiate, and sell their own practices have an extremely high failure rate. When they do succeed, they often receive far less money in the end than those who hire transition specialists to do the job.

A dentist who is seven years from retirement is considering selling early and working for the buyer. Is this a good option to consider?

It depends. If the selling dentist plans on dramatically cutting back production, then this option might be worth exploring. A drop in practice value and dramatically reduced profits are likely to occur in that scenario, so it's always wise to examine all possible transition scenarios before randomly cutting back on practice production. Otherwise, the dentist who sells before retirement but plans to continue working at a reasonable pace has the following risks to consider.

What if the buyer and seller don't get along after the sale? What if philosophical differences emerge between the buyer and seller? What if the buyer wants to take the practice in a different direction than the seller desires? What if the buyer wants the seller to hand over more patients sooner than the seller was ready (emotionally or financially) to give him or her?

If a battle ensues over these or any other issues, it's obvious who the eventual winner will be—the new owner of the practice. It's not a comfortable position for a seller-dentist to be in, and that's why I recommend that dentists retain ownership of their practices (in most situations) until they are a little closer to retirement. Three years before retiring is the soonest I recommend selling outright, and the closer to target retirement date, the better.

Many dentists interested in selling before retirement don't take the time to do a thorough analysis of their practice numbers and compensation before selling. One of the first things that should be done is to compare the two possible scenarios—selling now and working for the buyer and selling at a later date and perhaps even waiting until retirement to sell. In doing such an analysis, the following should be examined and compared very carefully.

First, look at the total compensation "package" the seller is receiving from the practice as the owner. This is determined by looking at the seller's direct compensation and adding to this figure, where applicable, any depreciation expense being taken to offset the owner's taxable income, minus any principal and interest expenses being currently paid for equipment or other purchases being used in the practice. Next, take into consideration all benefits received by the owner that are currently being paid for by the practice, including such things as continuing education courses that were rolled into family vacations. Last but not least, be sure to include expenses that may have been considered elective or creative on the part of the practice. These are often the hardest ones to remember, as they are the most easily disguised and often forgotten by he owner.

Keep this in mind: When the practice is sold, these benefits will not be paid by the buyer's practice, they will have to be paid for out of the seller's net compensation as the buyer's associate.

Once the approximate owner's compensation package has been determined, then a simple comparison can be made with the after-sale compensation that a seller would likely receive. This is determined by adding to the seller's expected compensation, as the buyer's associate, the payments being received by the seller for the practice, or in the event of a cash sale, the ongoing investment return on the after-tax sale proceeds received at closing. Remember: When an economic forecast is based in part on the longevity of the relationship between buyer and seller after the sale, think conservatively. It's best to have lowered expectations here and be prepared for the relationship to be shorter than expected. This way, disappointment as well as potential economic chaos can be avoided.

Once you've examined this before- and after-sale analysis, you can make an intelligent decision based on emotional and financial considerations. If selling early still looks like a good move, then go for it. Otherwise, proceed with caution until a little closer to retirement date.

How does a dentist know how much to sell his/her practice for in today's market?

There are a number of variables that will influence the market value of a dental practice, so there is no quick answer to this question. However, two primary factors stand out above the rest. The first one is the overall profitability of the practice and the second is the geographic location of the practice.

The greater the profitability (which would include the owner's total compensation and fringe benefits), the more valuable the practice will be to a prospective buyer. It is out of the practice's profit that the buyer will be making the payments on the practice. Therefore, the higher the profit, the more net income remaining for the buyer after making these payments.

In addition, a more desirable practice location means a higher market value. This is much like what exists in the real estate market, and it's why two nearly identical practices can sell for drastically different prices, and at drastically different speeds.

What things should a seller-dentist avoid that could destroy the value of the practice?

There are many events and circumstances that can destroy the value of a dental practice. The most obvious practice value destroyers are death or disability of the owner. Either of these events can lead to immediate destruction of practice value, particularly for those dentists who haven't planned ahead by having a built-in buyer for their practice in the form of a committed associate or partner.

Another common practice-value destroyer is bringing an associate without a properly structured buy-in or buy-out agreement. In the absence of such an agreement, an associate may feel no obligation to purchase the owner's practice in the future, even though the associate would enjoy the benefits of immediate practice expansion through such a purchase. When this stalemate occurs, it often makes it difficult for the owner to sell the practice to an outside party, particularly if the associate leaves and competes with the owner in the same geographic area. This situation is particularly tragic upon the death or disability of the owner—often the associate "inherits" the practice for a fraction of its value under these circumstances.

The casual practice of space sharing can be another serious destroyer of practice value under certain circumstances. Some patients assume that all the dentists are "partners" and often are willing to go to one of the other members in the event of their dentist's illness, death, or temporary absence from practice. Because of the potential familiarity that patients may have with the other dentists in this group arrangement, they could be more inclined to transfer to one of them in a practice transition rather than to the "new" associate or buyer. Potential buyers are often concerned about such a possibility and often choose practices to purchase that have no such potential complications associated with them. Another factor to consider: A buyer of a practice that is in a group setting faces built-in competitors, as well individuals that he or she must live with. These various conditions often create what is potentially an unmarketable practice.

What type of advisor should a dentist hire to help with the sale of a practice?

A new breed of consultant has emerged over the last decade—the transition specialist. These consultants focus specifically on the needs of the transitioning dentist—those considering associates, partners, mergers, or some type of buy-in or sale. Some were once practicing dentists, while others were previously practice management consultants.

It's advisable to work with a transition specialist that can offer unbiased consulting services, so that all available transition options can be explored before proceeding in any particular direction. Once a particular option has been chosen, the right timing for the transition should then be determined. Timing is critical because two dentists choosing identical transition options may find their implementation timeframes should be totally different.

There are nationally recognized transition specialists who can help dentists with planning and implementing their transitions. Depending on the dentist's location, some of these consultants may be near, while others may not, but they are all as close as your telephone and fax machine. When you choose a transition specialist, speak to other dentists who have used his or her services in the past. Consult dentists on both sides of the transition fence (i.e., associates as well as owners, buyers as well as sellers) to for their views concerning the individual you're considering as an advisor. It will do you little good to choose a consultant with whom buyers or associates aren't comfortable.

The Value of Your Practice

What steps should a dentist take
To maximize the value of the practice?

Practice value can be maximized in several ways. One of the best methods is to implement a sound practice management program, which can enhance the profitability of the practice by improving the overall systems and efficiency of the practice.

The potential net income of your practice is essentially what a purchaser is buying. The higher the net profits the greater the value of the practice. In addition to increasing your *overall* practice net profit, increasing your practice's *percentage* of net profit is equally important. The greater the percentage of profit, the greater the value.

You can also expand the value of your practice by bringing in an associate or by purchasing and merging with another practice in your area. Knowing the right time to sell part or all of your practice can add value as well. Selling too late or too soon can greatly decrease the value you receive, which makes constructing a sound plan of transition an investment to consider.

All things being equal, the greater the ratio of fee-for-service patients entering your practice, as opposed to managed care patients, the more desirable your practice becomes. This, in turn, drives up the value.

Prior to selling part or all of your practice, consider relocating if you are in a declining area. The investment will definitely enhance the value of the practice and may significantly boost practice productivity as well.

Consider replacing any outdated and/or poorly functioning equipment with newer and more modern equipment and technology. (This includes computerization where none exists.) Previously owned equipment that is 5-10 years old can often be used for this purpose, saving thousands of dollars while still accomplishing the necessary task at hand. If your office décor has become dated, consider giving it a facelift.

These improvements can go a long way toward enhancing the market value of the practice.

Regardless of the steps you may take to enhance the value of your practice, this value remains in a locked position for most dentists until retirement. Making advance preparations to successfully transfer this value through buy-in, pre-retirement sale, and traditional sale arrangements can greatly enhance the final selling price received. This is why your foundation for enhancing practice value lies in a sound plan of transition. Without such a plan, steps taken to enhance practice value are in vain.

How can a dentist insure the value of his or her practice?

The best way to insure the value of the practice that you've spent years building is to have a well-constructed plan in place for transferring this value to an existing associate or partner, or perhaps to a dentist you've been sharing your facility with. By constructing a clear and equitable plan of transition in advance of the relationship you form with another dentist, you will be assured of receiving the full value of your practice when it comes time to sell.

How will incorporating managed care into a practice affect its value?

Generally, practices with a large managed care base sell for less than fee-for-service practices of similar size, and I think this trend will continue. As described in Chapter 7, "Determining the Value of Your Practice," practice values are largely market-driven (i.e., driven by the *buyers*), and most buyers today seek traditional fee-for-service practices to purchase.

To avoid this potential loss in practice value, restrict the managed-care portion of the practice to a minimum, where possible, if maximizing its value is the goal. I recommend that dentists consider purchasing and merging with other fee-for-service practices in their area as opposed to going the managed-care route. As described in Chapter 5, "Practice Mergers," merging as a means of practice expansion can greatly increase practice value and allow the dentist to avoid pursuing options that could decrease the value of the practice.

Associateship to Co-Ownership

When is a practice ready for an associate?
And how will the owner-dentist know when he
or she is personally ready to bring in an associate?

A practice is usually ready for an associate when the existing patient flow results in limited appointment availability for new and existing patients. In addition, long-term practice goals as well as practice trends should be evaluated prior to making the decision to bring in an associate.

In addition to ensuring that the practice is ready for an associate, equal emphasis should be placed on whether the dentist is actually ready. Prior to bringing in an associate, the owner-dentist should first evaluate the number of hours per week required for maintaining adequate patient care. The owner should then determine whether he or she is willing to reduce his or her clinical hours in the practice in order to shift some patients to the associate in the beginning of the relationship. Generally, both patient overflow and willingness to transfer patients must exist in order to maximize the success of an associateship to co-ownership arrangement.

How will bringing in an associate
impact the value of my practice?

Practice value can be maximized and ensured by a well-planned and implemented associateship to co-ownership arrangement. The associate can help expand the market share of the practice, increasing its value and enhancing the net profitability. In addition, this arrangement secures and establishes the future buy-in and buy-out price of the practice, with the associate becoming a built-in buyer in the event of death, disability, relocation, or retirement.

How could an associate harm
the value of a dental practice?

Associates are typically thought of as helping the practice, not harming it. After all, an associate can expand the hours and services of the practice and take a lot of pressure off the owner. Bringing in an associate without a clear plan for the future in the form of a properly structured buy-in or buy-out agreement is a common destroyer of practice value. If the associate leaves the practice and takes patients, the damage is obvious. However, the greatest damage occurs when the owner attempts to sell part or all of the practice while the associate is present in the practice. Potential buyers are concerned as to the true ownership of the patient base and where the patients will go upon the associate's exit from the practice. Few dentists find the camaraderie or profit enjoyed from a previous associateship to be worth the loss in practice value. This is why I recommend all such arrangements be entered into very seriously, with a clear, equitable, and agreed-upon plan for the future.

Why do so many associateships and partnerships fail?

The majority of associateships and partnerships fail due to one primary reason: little or no planning was done *in advance* of the relationship. Few dentists take the time to analyze whether the practice is ready for an associate and then fail to discuss the long-term structure and goals behind the proposed relationship prior to "moving in together." They basically cross their fingers and hope the things they desire in the relationship will somehow work out. Sometimes, the desires of the parties are complementary, but they often can be conflicting. It's essential that all issues be discussed so both parties know where the relationship is heading.

I recommend constructing a preliminary analysis of the owner's practice to determine if the practice and the owner are ready for an associate. Then all present and future issues should be discussed openly and thoroughly. Important issues that should be addressed include the eventual buy-in date, price, and terms, how the associate's earned equity will be treated, and how the two dentists will be compensated as partners after the buy-in. Once the major issues are clear to both parties, they should then be put in writing in a clear and understandable format. Dentists who follow this path will greatly enhance their chances of future success.

Should a soon-to-be graduate consider an associateship leading to a buy-in as a practice establishment option?

An excellent option for new graduates to consider is to start as an associate in an established dentist's practice. As part of the process, a clear plan for buying into the practice at a specified time in the future should be established. This approach represents a very low-risk way to establish a patient base, build practice equity, and eventually earn owner-level income. In the future, the associate can repeat the same process, allowing new associates to enter the practice to buy-in in sequence.

New graduates may also want to consider the outright purchase of the practice in which they plan to associate, as opposed to buying part of the practice. Many new graduates have found that purchasing a practice and having the seller work for them an ideal way of assuring themselves of practice ownership early in their career.

Whether the transition arrangement leads to a co-ownership situation or an outright purchase will often depend on the target retirement date of the owner-dentist and the clinical and managerial readiness of the associate dentist. Either approach will help the new graduate establish a plan for eventual ownership, allowing equity-building and enhanced profitability.

What are the advantages to bringing in an associate?

Many advantages exist for dentists who bring associates into their practices. It's important to know these advantages so they may be weighed against any real or perceived challenges involved. Sharing the day-to-day workload is probably the single biggest reason most dentists initially consider associates. Other benefits include increased practice production, lower overall overhead (as a percentage of gross), greater net profit, and enhanced practice value.

Many dental offices are grossly underutilized and under-productive due to the limited operating hours. By spreading a greater number of gross dollars over what is predominantly a fixed overhead, profitability can be greatly enhanced. In addition, if the practice is referring out any procedures that could be provided by a competent associate, it just makes good sense to include an associate in your practice expansion plans.

What are the most common mistakes made when bringing in an associate?

Overall, the most common mistake made when bringing in an associate is failing to construct a long-term plan prior to the beginning of the relationship. Taking a wait-and-see attitude will almost always lead to misunderstandings over issues that usually surround the eventual buy-in.

A specific mistake commonly made is overcompensating the associate—that is, paying the associate at a compensation level greater than what's appropriate for an employee in a non-management, no-risk situation. I see many dentists who are not on top of their numbers, who are not aware of how their total compensation (as a percentage of gross) compares to the associate's. Owner-dentists are often too generous to their associates, and end up paying them a higher net percentage of their production than they make as owners. This creates an unfair situation for the owner and creates no incentive for the associate to buy-in. If the associate discovers that he or she will make a lower net percentage after buying in than what he or she was making as an employee, he or she will not appreciate the investment and will often view the buy-in as overpriced. In this scenario, the generous owner-dentist suffers a double-whammy: overcompensating the associate and losing the associate or having to accept a lower price for the buy-in.

What are the steps involved in an associateship leading to co-ownership arrangement?

A well-planned associateship leading to co-ownership has three distinct phases: the trial period, the post-trial period, and the buy-in.

The initial trial period phase lasts from 6 months to 1 year, allowing the owner time to evaluate the clinical ability and communication skills of the associate and for both dentists to develop and evaluate their professional relationship.

The next phase is the post-trial period. It is demarcated from the trial period by two things: The associate signs a non-compete agreement (if one hasn't already been put in place) and establishes a good-faith deposit fund. The fund consists of retained earnings of the associate that will be applied toward the future buy-in. It is during the post-trial phase that the associate's commitment level is enhanced.

The final phase is the buy-in, which generally occurs within 1 to 2 years from the date of the associate's initial entry into the practice. The time frame is usually dependent upon the associate's ability to produce enough income to fund the buy-in and make a reasonable living in the process. Once the buy-in occurs, the two dentists become co-owners (partners or shareholders). This phase continues until both co-owners bring in a new associate to become a third co-owner or the senior co-owner sells his or her remaining interest in the practice to the junior co-owner, allowing the cycle to repeat itself.

The buy-in establishes co-ownership of the practice between the associate and owner, sets in motion an exit plan for senior co-owners and lays the groundwork for future associates to become co-owners.

What's wrong with having an associate as a long-term employee only, without offering any ownership in the practice?

Associates with no interest in eventual ownership are often less motivated than those who wish to be owners and generally do not make good long-term employees. They often develop an "employee-mentality," with little concern or interest in the management of the practice, including overhead control. In some situations, these associates never aspire to ownership. In other situations, the owner's practice is used as a temporary "holding place" until the associate leaves to purchase an established practice or set up a new practice. This is where the "revolving door syndrome" originated, in which new associates enter and leave on an ongoing basis. (In fact, I know of many practices that have "spawned" five to six new practices in their community this way.) Staff and patient dissatisfaction often surfaces in this environment, which can certainly have a negative impact on the practice.

Practice Mergers

What's the difference between a practice merger and forming a group practice?

In a practice merger, one dentist buys and joins with the practice of the other, forming a single-practice, single-business entity. The selling dentist then works for the buyer in a phase-out arrangement. As the seller phases out, a greatly expanded practice is created for the buyer. A group practice, on the other hand, occurs when two or more dentists share the same office space but maintain separate practices. The primary reason for forming the group is the reduction of fixed costs between the dentists. In addition, there is generally no agreed-upon plan of transition within group practices vs. mergers.

What are some advantages of merging for a late-career dentist?

Merging practices is an excellent way for late-career dentists to transition out of practice. Selling to an already established and experienced individual can be a much more secure scenario for the selling dentist than the traditional approach of selling to a new and inexperienced dentist. A merger also allows late-career dentists the option to continue practicing dentistry after the practice sale, a more difficult scenario to duplicate with a new dentist who's not adding any additional patient base to the equation.

What are the advantages of purchasing and merging with another practice?

For the expansion-minded dentist, purchasing and merging the practice with another practice is an extremely efficient way to increase profitability and expand the size of the patient base. At the same time, the purchasing dentist eliminates some of the competition and prepares the practice for the entry of an associate who will eventually buy in to the now-expanded practice.

Purchasing a Practice

How does a dentist determine what size practice he or she should purchase?

In looking at practice size, there are two factors to consider: The physical size of the office and the production history of the practice.

As far as physical size is concerned, determine whether current and potential patient load can be adequately handled in the current space. If not, could the office space be expanded or laid out differently? Would staggering the hours of the practice be a solution? If the purchasing dentist is interested in expanding the practice in the future by merging with other selling dentists in the same area, think about how the facility or practice hours could be modified to accommodate such an expansion.

Another important factor to consider is the practice's production history, as well as its potential. Ultimately, the size of the practice purchased will probably be dictated by the dentist's prior practice experience and/or his or her overall comfort level with the current production numbers of the particular practice. It may also depend upon whether the selling dentist will help maintain the production of the practice by providing dental services during the transition and, if so, for how many days per week and for what period of time following the purchase. The seller's production will go a long way toward paying for overhead expenses and enhancing the overall profitability of the practice. If the seller will be staying and providing such services for some extended period of time following the sale, the size of the practice could be larger than the buyer would have normally considered buying. If the transition of the seller is properly structured, the buyer can gradually phase in (as his or her clinical speed improves) while the seller phases out.

In looking over information on various available practices, there are some specific things to look for. Examine gross collections for the last 3 years to determine what part was hygiene-related; what percentage of fees were received from private patients, insurance/direct reimbursement, prepaid/capitation/HMO, and/or Medicaid, and how many active patients are there in the practice. How many new patients are seen each month? What is the average number of patients seen by the dentist and by the hygienists daily? How many total hygiene days per week are there, and is there a non-surgical perio program in place? What is the collection percentage of the practice and what is the total accounts receivable? How many staff is employed and what are their salaries and benefits? What procedures is the practice currently referring out, such as endo, perio, pedo, surgery, and implant placement?

How will a purchasing dentist know if the price and terms of the practice are fair?

One of the first things to do is to make sure that the purchase price of the practice reflects fair market value, which can be verified by using the services of an experienced transition consultant. There are certain guidelines that have been established for the valuation of dental practices so buyers can be assured of paying a fair price. In fact, a formal valuation of the practice is always a good investment for a buyer to consider prior to purchasing. This tool enables the buyer to determine whether or not he or she is making a sound investment and may also be used to compare against any valuations that have been provided by the seller.

The terms of the purchase price are also important and will often make the difference between a successful end result and a poor one. The terms should be flexible enough to allow the buyer to pay the existing overhead of the practice, the payments on the purchase price, and still make a reasonably good living. The wrong terms can create a serious financial problem during the initial months and years following the purchase. There's good news regarding practice purchase financing—there are lending institutions available that are willing to make loans to dentists for the purchase of established practices. These institutions are also willing to offer a number of flexible payment plans that will give the buyer some financial relief during the initial transition period.

How can a dentist determine if the purchase of a particular practice will work for him or her financially?

The buyer of a practice should be provided with a projection of what the net income will look like during the time the practice is being paid for. Without this, there's no way of measuring the economic viability or true value of the practice being purchased. This financial projection is based on the present overhead and collections of the practice, less the practice payments. In order to construct an accurate picture, it will be necessary to determine what the "true net" income of the practice is—that is, the total compensation the seller is receiving from the practice, including all benefits paid on the seller's behalf. This projection should also reflect expenses borne by the seller that the buyer won't have, as well as expenses the buyer will incur that the seller doesn't have. Some of the seller's expenses would include excess supply costs, depreciation, continuing education and travel costs, and the rental amount the seller is paying should the seller own the facility.

Additional expenses that a buyer might incur that the seller doesn't have would include initial working capital and marketing costs, as well as the cost of any re-equipping or improvement to existing decor. Working capital is definitely a must, as it is needed for paying the initial expenses incurred during the first few months following the purchase. This is especially necessary in situations where the seller's accounts receivable are not to be included in the purchase price.

How should the seller's transition out of the practice be handled?

Two important issues come to mind regarding the seller's transition out of the practice. The first is how to successfully transfer the patients to the new owner and the second is how to maintain reasonable cash flow during the initial critical 3- to 6-month period following the purchase date.

A great deal of misinformation and concern surrounds the patient transition and retention process. After all, if the patients of the practice don't transfer, the buyer is left wondering "What did I buy?" When the patients are properly informed about the transition, the seller's exit should not cause a mass exodus of patients. Even though most people avoid change, patients are accustomed to this type of transition and have experienced this with their physicians and other professionals.

In addition, the staff should be well prepared with scripts for introducing the new dentist in person as well as over the telephone. A personal letter of introduction from the seller is also important.

Some practice transitions are very brief, requiring the transfer of the seller's patient base to the buyer as quickly as possible. This is particularly true when the buyer's income needs it or the seller's personal or health situation requires it. When the seller leaves the practice quickly, it may actually shorten the time required for the patients to transfer to the buyer. Contrary to what many dentists think, the successful transfer of patients depends mostly on the people skills of the buyer, the performance and attitude of the remaining staff, and not necessarily on the seller's presence after the sale

Should the seller continue working in the practice after the purchase?

In some situations, the buyer may want to protect the cash flow of the practice initially by having the seller stay with the practice, providing dental services during a transition period. This can be particularly important during the first few months following the purchase. Each transition should be handled on an individual basis. In some situations it is most advantageous for the seller to stay, while in others it may be best for the seller to leave as soon as possible after the sale, staying only long enough to finish up any cases in progress.

Another common mistake is allowing the seller to continue working in the practice for a longer period of time than the practice can support him or her. As discussed earlier, protecting the initial cash flow of the practice by having the seller work for the buyer can make a lot of sense in certain situations. However, before agreeing to such an arrangement, the buyer should make sure he or she has constructed accurate cash flow projections showing how this will impact the bottom line.

If the buyer is clinically and managerially ready to take on the practice, by all means do so, and limit, where possible, the amount of time the seller stays in the practice during the transition. However, if the buyer is not quite ready for the responsibility of the entire practice, see if the seller would be willing to stay and work in the practice following the purchase date. To determine how long the seller should stay, as well how much to compensate the seller, income projections should be constructed depicting various scenarios to make sure there will be sufficient income during the specified time.

What are some of the most common mistakes made when purchasing a practice?

Business decisions do not come without potential for mistakes, and purchasing a dental practice is no exception. Though the track record for dental practice acquisitions is excellent, there are still certain pitfalls to watch out for.

One of the first mistakes made is paying too much for the practice based on fair market value. A similar problem occurs when the terms of the purchase are not structured with enough flexibility to allow reasonably good cash flow during the payout period. The terms of the purchase (that is, how the payments are structured over time) are often equally, if not more, important than the price. Both of these problems can be eliminated by utilizing the services of an experienced transition consultant to value the practice and to suggest terms that will make economic sense for the buyer.

Another common mistake is allowing advisors to negotiate to death your proposed practice purchase. Some advisors have been hired for the job to act as a "hired gun." They feel almost compelled to look for as many things wrong with the practice as they can so their client will feel they've really "gone to battle." They often treat the situation like a divorce instead of a marriage, as you'd prefer. Remember: A win-win end result should be the goal, so be extremely careful that the practice transaction (as well as the relationship) isn't destroyed in the process of negotiating a fair deal. I have seen many excellent opportunities lost this way—that is, great practice opportunities that were negotiated to death by the advisors, only to be lost to another buyer who recognized a good opportunity when he saw it.

What type of lending institution should be used for financing the purchase of the practice?

Another common mistake is using the wrong lending institutions for financing. Traditional banks are notoriously clumsy when it comes to approving loans for the purchase of an established dental practice. They often act like they are doing you a favor by even discussing the possibility of such a loan. Nothing can be more frustrating to a buyer than losing thousands of dollars in "lost practice income" while waiting weeks and months for the loan to be approved, the funds to be distributed to the bank lawyers, and the closing date to be agreed upon. Also, banks often charge a lot of hidden fees. I recently had a client charged more than $14,000 in loan origination fees, points, closing costs, and bank attorney fees on a loan. Some banks make unusual requests. I had one banker tell me he would be happy to loan my dentist-client $150,000 at 10% interest if my client would just put a $150,000 CD (at 5% interest) in the bank as collateral. I told him, "If my client had access to $150,000, why would we be talking to you?"

Some of the new lending institutions that have emerged in the last few years will loan up to 100% of the value of the practice based on appraisal. The funds are often available within days of providing the bank with the requested information. This can be a great benefit to both parties, but it is especially helpful to the buyer, who is usually anxious to begin making an income. I highly recommend investigating these new sources of practice purchase financing. They know the process, they service their loans quickly, and they understand the needs of dentists.

Who should be used as an advisor to oversee the purchase of the practice?

A common mistake I see young dentists make is seeking advice from the wrong people. Often they will talk to other dentists they may know rather than seeking out an experienced transition consultant. Another is using advisors with titles that sound like they ought to know what they are doing, but often they have had little or no actual experience in handling dental practice transitions. Be sure to hire a consultant who is willing to give you a list of referrals of other buyers and sellers who were happy with the results and felt that they were treated fairly. Hire one with a win-win attitude.

New Practice Start-Up

What are some of the most important factors to consider with a new practice start-up?

There are several key factors to consider when structuring a plan for establishing a new practice. Some of the most important factors include:

- location

- the economy and demographics of the area, as well as the number of dentists in the area

- the availability of office space

- the size of the office and amount of equipment to start with

- the major employers in the area and any dental benefits offered by those employers

- whether to lease or to purchase the facility or equipment

- how to begin introducing and marketing the practice to the community

- how and where to get financing

Just how important is the location of the new practice?

"Location, location, location" is a popular phrase used in the real estate industry to point out the importance of protecting one's investment when buying a home. The same holds true when determining where to place a new practice.

Selecting an area is a personal decision and many factors will affect this decision—some emotional, some financial, and others based simply on timing and availability.

In seeking the right location, ask the following questions:

- What type of community do I want to live in?

- What type of climate do I enjoy?

- Do I thrive on the excitement of city life or do I long for the peace and quiet of the country?

- What recreational opportunities are available in the area?

- Are there career opportunities for my spouse? How are the schools rated for my children?

Choosing a location that best meets your personal needs is the first step in building a solid foundation for your future happiness in the practice. It is not, however, the only step.

In selecting a practice location, it is equally important to evaluate the community's ability to meet your professional and economic needs. This will require some investigative research on your part.

As a starting point, I recommend meeting with advisors from the local Chamber of Commerce to find out about the community's business outlook. They can provide you with local economic data such as population trends and average household income. They can also answer questions about the quality of schools and the overall quality of the community.

It's important to ask questions with an eye toward future growth and development. That requires that you not think about the location of your practice as something static, but as continually evolving and growing.

Consider networking with other professionals in the area, including dentists.

Speak with local dental supply representatives. They are often a good source of information and can share with you obstacles that other dentists may be facing.

Overall, the best areas for a new practice start-up are those that are experiencing growth but have a few dentists for you to compete with.

It takes a tremendous amount of hard work and due diligence to start a practice from scratch. Your location will play a vital part in your success. Make the decision about location carefully and intelligently.

Should a recent graduate consider a new practice start-up?

There is no substitute for knowledge and real working experience. If a person wants to open up a restaurant, he or she should first work in a restaurant; likewise, it only makes sense that a new graduate gain practical working experience before staring a practice. I recommend that new graduates work as associates for at least one year to gain private practice experience prior to setting up a new practice.

Associating with an experienced dentist affords an opportunity to both sharpen technical skills and gain valuable practice management experience. This period also affords time to gain sufficient hand speed ability so that when you do open your own practice, you'll be able to treat an adequate number of patients.

Though many associate positions offered today are part of a long-term arrangement (usually leading to some type of co-ownership), there are dentists who are looking for temporary associates to work in their practices. Many of these dentists are looking to ease their workload and don't wish to make any long-term commitment. Dental clinics are also an option for dentists looking to associate.

Also, consider maintaining a part-time associate position during the start-up phase of your practice. That way, you have a built-in source of income while waiting for your practice to take root.

What size office is appropriate for new practice establishment?

There is no ideal size for a facility. Your work style and professional goals will determine the overall size.

I know dentists who saved thousands of dollars a month by utilizing only 800 square feet; but while they saved money on facility costs, they also experienced lost potential due to the productivity limitations of their facilities. It's one thing to downsize an existing successful practice into a niche practice. It's another thing to start a new practice with space limitations.

Conversely, I know dentists who invested in the ego palaces of the 1980s; many of these dentists lost hundreds of thousands of dollars from the enormous monthly debt burden.

I recommend a total of three or four treatment rooms for a solo practitioner. These should include a hygiene operatory. In the beginning, equip only two of the operatories and plumb the remaining ones for future expansion. Always work with a licensed general contractor who is in good standing, someone that comes recommended by others. Supply dealers are often a good referral source and may even have in-house talent to help you.

Here is a tip: Find out if there is space available that was previously occupied by another dentist who may have retired or moved to another facility. With leasehold improvements already in place, construction time and thousands of dollars could be saved in the process.

Should the equipment be purchased or leased?

For many dentists, leasing is an easier way to get started than going through the typical loan process at a commercial bank.

There are advantages to leasing. Up to 100% financing is usually available and lease terms can often be structured beyond normally available loan terms.

Also, leasing may provide more advantageous tax breaks by allowing the cost of the equipment to be deducted more rapidly than with purchasing.

But don't forget to do your math when comparing the two. And be sure to consult with your tax advisor to determine which option is better for your particular situation.

What expenses will the dentist need to consider budgeting for the first year?

A financial budget and business plan is essential in structuring any new business—including a dental practice. It's important to know where the practice stands financially at all times, including production goals that must be met by certain dates. Knowing the numbers will set you free from the emotional anxiety that breeds from the unknown.

Some initial practice expenses include rent, utilities, telephone, equipment, loan or lease payments, the cost of an initial supply inventory, and the total salary costs of the initial staff members. One combination assistant-front desk person is often workable in the beginning, to be followed by a separate front desk person, and eventually, a hygienist. This is why it's important to obtain financing for initial working capital. This capital helps pay for expenses incurred prior to the time the practice begins collecting for services provided.

INDEX

A

Absentee ownership, 10
Accountants, 237
Accountant-valued practice, 293-294
Accounts receivable, 201, 206-209, 225:
collection, 207-209
Acquisition-merger profitability, 105-113
Advantages (transition), 54-59, 113-122,
318, 321
Advertising, 137
Advisors, 231-240: questions to ask your-
self, 234-235; transition specialists, 235-
237; accountants, 237; lawyers, 238;
team approach, 238; financial plan-
ners, 238-239; lending institutions, 239;
traditional bankers, 240
Affording to buy, 297
After-hours coverage, 221
Age staggering, 122
Allocations of purchase price, 201, 205-
206
Amortization, 78, 225-226
Arbitration clause, 223-224
Area desirability. SEE Location of prac-
tice.
Asset summation, 148-149
Assets included/excluded, 201, 203-205,
224-225
Associate benefits, 222
Associate compensation, 66-67, 69, 188-
192, 221-222, 302: over-compensation,
69
Associate employment agreement, 219-
224
Associate laboratory expense, 67-68
Associate profitability, 50-53
Associate questions, 63
Associate revolving-door syndrome.
SEE Revolving-door syndrome.
Associate status, 69-70, 220, 320
Associate with no contract, 291

Associate's duties/responsibilities, 220
Associate's earned equity, 89-92
Associate's fees, 222
Associateship to buy-in arrangements,
76-81, 115-116
Associateship to co-ownership, 17, 49-
94, 219-229, 316-320: profit expansion,
50-53; solo practice, 53; relationship
dynamics, 53-54; advantages, 54-59;
precautions, 59; long-term planning,
60-62; practice owner questions, 62;
associate questions, 63; transition
checklist, 63-69; associate status, 69-70;
phases of transition, 71-89; trial period, 71-72; post-trial period, 72-75; buy-
in, 76-81; buy-out, 81-89; special cir-
cumstances/considerations, 89-94;
agreements, 219-229
Associateship (prior to), 187-188
Associateships don't work, 294-295
Auto-vehicle expense, 170-171

B

Bank accounts, 225
Banks as lenders, 240
Budgeting (new practice), 330
Built-in buyer, 58
Business equipment/supplies, 132-133,
135
Business plan/budget, 133-134
Business-management plan, 135-136
Buy low/sell high, 114
Buy-in agreement, 219-229: associate
employment agreement, 219-224; pre-
buy-in terms/conditions, 220, 224-225;
buy-in checklist, 220, 225-226; co-own-
ership agreement, 220, 226-227; buy-
out agreement, 220, 227-229
Buy-in checklist, 220, 225-226
Buy-in date, 80, 225: deferral, 80
Buy-in practice revaluation, 91

Vacation, 222

Valuation of practice, 141-195, 296, 299-
301, 309, 314-317: factors, 159-166; at
buy-in, 296; considerations, 299-301;
impacts, 316-317

Value determination, 141-195: history,
142-144; understanding practice value,
142-146; practice valuation guide, 142,
146-166; profit and loss statement,
142, 166-172; preserving practice
value, 142, 172-183; reality
check/appraisal, 142, 183-192; valuation factors, 159-166; enhancing practice value, 192-195

Value destroyers, 172, 312-313

Value of referrals, 301-302

Value protection, 57, 142, 146, 172-183,
192-195, 314-315

W

Waiting too long, 24-26, 179

Warranties/acknowledgements, 202, 211-
219

Weighted averages, 153-158

When to plan, 23-24

Work before details, 295-296

Working facilities and expenses, 222

Workload sharing, 56

Worm farm failure, 84-86